HOW TO ATTAIN AND PRACTICE
THE IDEAL SEX LIFE

This book is a translation by Norman Haire, CH.M., M.B., from "Das Sexualleben in seiner biologischen Bedeutung". It is intended for circulation only among mature persons, twenty-one years of age or over.

How to Attain and Practice the Ideal Sex Life

By

Dr. J. Rutgers

**Ideal Sex and Love Relations
for Every Married Man and Woman**

Intended for Circulation among Mature Persons only

CADILLAC PUBLISHING CO.   NEW YORK

MARGARET SANGER TELLS OF HER VISIT TO DR. RUTGERS AND HIS GREAT INFLUENCE ON THE COURSE OF MODERN LIFE

From "My Fight for Birth Control", 1931, Chap. VIII, p. 107 ff.

MY VISIT to Holland in January, 1915, was doubtless the most instructive of all my travels, and from it I derived the greatest benefit.

During my arduous studies in the reading room of the British Museum I gathered... that Holland stood out as the one nation in Europe where some force was automatically at work on... constructive race building... Here the death rate had fallen faster than the birth rate, which was a natural increase in the population of 16 persons per thousand, meaning that the population of Holland was increasing faster than that of any other country in the world!... Again I found a gradual lowering in the rate of deaths among mothers and children; a reduction in the proportion of stillbirths and abortions; and indication of a smaller amount of venereal disease; and a decrease of professional prostitution. The tables of maternal mortality gave Holland the lowest figure...

Speaking neither Dutch nor German... I could not telephone to Dr. Rutgers. So at nine o'clock the same morning I wrote his address on a piece of paper, hailed a taxi and set forth to call on the veteran of Dutch Neo-Malthusianism. Never shall I forget the feeling I had when, in response to my ring, a small, square aperture in the upper part of the door opened in an uncanny way, and a face, wizened, aged, and inquisitive, appeared in the frame window. Finally after I had explained my mission, the doctor opened the door. I was ushered into his library to wait until he was dressed. We then went out to a second "breakfast" together at a nearby cafe, where we talked until noon, about the situation in Holland and the difficulties in America.

From Dr. Rutgers I learned much of the complexities of the technique of contraception... The following day, I began my daily visits to his office which continued for several weeks... The fact that each woman had to be examined by Dr. Rutgers before the method of contraception could be advised presented an entirely new aspect of the situation to me. I began to delve with deep interest into the whys and wherefores. I bombarded the little man with questions concerning each case. At some sessions there were as many as ten or even fifteen women in his office seeking instruction. These I advised and fitted under his guidance without knowledge of the Dutch language.

Besides myself, two midwives were learning the technique from Dr. Rutgers. They came each morning to equip themselves with knowledge preparatory to starting a center in the outskirts of The Hague. There were already over fifty such centers, which Dr. Rutgers called "clinics" ...

The nurses or midwives were trained by Dr. Rutgers as "experts" in hygienic methods of family limitation. They were then set up in practice in various towns or cities throughout Holland...

Besides these official clinics for which the Neo-Malthusian League was responsible, I found many commercial places, run as supply shops, where any woman or man could purchase any contraceptive article desired regardless of needs or conditions...This method was strongly disapproved by Dr. Rutgers and the Dutch Neo-Malthusian League. They directed their propaganda against commercializing this great service.

Records, detailed and full, had not been kept until Dr. Rutgers took charge, follow-up had not seemed necessary, and the great opportunity of giving to the world case histories or mass facts over a period of forty years upon which scientific data could be based, was lost to the world forever...

Dr. Rutgers' object was to direct the teachings of family limitation into homes where there was poverty, sickness, or disease... There was a gentle and sympathetic follow-up into the homes where death had taken a child. The condition of the home and the attitude of the mother was reported to the League's officers, and proper advice was given according to the circumstances. I found that the infant mortality rates of The Hague and Amsterdam were at that time the lowest of all cities in the world...To Dr. Rutgers we owe the idea of training nurses and sending them into congested quarters to teach contraception to the overburdened mothers of the poor...

I visited Dr. Rutgers again in 1920, and found a sad and unhappy man, ever willing that the younger generation should try its hand, but realizing how much they were lacking in experience. When, in 1921 Dr. and Mrs. Drysdale and Dr. Haire and I went to Amsterdam to attend a contraceptive conference, Dr. Rutgers' health would not allow him to join us. He died in September, 1924. His death was ten years too soon. Today the influence of his work goes on spreading itself sanely, quietly into the lives of people who are not afraid to think.

The results of my visit to Holland were to change the whole course of the birth control movement, not only in America but in England and Europe as well.

TRIBUTE TO THE GREAT HUMANITARIAN
PHYSICIAN, DR. J. RUTGERS,
AUTHOR OF THIS BOOK

WHILE the present pages were in the press, the sad news reached us of the passing away of the esteemed and beloved author of the original work "Das Sexualleben". His genial nature, of which we as publishers and translators have had many proofs in his letters to us, endeared him to the thousands in his native land, in Germany and in Switzerland, where he was well known as one of the most active members of the Zürich Society of Natural History (Naturforschenden Gesellschaft, Zürich).

His son, Dr. F. J. Rutgers, at present practicing in Zürich, and himself a member of the above Society of Natural History, has with filial piety written an encomium of his father's life and work, which appears in the transactions of the Society. It is here translated by Mr. Clifford Coudray, who collaborated with the late author during the last two years.

Johannes Rutgers, M.D. (Leyden, Holland) was born in the little Dutch village of Hallum, in Friesland, the fifth of six children of the local pastor. Both father and mother, of old and learned Dutch family, were his first schoolmasters. Like Cornelia of Roman fame, the good mother taught her sons herself, and under her able tuition, the young Johannes matriculated at Groningen University. He was a lover of nature even at that early age, and threw himself with ardour into the study of plants and flowers and insects. This is reflected in his greatest work, "Das Sexualleben", when he refers so often to the analogy between plant life and that of man and the lower animals. At twenty-two years of age he was ready to enter the church, having terminated his theological studies with success, although too young to be appointed to a curacy in Holland. He got his first call at the age of twenty-four, shortly after his marriage with Cornelia Abresch, also daughter of a clergyman. By her he had four children.

Soon after this marriage, however, he resolved to take up the study of medicine, first in Groningen and later in Leyden. where on the seventh of July, 1879, he received his M.D. degree.

He then bought a practice in Rotterdam, where he worked untiringly in the interest of all his patients, rich and poor. His sound good

7

sense, his unfailing patience and general lovableness, led his patients one and all to cherish the greatest affection for him.

His rule of life was: to be of use in the world, to help the afflicted. Personally he was incredibly selfless, and simple in his ways. Apart from his practice, he devoted himself exclusively to natural history. For instance, while he was at the busiest period of his extensive practice in Rotterdam, he experimented, in the year 1887 with the digestibility of various kinds of vegetable albumens on his own body. For whole months at a time his only food consisted of carefully weighed quantities of vegetable albuminoids, completed only by the weighed quantities of the other indispensible food-stuffs, free from albumen.

After the death of his first wife, he married, on the third of August, 1885, Marie Hoitsema, and their life was a most happy and united one, right down to his recent death. Frau Marie Rutgers took the liveliest interest in all her husband's work and experiments and cooked and weighed out the peas and beans, etc., for her husband's repasts, while she cooked other things for the children, sharing the doctor's meals herself. Frau Marie was also celebrated throughout Holland as protagonist of Women's Rights. The result of these food-experiments on both husband and wife (that hitherto had only been made by Professor Voit of Munich on dogs) have appeared in Kuhne and Voit's "Zeitschrift für Biologie", Munich. Professor Voit wrote at the conclusion of these reports: It needed a Dutchman's patience to carry it out.

For many years the late Dr. Rutgers was Editor of the "Niederlandisches Medizinischen Jahrbuch" and conducted the scientific reports, also those on new and old Pharmaceutical preparations and posology with distinguished success.

In the month of May, 1904, to the great regret of all his patients, Dr. Rutgers retired from his great practice in Rotterdam and settled in The Hague, in order to consecrate the remainder of his useful life to pure science, that of the Sexual Life being to him of primary importance. His observations during his long years of practice had provided him with rich material for such a work. He became celebrated for his pioneering in the questions of Eugenics and Birth Control, to combating Prostitution and Venereal Diseases. He devoted not only his time, but gave large sums of money to the education of the masses in these essential things.

His works on these burning topics have been translated into every European language, including Esperanto, especially his pamphlets on Contraception.

His greatest books are entitled "Rassenverbesserung" with its English translation ["Racial Improvement"] by Clifford Coudray,

B

M.P.S. London and L.Sc. Paris, and the still larger volume, in six parts, "Das Sexualleben" — translated into English by Norman Haire, Ch.B. Sydney ["How to Attain and Practice the Ideal Sex Life"]. This work may be taken as a monumental compendium of the subject in the light of present day knowledge, illuminated here and there not only by the deep human knowledge of the late Dr. Rutgers, but also with sparks and flashes of his inexhaustible good humour and native wit.

Dr. Rutgers fell asleep in his daughter's home in Heerenveeren, a little town in the North of Holland; and died as he had lived, respected, beloved, and at peace with all men.

R. A. Giesecke and *Dr. F. J. Rutgers,*
Society of Natural History.

NEW ORIGINAL VIEWPOINT ON THE
SEXUAL LIFE
Vast Practical Experience of the Author

IN introducing this book to the English public I am at a disadvantage, in that the manner of publication compels me to write a foreword at a time when I have completed the translation of but one-quarter of the book, and, indeed, read but little more of it. The original German edition reached me only section by section, and pressure of professional work, together with lecturing and my own literary work, has prevented me from reading it all as yet.

For this reason it may be wise to explain that the translator is not necessarily in agreement with all the opinions expressed by the author, though so far as I have read I have not found any important ground for disagreement.

Dr. Rutgers is known in England chiefly as one of the pioneers and leaders of the Dutch Birth-Control movement, to which we British and American advocates of Birth-Control owe so much. But this volume shows him to be a profound thinker, very widely read in the literature of his subject, of vast experience in the practice of his profession, possessed of a strong critical faculty and an unusual capacity for independent thinking. This last attribute is perhaps the most characteristic and the most valuable. He accepts nothing simply because it is customarily accepted. He examines it for himself, weighs the *pros* and *cons* impartially, and either makes his decision in accordance with the weight of evidence, or if the latter is insufficiently conclusive leaves the decison until some fresh evidence shall have been obtained. His originality is delightful, and even where one may not agree in every detail with his conclusions, one feels that one has been led to see things from a new viwpoint.

90 Harley Street, London

NORMAN HAIRE, Ch.M., M.B.

10

TABLE OF CONTENTS

This very detailed table of contents has been arranged — for easy reference — to combine the purpose of contents and index for the convenience of the reader.

Tribute to the Author, 7
New Original Viewpoint on the Sexual Life, 10
Foreword: Aim of the Author, 25

Part I.
ANATOMY AND FUNCTION OF SEX ORGANS IN MAN AND WOMAN
Sex Attraction . Sex Health . Hygiene . Rejuvenation

CHAPTER   PAGE

1. Two Main Sources of Our Sex Life   **29**
The Male and Female Sex Organs

2. Sex Glands of Man and Woman (Gonads)   **31**
The Very Foundation of the Sexual Life
The Production of Vigorous Young Cells

3. Sex Experiments of Nature   **32**
Development of the Two Sex Systems
Appendix: Hermaphrodism; Cases

4. New Sex Experiments and Discoveries for Improving Sexual Life   **37**
"Rejuvenation Treatments" for Increasing Sex Potency of Man and Woman
Success in Treating Impotent Men
Curing Frigidity in Women
Changing Male into Female and Female into Male by Sex Operation
Implantation of Sex Organs of Opposite Sex
Biology of Sex Attraction
The Toxin of the Ovaries Causes Attraction towards the Male
The Toxin of the Testes Causes Attraction towards the Female
A Modern Operation that Makes a Normal Man of a Homosexual: Cases

Happy Marriage of Dr. Lichtenstein's Transformed Homosexual
Appendix: Comparison of Hermaphrodism and Homosexuality

5. Sex Changes in Mature Male and Female   **44**
New Cell Formation after Puberty
Conditions which Stimulate Sex Desire: Foods. Alcohol. Massage. Drugs Inhibiting Sex Stimulation. Devices which Increase Sex Energy: New Methods
What Should Be Avoided by Persons Too Easily Aroused Sexually
The Act of Copulation is the One Physiological Human Function Requiring a Partner for Its Performance

6. Unique Journey of New Sperm-Cells   **48**
The mysterious Workshop of Nature
The Two Life-giving Explosives in the Testicle that Convulse the World
Passage of Sperm-Cells along Walls of Vagina like a Great Ocean Voyage
200 Million Sperm-Cells in a Single Ejaculation
This Fecundity is Nature's Device to Ensure Continuance of Man

CHAPTER   PAGE

7. Nuptial Flight of New Sperm-Cells   **52**

First Rapture of Nuptial Flight
History of Sex Evolution

8. How Sexual Pleasure Vitalizes Our Life-Energy   **54**

Conscious Control of Sex Impulse
Voluntary Control of Internal and External Genital Muscles
Three Excretory Systems
Secretory Aspects of Sexual Life

9. The Male and Female Sex Organs   **57**

The Sex Organs of Woman
   The Uterus or Womb of Red Muscle
   The Antechamber and Vault of the Vagina
   Spasmodic Contractions during Coitus: Avoiding Injuries to Husband
   Length of Vaginal Canal: Its Remarkable Powers of Expansion
   The Clitoris in Woman
   Position of the Ovaries
The Sex Organs of Man
   The Penis and Testicles
   The Prostatic (Presiding) Gland: Special Function in the Act of Love
   New First True Idea of the Sexual Function Here Given

10. The Genital Canal in the Sex Act   **63**

The Physiology of Erection and Desire

The Throbbing that Produces in Us a Warm Feeling of Glow and Pulsation
Direction of Erection Resultant of Two Forces: Blood Pressure and Gravity
How Blood Pressure Effects Our Sex Life
Tight-fitting Clothes Diminish Coital Powers
What the Savage Races Can Teach Modern Civilized Man

11. The Glans and Prepuce in the Sex Act   **70**

The Male Glans and the Female Clitoris in Technique of Coitus
"Nature Shames Our Machines with Her Devices"
Mutual Adaptation of Man and Woman

12. Effect of Circumcision on Sex Health   **73**

Facilitates Sex Cleanliness
Removes Frequent Cause of Masturbation
Decreases Possibility of Venereal Diseases

13. Modern Methods of Sex Hygiene and Sex Health   **76**

Vigorous Metabolism and Health
Modern Methods of Genital Cleansing
How to Cleanse the Male Genital Canal. Automatic Cleansing
How to Cleanse the Vulva and Vagina. Disinfecting Solutions. Washings

Part II.
SEX HEALTH AND THE PERFECT SEX ACT
Physiology and Practice by Married Lovers

CHAPTER   PAGE

14. *Introductory*: Scientific Duty of Author Not to Withhold Anything of Service   **83**

Now Physiological Functions of Sexual Life to be Described in Detail

15. The Three Human Excretory Products   **85**

Surprising Effects of Yoghurt and Oil of Turpentine
Use and Abuse of Stimulants and Sterility
Source of Genital Disease and Sterility

CHAPTER	PAGE

16. Digestion of Food and Sex Health   90

Science Should Not Make a Mystery of Anything
Studying the Conscious Control of Our Bodily Functions

17. Urinary Secretion and Its Lessons for Sex Health   95

Dangers of Artificial Overstimulation
Diet Can Work Wonders
Too Great Repression of the Function Most Unwise

18. The Production of Semen. The Seminal Apparatus   98

The Processes of Sexual Secretion and Periodicity in Man and Woman
The Erection-Curve. The Emission-Curve
The Change of Life No Hindrance to Sex Act

19. False Popular Notions of Sex that Imperil the Young   102

The Monthly Sexual Secretion of Woman
Infectious Prostitution versus the Natural Safety Valve
Modern Hygiene and Sex Cleanliness
How the Mother Can Lead the Son to Ideal Sexual Life

20. The Physiology of Erection and Ejaculation   105

Male and Female Sufferings in the Sexual Life
Virile Powers in Childhood and in Old Age
Law of Frequency of Erection. Psychic Influences
Storing Up Energy for Healthy Sex Act
Paths which Calm and Soothe Sex Excitement
Converting Sex Passion into Love

CHAPTER	PAGE

21. The Erection and Climax in the Sex Act   110

Attainment of Supreme Happiness
How the Ideal Sex Climax of Married Lovers Is Accomplished.
Massage in Perfect Sex Technique
Male and Female Erection and Mutual Massage
Importance of Coital Massage

22. The Role of the Husband and Wife in the Sex Act   113

Modes of Sex Intercourse for Husband and Wife
Natural Methods of Birth Control
The Spanish Method
The "Karezza" Method (Zugessant's Discovery)
The French Method
The "Right" Mate
Curve of Sensation in Woman; in Man
Woman's "Sexual Ecstasy." Man's "Culminating Point"
Sexual Division of Labor in Perfect Sex Act
(See also Chapters 27, 29, 54 and 57.)

23. Practical Benefits of Sexual Relations Between Married Lovers   117

Health Improvement by Ideal Sex Act: Intensification of Our Vital Energy and Joy of Living
Study of Sex Emotions Scientifically Far too Neglected: Vital to Happiness
How to Make Sex Life as Strong and Beautiful as Possible (to be Studied)

24. Normally Functioning Sexual Life as Health Stimulant   120

Modern versus Old-fashioned Medical Methods
Hygienic versus Dangerous Sexual Relations

13

CHAPTER   PAGE

Starved Sexual Life and Illness
Marital Intercourse as a Remedy;
Not Diseased Prostitution

25. Importance of Massage in Ideal Sexual Life
123
Energetic Vitalization of All Life's
Functions by Caresses, Em-
braces, Climax of Passion
Ideal Ardent Sex Act of Married
Lovers Great Health Stimu-
lant
Marvelous Cures of Internal Or-
gans by Thure-Brandt Mas-
sage

26. Increased Energy Through Ideal Sexual Life   127
Strength of the Sexual Life:
Source of Supreme Happiness
or Disaster
How the Sexual Life Can Increase
Our Energy
Sexual Passion Stimulates the
Processes of Oxidation
Exciting Motives in a World Full
of Lovers

27. How to Overcome Physical Hindrances to the Practice of the Ideal Sex Act by Married Lovers   129
Choice of Ideal Sex Partner
Planned Procedure on Wedding
Night and during Honey-
moon
Avoiding Grave Mistakes of
Newlyweds

CHAPTER   PAGE

Overcoming Bad Position of the
Sex Organs
Best Positions for Perfecting Sex
Act for Husband and Wife
Forced Positions
Scientific Mastery of Coital Tech-
nique for Different Types of
Women
Avoiding Sex Injuries
Sexual Dangers from Sedentary
Habits
Ideal Love Life and Married Hap-
piness

28. Social Restrictions on Sexual Intercourse
135
Sex Restrictions of the Single and
the Married
Periodical Prohibitions
Sex Restrictions on Professions
Prohibitions Intensify Sex Im-
pulse
Ideal Sexual Life for All: Aim of
Sexual Reform
Regulated Sex Satisfaction Im-
perative for Enduring Love
The Passion-Curve in Ideal Love
Guidance and Education in the
Art of Love

29. The Four Categories of Human Sexual Satisfaction   138
Highest Ecstasy Between Two
Lovers in Ideal Marriage
The Best and Gentlest of All
Methods
The Other Three Kinds of Sexual
Relief or Satisfaction
The Problem of Masturbation and
Nocturnal Emissions
The Question of Homosexuality

Part III.
MODERN METHODS OF SEXUAL CONTROL
that Make for a Healthier and Happier Sex Life

CHAPTER   PAGE   CHAPTER   PAGE

30. *Introductory*: Sexual Control Enriches Our Love Life   145
New Generation Requires Finer
Pleasures and Gentler Love-
Making
Conscious Sex Mastery and Con-

trol: The Spurs and Bridle
to Sex

31. Control of the Produc- tion of Semen   148
Normal and Abnormal Production
of Semen
Effects of Drugs on Sex

CHAPTER   PAGE

Quinine and Excessive Use of
Alcohol

Dangers of Powerful Sex Stimulants

Aim: Fulfillment of Sexual Ideal
of Every Adult

32. **Strengthening the Sex Virility of Man. Diet and Sex Control**   151

Mechanical and Chemical Sex
Stimuli

Smoking. Clothes. Exercise. Food.
Alcohol and other Beverages

How They Effect Our Sex Feelings

Alcohol and the Powers of Resistance

Tea, Coffee, Chocolate and Sex

How the Meat Diet Strongly
Effects Sex: Beef or Veal?

Do Eggs Increase Sexuality?

How do Wine, Beer and Cigars
Affect Sex Control?

The Hot or Cold Bath. Overheated
Rooms

Treatment in So-called Massage
Establishments

How the Sexual System Reacts
to Nerve Excitement

Diverting Psychic Sexual Stimuli
into Other Channels

Drugs and Foodstuffs which have
a Calming Action on the Sexual System

Aphrodisiacs and Anti-Aphrodis-
iacs

Other Factors in Regulating the
Sex Life

33. **Increasing Our Sex Powers of Resistance**   159

Modern Scientific Methods. How
Our Modern Society is Mak-
ing for Healthier and Happier
Sexual Life

Sacrifice of Sensual Pleasures as
Ideal Love Awakens

CHAPTER   PAGE

34. **Conscious Control of Our Sexual Life**   162

Methods for Control of Passions
and Habits

Function of Ideal Higher Education

35. **Practical Use of Sug-gestion and Hypnotism in Sexual Control**   166

Complete Relaxation. Simple
Method of Self-Hypnosis

Putting Oneself to Sleep at Will

Control of Sexual Fancies and
Excitants

36. **Control of Sexual Dreams**   169

Sexual Life Revealed in Dreams

Important Lessons on the Im-
provement of Our Whole
Sexual Life Taught in Our
Dreams

37. **Modern Methods of Sex Education**   172

Sexual Life and Its Problems to
Teachers and Parents

Directing the Awakening Sexual
Life

Keeping Sex Secrets from Pru-
dish Parents

Ignorant Girls as Ready Victims of Seducers; Case Histories

Parents Should Develop and
Ennoble Sex Life of their
Children

Dangerous Results of Represent-
ing Normal Sex Act as Something Repulsive

Sex Education in Methods of
Sex Control

Co-education and Sexual Life

Dangers of Sex Separation
(Homosexuality)

Sex Relations in Grammar
School; High School; Uni-
versity

Sex Case Histories

How to Dress Boys and Girls
for Best Sex Health

Sex Hygienic Clothes and Habits

15

CHAPTER   PAGE

38. Practical Object Lessons in Sex Instruction for Different Ages 178

Introducing Child to Mysterious World of the Sex Life

Ignorance Leads to Sex Secrecy and Evil Influences

Astonishing Sex Case Histories

CHAPTER   PAGE

Practical Object Lessons in Sex Instruction for Parents and Teacher

Sex Talks of a Mother with her Child

Sex Instruction for Secondary Schools

Homes that Interfere with the Teacher

How the Teacher Can Immunize the Child Against Profane, Narrow-minded People

Part IV.
EVOLUTIONARY DEVELOPMENT OF ALL FORMS AND MODES OF LOVE INTO THE COMPLEX SEXUAL RELATIONS IN MODERN IDEAL MARRIAGE

39. *Introductory*: Practical Importance of a Study of Sexual Evolution 185

To Arrive at Objective Standards of Sexual Life

The More We Grasp Actual Facts, the Less Shall We Go Astray

Happiness Depends Largely on Our Sexual Life

40. How Human Sexual Life Developed 186

Study of the Evolution of Reproductive Processes

Hermaphroditic Period of Transition

From Hermaphrodism to the Separation of the Sexes

Advantages of the Sexual Method

Sexual Rebirth

The Principle of Complementary Periodicity

Why the Sex Impulse Imbues Us with Life-Energy

41. How the Human Sex Organs and the Brain Developed 197

Enormous Mutual Influence of Brain System and Sex System

Development of Sexual Functions and Progress of Civilization

The Two Great Powers of Human Life: Brains and Sex

Happiness Requires the Stimulation of the Sex Life

Hygienic Dangers of Sexual Excess

Sex Passion Stimulates Intellect Powerfully

Ethical and Hygienic Dangers of a One-Sided Intellectualism

42. How the Sexual Passion Developed 202

How Sex Relations Develop into Love

Affection and Mutual Sex Satisfaction

Union between High Aspirations and Sexual Love

Pagan Sex Feelings. Mystic Sex Feelings. Idealistic Sex Feelings

43. From Cold-Blooded to Warm-Blooded 206

Variety Comes to the Love Life

Tenderness Enters the Sex Relations

Higher Development of the Sexual Life and Warm-Bloodedness

The Procreative Act is Now the Climax of Emotion

44. From Human Rutting Periods to Permanent Sexual Life 210

Control of Sexual Life One of the Greatest Triumphs of Man

Sexual Excitability and Frequency of the Sex Act

Savage Human Rutting Periods

16

CHAPTER   PAGE

Man learns to Control His De-
sires and So Increase and
Multiply His Pleasures
Higher Sex Life of Man and
His Supremacy among the
Species

45. From Group Relations to Private Affairs   213

Regulation of the Sex Life for
Production of a More Vigorous Race
Development of Higher Sex Systems

46. Sexual Freeing of Woman   216

Modern Woman the Life Com-
panion and Sex Mate of
Man
In Married Love of Two Kindred
Souls: The Supreme Height
of Passion
Nature and the Power of Sex
Win Freedom for Woman
against her Enslaving Insti-
tutions

47. The Science of Sex Attraction and the Art of Courtship   218

Lures Practised by Modern Wo-
man. Modern Free Woman
A Higher Type of Lover and
Mother
Sexual Intercourse in Modern
Ideal Marriage a Mutual Sur-
render of Two Lovings Souls

CHAPTER   PAGE

48. The Coming of Birth Control and Voluntary Motherhood   221

Decrease of Size of Families: Sex-
ual Prohibitions a Check on
Births
Brutal Preventives. Private and
Social Perils of Overpopula-
tion
Practical Modern Method of Birth
Control Frees Womanhood
Racial Improvement through Con-
trol of Births

49. The Two Distinct Functions of Married Love   223

In Savage Society Childbirth Not
Associated with Sexual Inter-
course
How it Was First Scientifically
Discovered and Proven that
the Sex Act between Man
and Wife Produced Fertility
The Higher the Living Being the
Fewer the Offspring: Fixed
Law of Nature
Honoring Sexual Love a Modern
Conception

50. Perfecting the Sexual Life   226

Overcoming Sexual Pride and
Sexual Rivalry
Power of Female Sex Attraction
and Male Domineering
The Sexual Life in the Near
Future

Part V.
MODERN ART OF LOVE . BEST TECHNIQUES FOR ITS PERFORMANCE IN IDEAL MARRIAGE BY ALL AGES AND TYPES OF MEN AND WOMEN

CHAPTER   PAGE

51. *Introductory*: Study of All Vital Fields of Sex Science Is Essential for Comprehension and Control of Sexual Love to Bring About Best Health and Happiness Possble   230

CHAPTER   PAGE

52. Dangers in the Sexual Life of Children and How to Prevent Them   232

Highly Sensitive Bodies of Chil-
dren: Ever New Sensations
Child a Sexual Being in a Sexual
World
Preparatory Education in Sex
Differences

17

CHAPTER	PAGE

Dangers of Innocent Sex Charm and Coquetry of Girls : Elderly Men

Child as Consummate Coquette : How to Avoid their Playing with Fire before Ripening of Sexual Feelings : Mistakes of Judges and Teachers

Crudest Realism as well as Sexual Idealism in Child

Overcoming Threatening Dangers of Precocious Excitation

Training the Healthy Child : Loving but Firm Treatment

53. How to Guide the Sexual Life of Children in Preparation for Ideal Married Love in Later Years   236

The Two Most Important Methods

First External Stimulation at Puberty

Modern Improved System for Realization of Sex Ideal

Developing Sexual Altruism

Childish Sex Infatuations

Sexual Love Reproduction of Mother Love in a New Form

Tender Love in the Newly Married Leading to Ideal Sex Act

Mother's Advice in Sexual Errors

Settling Many a Sex Problem Never Before Solved!

Infatuation of Boys for Women

Coarse Love-Making of Uninformed Men Leads Girls to Lesbianism

Mother Love versus the Evils of Legal Sex Prohibitions

Maternal Love Refines and Ennobles the Sexual Life

Intense Mother Love Best Preparation for Later Ideal Sexual Life and Marital Happiness

54. The Modern Art of Mutual Satisfaction for Married Lovers. Sexual Tenderness   241

Its Practise an Essential for Complete Marital Happiness

Art of Love for the Engaged: A Foretaste of Later Delight

Sexual Tenderness Produces the Most Intense Effect : Breathing, Body Warmth, Eye Flashes. Awakening of the Sexual Glow. Sexual Charm

Sex Control of Sweethearts through Anticipating Future Pleasure in Ideal Marriage

Avoiding the Rocks and Shoals to Enjoy the World so Rich in Pleasures for Married Lovers

Gentlest, Most Delicate Caresses Lead to Ideal Sex Act

Modern Technique of Massage Described in Detail as the Most Important Preliminary to the Ideal Sex Act

55. Awakening of the Sexual Passions   245

How the Psychic Life is Stimulated by Increased Blood Pressure

How Sex and Love Lead to Climax of Happiness

Physical and Psychic Function of Penis in Man and Clitoris in Woman

First Imperious Glow in the Boy and Girl at Puberty

Beneficial Health Effect of Ebb and Flow of Erection

Suffering in Advanced Age from Disappearance of Erection

How to Counteract Ills in Advanced Age

Methods to Replace the Failing Erection

Great Importance of Sex Erection for Relief of Blood Pressure in Brain

Why Only Man, because of His Immense Brain Power has Strong Erection

Why in the Lower Species of Animals with their Limited Brain Capacity Strong Erection does not Exist.

"Erection is one of the Most Important Functions of Life and the More So the More Highly the Brain Is Developed"

Erection is the Regulator of Healthy Blood Circulation

Important Advice on How to Remain Sexually Young a Long Time

CHAPTER   PAGE

How to Husband Strength so that
the Sexual Life in Marriage
May Attain its Full Power

56. Imperious Approach of Sex Maturity   250

Overwhelming Sex Urge Stimu-
lated by the Hormones
Imperative Need for Liberation of
the Tension
Fighting the Hardest Battle in
the Solitude of the Night
How to Relieve Nature's Painful
Urge
Masturbation too Childish. Pros-
titution Repellant and Dan-
gerous with Disease. Noc-
turnal Emissions: Nature's
Kindness. Casual Relations
Open to Grave Complications
The Ideal: To Find a Kindred
Spirit and Sex Partner in
Married Love

57. The Art of Love-Making for Different Ages and Types of Men and Women. Ideal Sex Techniques for Married Lovers   253

The Modern Art of Love for the
Husband
Sexual Gallantry of Husband in
Modern Ideal Sex Act
"Frigid" Women: Victims of
Man's Lack of Gallantry
Man's Initiative in Sex Act In-
considerate to Woman
Attaining Intensest of All De-
lights
Simple Method of Delaying
Climax
How to Prevent the Dulling of
Female Sensitiveness
Allowing the Wife to Take the
Position of Advantage in
Coitus
Ideal Mutual Climax
Ernst Klotz' Method of Coitus
for Wife's Benefit
How to Know When Wife De-
sires to be Loved
The Modern Art of Love for the
Wife
Ignorance of Parents a Grave
Danger to Passionate Girls

CHAPTER   PAGE

Brutal Excitement of Mastur-
bation: Obstacle to Ideal
Marriage
Unfavorable Position of Wife:
Ordinary Position too Fa-
tigueing
Wife as Master in the Act of
Love
A Scientifically Interesting
Method
Reaching the State of Idealized
Highest Love
The Use of Odors and Perfumes
According to the Type of
Lover: For Coarser Natures.
For Highly Refined Persons

The Art of Love for Impotent
Husband or Frigid Wife

Disappearance of Frigidity

Preventive Measure and Conjugal Happiness

Altruistic Mutual Aid

Method of Satisfying Impotent
Husband

Steps toward Arriving at Harmonious Sex Satisfaction in
Ideal Marriage

Overcoming the Three Great
Disappointments for Happi-
ness of Engaged and Married
Lovers

Best Positions for Harmonious
Satisfaction

Each Married Person to Study
the Erotically Sensitive Spots
Most Stimulating to His
Partner

Differences in Stimuli Rising
out of: Temperament, Habits,
Age, Associations, Moods and
Circumstances of the Moment

Gentle Caresses Most Effective.
Great Mystery of Individual
Love.

In Real Idal Marriage Sex
Harmony Grows with the
Years

Ideal of the Full Love Life and
Aged Lovers

Regulating the Sexual Life for
Maximum Health in Ad-
vanced Age

Greater Mutual Considerateness
in Modern Marriage

19

58. Art of Choosing a Mate for Ideal Marriage. Types of Men and Women According to Degrees of Sex Intensity　260

The Ten Degrees of Sex Behavior in Love-Making
How Appearances Deceive in Judging Sex Temperaments
Serious Errors in Choice: How to Avoid Them Before They Wreck Our Lives
Southern Temperaments
Oriental Temperaments
Cold Climate Temperaments
Misleading Temperaments of Women

59. Various Human Sex Types that Nature Produces　263

Heterosexuals. Homosexuals. Ambisexuals. Future Sex Types
Importance of this Study to All Persons For Personal and Social Reasons
Better Insight to Our Own Position in the World
Wider Tolerance for Those Who Differ from us Sexually by Birth

60. Dangerous Age and the Ideal Sexual Life for Maximum Health　267

Sexual Age
The Sexual Apparatus: The Law of Gradual Decline
Fading of the Overblown Flower
The Second Youth of Modern Woman: Sexual Sensibility Retained
Sex History of Husband in Married Life
Complicated Preparations for Coitus.
Sexually All Ages are Dangerous
Gentler Excitements to be Chosen
Husbanding Vitality: Marriage With Young Woman?
Importance of Sexual Rest
Squandering Strength
How Medical Aid Can Be Bene-

ficial
Unwise Prescriptions
Operative Method to Restore Power of Climax
Sex Rejuvenescence and Renewal of Youth

61. Practical Advice for Aged Married Lovers　272

The Sexual Life of the Aged Man
Awakening the Slumbering Passions: Its Dangers
Alcohol and Debauchery Perilous
How This Period of Life May Be Crowned with Blessings
A noble Repose: The Ideal in Old Age
Happiness in a World of Love Memories
Normal Exercise of Sex Function that Ensures Lasting Preservation of Strength
The Best Book for an Old man
The Sexual Life of the Aged Woman
Changes in Female Sex Anatomy
Stoppage of Sexual Congestions: Hygienic Substitutes. Home Gymnastics and Massage, Baths, Walks, Rubdowns, etc.
The Grave Mistakes of Relatives of the Old
The Excretory Functions
Lessening of Sensibility to Pain and Pleasure
How to Reduce Troubles of Old Age to a Minimum
Happy Sexual and Family Foundations in Flower of Manhood
Looking Back with Joy on Earlier Love Life

62. The Sex Periods of Our Life History　276

1. Period of Absolute Sexlessness
2. Period of Hermaphrodism
3. Period of Sex Relations between Man and Wife. Renewal of Strength in Mutual Satisfaction
How to Shape the Sex Life According to the Sex Periods

CHAPTER   PAGE

Criminality of Exciting a Child
Criminality of Demanding Un-
    natural Chastity in the Ma-
    ture
Mistakes of Judges and Moral-
    ists
Duties of the Physician
The Trio: Masturbation. Per-
    fect Coitus. Impotence

CHAPTER   PAGE

From Childish Naivete to Senile
    Exhaustion
Exceptional Cases in Extreme
    Precocious Sexuality
Premature Old Age
"Eternal" Youth
Abnormal Types
    Sex Crimes in Old Age
    Blind Frenzy in Youth

Part VI.
HEALTHIER SEX RELATIONS AND TECHNIQUES
Avoiding Ever-present Sex Dangers and Injurious Methods of Satisfaction

CHAPTER   PAGE

63. *Introductory*: Aim of this Book: To Help Make Modern Sexual Life a Source of the Greatest Human Happiness and Delight 280

Sexual Life as Source of Life-
    Energy
Greatest Happiness and Joy
    (through Ignorance a Source
    of Misery and Despair)
Preachers of False Morality as
    Poisoners of Life's Happi-
    ness
This is the First Time Sexual
    Passion has been Really
    Evaluated by Science!
Removing Prevailing Errors and
    Evils of the Sexual Life
Correcting Innumerable Sex Mis-
    takes

64. How to Attain the Optimum in the Sexual Life. Avoiding the Dangers of Sex Poverty as well as of Sex Excesses 283

Too Much and Too Little Sexual
    Life: Both Bad for Mature
    Men and Women
Prostitution Result of Unnatural
    Restraints to Ideal Love
Tragedy of Unsuitable Sex Re-
    lations
Avoiding Frightful "Regularity"
    in Marital Intercourse
Squandering of Sex Strength

CHAPTER   PAGE

How to Attain the Optimum in
    the Sexual Life, not the
    Minimum: Aim of True
    Morality
The Married Life of Fully De-
    veloped Couples
Rendering Each Other Happy
    through Sex Relations
Ideal Sexual Life in Accord with
    Nature's Laws (not Preach-
    ers')
Each Sex Act between Married
    Lovers to be a Renewal of
    Love
How Often to Indulge during the
    Different Sexual Periods of
    the Married Life for Har-
    monious Love

65. Miserable Substitutes for Ideal Sex Satisfaction which Are Scorned by Our New Generation 287

Masturbation: Its Diagnosis and
    Cure
Different Kinds of Masturba-
    tion: in Babies; in Children;
    Mutual Masterbation in Chil-
    dren; at Pubery, with Emis-
    sion; Great Care to be Taken;
    Boarding Schools (Homosex-
    ual Practices); Barracks;
    Masturbation during Mar-
    riage; Melancholic Masturba-
    tion; Senile Masturbation
Various Systems of Cure of
    Habitual Masturbation: in
    Children; in Adults

21

CHAPTER   PAGE

Soothing Healthy Effects of
Normal Loving Copulation
versus Substitute Evils
Loving Care, Not Frightening
of Patient, the Right Way
Ignorant Guides Drive Patients
to Despair — far Worse than
the Vice Itself!
Harmful and Harmless Appli-
ances
Present Forms of Marriage versus
Ideal Marriage as Outlined in
this Work
Sour Fruits of Our Present Sex
Morality
Sexual Reform Movements and
Programs
State Should Require Medical
Certificates of Health as First
Step to Insure Married Love
and Healthy Progeny
Free Love Associations versus
Indissoluble Unions
Ideal Married Love versus Free
Love Unions
Ideal Organization of the Sex-
ual Life
Monogamy versus Legal Mo-
nogamy
Marriage is Immoral without
Mutual Love
Assurance of Marital Happi-
ness: the Qualities to Choose
Widowhood: Its Ills; "Widow-
Prostitution"
The "Dangerous Age": Wid-
ow's Melancholy
Prostitution, the Mockery of Love,
is the Antithesis of Ideal
Marriage
Forms of Prostitution
Prostitution as Cause of Un-
married Women
Great Carrier of Sex Diseases
Brothels Hotbeds of Infection
Poisons the Family Life
Dread Perils of Prostitution to
the Young: The Wreck of
Health and Happiness in One
Night!
The New Generation Has High
Sex Ideals; Scorns Miserable
Makeshifts
New Era of Mutual Sex Life
versus Era of Crude Desire
for Orgasm
The New Generation versus
Prostitution: Wants Pleasures

CHAPTER   PAGE

of Companionate Love; Re-
pelled by Mercenary, Dis-
eased Prostitution

66. Sexual Restraint versus
Complete Sex
Abstinence   298
Normal Sex Exercise Stimulates
Growth and Strength
Increase of Sex Potency and Will-
Power
Dangers of Excessive Intercourse
Compared to Dangers of No
Satisfaction at all for Mature
Persons
Learning What Sexual Happiness
Really Is!
False Unscientific Notions of
Theoretical Teachers
From My 25 Years' Experience
as a Practitioner
Sexual Life Histories of My
Patients
Sex Abstinence Interrupted with
Occasional Liaisons: Dangers
of this Course
Cases of Sex Abstinence of
Adult Virgins
Psychical Disturbances
Enforced Sex Abstinence and
Hysteria
Unbalancing the Nervous Sys-
tem
Case of Typical Erotically De-
lirious Type
What are the Remedies? What
about Marriage?
Psychoanalysis
Case Histories of Three Sisters:
How Differently Sex Absti-
nence Affected Each
Case Histories Showing Intoler-
able Nymphomania; Seduc-
tion; Insanity
Suicide of Sex Abstainers
Effects of Sustained Sex Absti-
nence on Intellect: Often
Leads to Perverse Sex Prac-
tices: Sadism; Lust-Murder
Criminal Sex Occurences Result
from Hypocritical Upbringing
Normal Exercise of the Sexual
Functions Is an Essential
Condition for Full Health and
Full Vitality; for Renewal
of Life-Energy
Decided Therapeutic Effects
of Sexual Satisfaction

CHAPTER   PAGE

Auto-Intoxication of Sexually
Abstinent Women

Blood-Poisoning

Outline of Deleterious Influences on the Various Sex
Periods

Hygiene of the Future Striving
for Ideal Mode of Sex Living

67. Sex Sublimation versus Beautiful Sex Relations in Married Love   307

"Higher Things" versus "Base"
Sexual Life

Sex Sublimated Dangerous as
Teachers of the Healthy
Young

How the Sex Sublimated Un-
knowingly Fall into Perver-
sities

Morbid Influence of Sexually
Crippled Talented Persons on
Literature, Science, Art and
Racial Health

Harmonious Sexual and Spiritual
Development: Makes Impera-
tive the Crushing of Pesti-
lential Influences of Past
Ages: Imitating their Errors
Puts Weight on the Joyous
Soul of Modern Man

68. Degeneracy of the Sex Life. *Facts that Should Be Widely Known by Parents, Teachers, Judges, Ethical Leaders*   310

Aged Degenerates: In their Quest
for Abnomal Stimuli to Lost
Sexual Forces, they are Led
to Cruelty to their Unhappy
Sex Partners, Lust-Murders
and Violations

What Causes these Perverse
Acts? Modern Science Says:
Psychic Derangement; Ab-
normality in Erogenous and
Erotofugal Zones; False Ed-
ucation and Training; Over-
Refined Upbringing; Errone-
ous Impressions in Childhood;
Discrediting the Sexual Urge
instead of Perfecting it
Causes Sex Crimes and Sex

CHAPTER   PAGE

Pathology; Ignorant Official
Moralists

How to Treat Cases of Sex Degeneracy in the Humane Light
of New Science

"The More Heavily Such Cases
are Punished, the More Likely They are to Become Epi-
demic"

Mistakes of Judges

Two Modes of Treatment: Se-
clusion (in an Institution) or
Sterilization of Sufferers from
Hereditary Perversions

Preventing Propagation of Dangerous Diseases

Rendering a Man or Woman
Non-Productive: A Simple
Operation that has no Harmful Effects on Health, Potency
or Sensation

Futility of an "Appeal to Reason" in Perverse Sexual Life
Caused by Mental Derange-
ment

Useless to "Try to Teach Him
Better"

When is a Case of Sex De-
generacy Criminal? When
Pathologic?

Evils of Sex Laws Made Only
by Men

69. Unconscious Powers of Influence on Our Sexual Life   314

Replacing the Unconscious Sex
Urge by a Conscious Will
Power

Dangerous to the Sexually Uninformed

Psychology of Sexual Shame and
Modesty

Blushing from Guilt versus Blushing from Embarrassment

Important and Difficult Distinction in Judging Innocence or
Guilt

Fear a Poor Motive for Good
Behavior

The Feeling of Shame a False
Foundation for Ethical Education

CHAPTER	PAGE
Shame of Nudity Beginning to Disappear, but Bashfulness in Exposing Sex Organs Persists	
Nudity in Art; In Medical Consultations	
Conquering False Shame and Rising Superior to it	
Bringing the Sexual Life under Control of Reason	

CHAPTER	PAGE
70. Making the Sexual Life a Thing of Beauty	319
The Beauty of the New Sexual Life	
The Ideal: To Devote Every Effort to Render the Sexual Life a Thing of Intense Beauty	

THIS BOOK is not a treatise on Sexual Hygiene or Sexual Ethics. It aims primarily at establishing a firm basis for both, by means of a clearer insight into the nature of the sexual life.

All too seldom have attempts been made to fathom the profundities of the sexual life and to forge every link in the chain of causality from the minutest physical processes to the sublimest idealism of passion. Only by so doing can we fully elucidate this central problem of our existence and learn to control its impulses.

That nobody had, so far, properly attempted to do this was due not only to prudery but also to the fact that sexual phenomena run so little parallel with the other phenomena of growth, that even a scientific study of the subject is beset with countless, almost insuperable, difficulties.

To investigate the interdependence of *all* phenomena is the greatest of the tasks of Science.

Such a study will prove most valuable for one's own personal education, and quite indispensable for doctors, clergymen, and teachers, who desire to give guidance to the masses in the more intimate problems of life. Their attempts have hitherto almost always failed because they themselves were insufficiently instructed in the subject. Even in medical text-books the sexual passion with its intricate problems has been to this day almost entirely neglected, and yet every adult feels only too keenly in his own soul that in this sphere are found the most important mainsprings of conduct, determining happiness or misery, sickness or health. We doctors have to pick up in our practice all that should have been taught us at the medical schools. The material on which I base my observations I collected as a family physician in a large city (Rotterdam) but it was not until I had given up my practice that I found sufficient leisure to elaborate it. I have endeavoured to present it in a form which can be understood by educated laymen as well. How many unmarried people are there whose love-life has been unsatisfactory, how many married people whose marriages have fallen short of the ideal, how many parents who are anxious to bring up their children wisely, but do not know how.

One of the greatest triumphs of modern democracy is that all problems which are significant for conduct and happiness in life are becoming more and more the concern of all, instead of remaining limited to savants

This endeavour to make myself comprehensible to lay people has other advantages as well, for often it is only when we try to avoid the traditional technical terms that we feel the need for a clearer proof of our theories.

Up to the present, scientific students of the sexual life have always gone astray because they have considered procreation as its final goal, and have looked on sexual pleasure as a mere by-product, whereas in reality it is often the other way about.

In order to avoid this cardinal error, and to evaluate correctly sexual pleasure in its biological significance, I have in this book taken the male, rather than the female, sexual life as my starting-point, especially because, owing to the more superficial situation of the sexual organs in man, the physical aspects of his sexual life are more easily observed, while in the female the connection between psychical feelings and physical urges is much less apparent, and often scarcely perceived by herself. For woman, love is a veiled secret; for man, a naked truth. As an object for study I prefer to begin with the naked truth.

Woman will then be better able to ascertain for herself, and to describe, how she feels the life-impulses.

DR. J. RUTGERS

Part I.

ANATOMY AND FUNCTION OF
SEX ORGANS IN MAN AND WOMAN

Sex Attraction . Sex Health . Hygiene . Rejuvenation

Chapter 1

TWO MAIN SOURCES OF OUR SEXUAL LIFE

MOST errors arise not from absolute ignorance but from an inexact conception of just those things which one thinks one knows best. This is especially true in the sphere of sex. The simplest and clearest possible presentation of the underlying physical phenomena should therefore always be given first.

The physical foundation and starting point of our whole sexual life, with all its weal and woe, with all its profound agitations and emotions, are to be found in two minute organs, two small tumours, which in the adult body furnish the reproductive cells. These are, as everyone knows, in the male the two *testes* or *testicles,* hard and round, as big as a finger-joint, which produce the sperm-cells; in the female the two *ovaries,* in shape and size like a dried plum, which furnish the egg-cells.

These two types of organs are often grouped together under the name of *Gonads,* or *Sexual Glands.*

It is essentially the testes or the ovaries, as the case may be which determine the sexual difference, because they produce the reproductive cells and also because of the specific chemical constituents which they pour into the blood stream.

The most extraordinary thing about the testicles is that they migrate from the abdominal cavity where they are developed, in order to form a special outgrowth at the bottom of the belly. The testicles in man, like the ovaries in woman, are originally developed fairly high up in the abdominal cavity on either side of the lumbar vertebrae. But in the higher mammals and in man the testicles leave their original situation before birth and move lower and lower, like a hernia, forcing a passage right through the muscle fibres of the abdominal wall and pushing the peritoneum before them. They never break through the skin, but at last, approaching each other in the groins, they drop into two folds of the skin at the lower part of the body between the thighs. These folds are a continuation of the gluteal folds, and analogous to the folds which in the female form the *labia majora.* In the male, however, they grow together to form a single sac called the *scrotum* containing the testicles, divided by an internal septum. The raphé in the median line of the body, where the two halves of the scrotum meet, is clearly seen even in the adult.

The two testicles are quite palpable in the scrotum, and so also is the *sperm-duct* (seminal canal) on each side. The latter feels like a thin hard cord. Fortunately, the two testicles hardly ever hang at the same level, otherwise they would often be squeezed together and cause pain. This is easily understood, as they had to accomodate themselves to each other even *in utero*.

Anteriorly, i.e., seen from in front, the scrotum is partially covered by a continuation of the urinary passage, the copulatory organ (the *membrum virile* or penis).

In girls, the ovaries migrate downwards a little before birth and take up a position about the level of the upper margin of the pubic bone.

Even if the descent of the testicles was originally a pathological process, it must be admitted that this migration of both testicles to the exterior of the body, is to be considered as a wholly important event in the history of evolution. Thus, these organs at once become far more accessible than previously to external and voluntary stimulation. This intensifies the male sexual life very considerably and brings it more completely into the realm of consciousness. The increased vulnerability and the possibilities of subsequent hernia which inevitably accompanied this change would certainly count little against the gigantic advantage. This is shown most clearly by the fact that in the survival of the fittest the descended testis has gained the victory, and that the higher orders with their increased sexuality have reached a higher stage of development.

Chapter 2

SEX GLANDS OF MAN AND WOMAN (GONADS)

THE TWO kinds of organs hitherto discussed—testicles and ovaries—are frequently grouped together under the same of Sex Glands. But are they really glands? This question is not an idle speculation; it concerns the very foundation of the sexual life.

We shall never have a proper insight into the nature of the sexual life, as long as we consider this function merely as a glandular secretion. To do this, is to overlook the most important point. Sexual life is something *sui generis*. It is the originating of new life, going hand in hand with secretion. In the male the function of secretion, in the woman the creation of new life is predominant.

I have discussed tumour-formation rather fully here because the first mis-en-scène of the sexual life is a kind of tumour-formation—the first modification of growth in contrast with ordinary vegetative growth.

Now there are two special organs in the male: the two *testicles*—which though constructed like a typical gland do not at first secrete anything at all. Only at puberty do they begin to secrete countless fresh vigorous young cells—the male *sperm-cells*—mixed with a lot of mucus, just as if it were an ordinary glandular secretion.

This production of fresh vigorous young cells which will give rise to the next generation does not fit into our conception of a glandular secretion. For the substances secreted by a gland are its waste products, mixed perhaps with dead and disintegrated cell-fragments.

Chapter 3

SEX EXPERIMENTS OF NATURE

AFTER these preliminary attempts to find our bearings, we shall start from the very origin and consider the fertilised ovum as it lies in the uterus, in its most primitive embryonic condition, before it is attached to the uterine wall. At this period it derives a scanty nourishment from the maternal serum in which it floats. Not till later, at the end of the first three months, when the original store of energy possessed by the fertilised ovum is coming to an end, do a few blood-vessels grow from the embryo towards the uterine wall, where they ramify to form the placenta (afterbirth). Through this, by osmosis, the blood of the embryo obtains nourishment from and gives up its waste products to the blood of the mother. The offspring is now no longer known as the embryo but as the *foetus* and lives as a parasite on the maternal circulation until its birth. Thereafter it has an independent existence, feeds on other organisms, and grows, at first swiftly, but with gradually decreasing energy until puberty.

The first or embryonic stage is a very primitive one. The gill-clefts are beginning to form the face. The whole body is still open in the medial line anteriorly. Two *primordial kidneys* subserve the scanty urinary function. Four small eminences appear about the third week, which will soon develop into legs and arms. All external evidence of sexual differentiation is still lacking.

At this stage one cannot discern even any *internal* sexual differentiation. Development proceeds quite systematically. Every process of growth takes place by normal cell division and all the different tissues develop *pari passu* without mutual interference. When the embryo has developed to a certain point and the primordial kidney (*Wolffian body*) is completely formed, a new phenomenon occurs. There now appears at each side of the lumbar column, a thickening of the epithelial layer which lines the interior of the body cavity. These gradually develop as small growths or tumours. They are the first rudiments of the bilateral reproductive tumours. The first evidence of this change to be seen under the microscope is a tendency of the epithelial cells and the underlying connective

32

tissue to invade each other. This increases until the epithelial cells become separated into small aggregations surrounded by connective tissue.

Here, too, the segregation of these cell-masses has most far-reaching consequences—it is the beginning of the whole sexual life. In the ordinary course of events these cells would have become differentiated to form a surface epithelium, and, when old and degenerated, would have been cast off as dead cells. Now, however, that they are buried deep in other tissues they retain their original embryonic characters, no matter how much they are multiplied by cell division. When at last the time of their final cell division comes, they will reach the surface as young cells.

These isolated masses of epithelial cells may develop further in one of two different ways. This is the starting point of a divergence which becomes an actual sexual differentiation at puberty. In some embryos there is always one cell in each mass which attains a larger size and will eventually develop into a mature *egg-cell*. Such an embryo will eventually become a female. The formation of such egg-cell rudiments continues until the end of the second year of extra-uterine life.

In other embryos, however, i.e., in those which are to become males, all the cells of each aggregation undergo multiplication and form a large number of tiny cells which become arranged close together round a small central cavity. These tumours continue to grow and come to invade two neighboring glandular organs which are situated on either side of the vertebral column. The latter are the primordial kidneys (Wolffian bodies) which by this time are functioning. They are invaded, and the tiny cavities, which have meantime elongated to form tubules, join with the microscopic tubules of the primordial kidney. The two elements now form a compound organ known henceforward as the *testis*.

Later on, in the adult male, only the efferent sexual canal is derived from the Wolffian body, while the reproductive cells are furnished by the other part of the testis which corresponds to the original reproductive tumour. The two Wolffian bodies cease to function as secretors of urine and are replaced by two new, active, fully developed kidneys. But even in the adult testis, the typical glandular structure remains so obvious that, at first sight, one would think it was only a typical gland.

So on each side the epithelial protuberance develops into a mass which bulges out more and more and finally separates off from its base. In this way, the two testes lose their support posteriorly and come to sink down anteriorly. They are now only suspended by their efferent ducts which are, so to speak, their pedicles. They sink downwards in a graceful curve on either side of the urinary bladder until they reach first the inguinal region and finally the scrotum (vide chapter 1).

So later, after puberty, when the sperm-cells are voided, they follow the original urinary passage of the Wolffian body which at first ascends steeply, until the two sperm-ducts approach each other from right and left to join the unpaired urethra deep in the abdominal cavity.

In the same way two reproductive masses of the female type become separated from their bases, but remain attached by a few strands of connective tissue, so that the two ovaries do not sink down nearly so far as do the testicles. Furthermore, there is no coalescence with a glandular organ, so an ovary is considerably smaller and flatter than a testicle, of simpler shape, just like a tumour. For in embryos which undergo female development, the Wolffian bodies and their efferent ducts disappear, leaving only a few vestiges. For this reason, when in the course of time the egg-cells become ripe, they will not be so fortunate as to find an efferent duct ready for them, as do the sperm-cells. After puberty, each time an egg-cell ripens, it must, like an abscess, force its way straight through the ovarian tissue by destruction of the surrounding cells. It reaches the surface of the ovary, bulges outwards, and, leaving traces of hemorrhage and scar tissue behind, it becomes free and falls into the abdominal cavity. And what follows?

Fortunately, in every embryo, there is on each side not only the Wolffian body, with its duct, but also another canal. This opens exteriorly at the lower pole of the body and remains open at its inner end within the abdominal cavity.

Finally, we come to the external "genitals" which we may better call the external efferent-duct-system of the embryonic Wolffian body and the rudimentary pronephros, for only after puberty will this system be used for sexual purposes.

Both of the above-mentioned efferent canals lead to the lower pole of the body of the embryo, where their orifice forms a small protrusion called (in anticipation) the genital eminence. Later on in embryonic life, when the body cavity is closed and the genital eminence has become a small protuberance, it is still difficult to decide from this small papilla, whether it will develop into a *clitoris* with a short urethra or into a *penis*. Likewise, a pair of folds between the thighs may grow together to form a *scrotum* or remain separated to form two *labia majora*. Not before the tenth week after fertilisation, i.e., towards the close of the embryonic period, does the future sexual differentiation begin to be evident externally. In the male, the urethra becomes lengthened and is joined on either side by the "seminal" canals. Long before birth, these organs take on their permanent form. Although for many years the whole apparatus will continue to grow *pari passu* with other organs, yet the genital function will remain in abeyance, and meanwhile only the urinary system will be active.

Appendix on Hermaphrodism

Thus we see that the sexual differentiation is not so easy to determine as is generally supposed. At the very beginning of embryonic life, the genital masses are non-existent, and later, even when they do develop, it is at first impossible to decide how they will differentiate. As has been shown, the external genitals, too, are at first quite undifferentiated.

Not infrequently, especially in cases of arrested development in boys, this uncertainty may persist until puberty or even later. In such cases, one speaks of hermaphrodism or double sexuality because, although such individuals may not really be double-sexed, still they have some attributes of each sex. So, in ancient days, the imagination of man pictured double-sexed individuals who were termed hermaphrodites, because they combined the attributes of the god Hermes (Mercury) with the goddess Aphrodite (Venus). A real functional hermaphrodism is found only in some lower animals such as snails and earthworms, where every adult individual is capable of both male and female activity. Whenever they copulate, two male projections may be noticed, which deposit the semen. In the vegetable kingdom, in the same way, most flowers contain both male and female organs.

In the history of evolution of species, the hermaphroditic condition is a transitional stage between asexuality and sexual differentiation. (Vide chapter 40.)

In our individual development, a similar stage can be traced. We have seen above that during one period of the development of the embryo there exists a condition of double sexuality which is transitional between asexuality and sexual differentiation. This is true, however, only of the duct system. During this period, the efferent duct of the Wolffian body and that of the pronephros exist side by side. This conforms to Haeckel's law of a certain parallelism between phyligeny and ontogeny. In the adult body, each sex has only vestiges of the efferent duct system of the other sex.

Only Professor L. Pick of Berlin was once able to demonstrate the ovarian portion of an ovotestis with ripe egg-cells and the

35

testicular portion with rudimentary sperm-cells (*gametogonia*). This was the first time that the true hermaphrodism of the reproductive cells was established in man, or, indeed, in any mammal. The microscopic slides of this case were taken from one Augusta Persdotter, aged forty-three, and were prepared by the Swedish savant, E. Salén, 1898. After the death of the latter they were re-examined by Professor Pick in 1913 when these findings were established.

Chapter 4

NEW SEX EXPERIMENTS AND DISCOVERIES
FOR IMPROVING SEXUAL LIFE

FOR some considerable time, the true significance of several small, functionally obscure organs in the human body has been a vexing question. Finally it was found that they contain important chemical constituents which they pour into the blood-circulation. These substances are of great importance for the body-metabolism.

It has been observed that after radical extirpation of such an organ as the thyroid gland for exophthalmic goitre, the patient begins to suffer from general trophic disturbances, such as puffiness of the skin, dry epidermis, slowing of all mental activities, which might go on to complete imbecility. These symptoms will at once abate if the patient is given small portions of the thyroid gland, e.g., that of the sheep, or thyroid extract. It was further noted that the same treatment proved effective in the case of patients suffering from the same symptoms, which had manifested themselves spontaneously, without any operation. A small portion of this organochemical substance acts as a stimulant to the tissue metabolism. It cures obesity, renders the epidermis lustrous, and even improves cretinism, whereas a larger dose acts as a heart-poison, which may be observed by the acceleration of the pulse-rate. As far as the sexual life is concerned, it may be added that, in a child in whom the thyroid gland is removed at an early period of its life, sexual maturity is retarded or prevented altogether.

At first it was believed that organs which furnished such extremely active substances, represented a new type of gland. As no efferent duct was found, their activity was referred to as "internal secretion", a term which is self-contradictory. But more and more such organs with active products were subsequently discovered, e.g., the thymus, the supra-renal bodies, the hypophysis (pituitary), etc.

The physiological effect of muscular tissue, especially of its extract, which acts as a stimulant and in excessive doses increases the pulse-rate, but is a cardiac poison[1], had been known for some time, as was the fat-reducing effect of the Banting cure.

Thus, it became increasingly clear that all living organs contain typical chemical substances as the metabolic products of their ordinary cell-life. These katabolic substances are passed into the circulation by means of the lymph. We should only use the term *gland* when we find the typical structure of a gland, especially when a duct is to be found which serves to convey the waste products towards either the external surface of the body or the internal surface of the alimentary canal. All other tissues and organs, not excluding the above mysterious ones, give up their waste products to the circulation by means of the lymphatic system.

Our normal health depends chemically on the neutral equilibrium of all those substances contained in the blood-stream either as food for the tissues or as their waste products. Organochemical therapy aims at adding those substances, of which in a given case there may be an insufficient quantity.

These considerations suggest a reason why, in the human body, all sorts of rudimentary organs which have long lost their significance, still persist, instead of having been eliminated. This is probably due to the fact that on account of their organochemical constituents, these organs are still of some value in the struggle for existence. Indeed, the recent study of organochemistry began with the consideration of these very organs.

It was also noticed that if the testicles or ovaries were removed, the patient became feeble and debilitated. Hence, the organochemical effect of these organs was also studied. Brown-Séquard experimented with extracts of bull's testicles and met with some success. But far more definite results are obtained if, instead of administering extracts to the experimental animal, the living organs are implanted into it, e.g., into the muscles of the abdominal wall. Only by this procedure is a permanent effect likely to be obtained.

By experiments of this sort on animals, it has been proved that the organochemical substances derived from the testis or ovary are of paramount importance for the development of secondary sexual characters[2].

1. The danger of a meat diet in nephritis, and in the toxaemias of pregnancy with unconsciousness and nephritis are perhaps to be attributed to the same organochemical substances. A pregnant woman is doubly endangered, since she receives in her circulation not only the waste products of her own muscular tissue but also of the foetus. Under these conditions a meat diet constitutes a third source of danger.

2. There is a heated controversy as to which cells in these organs produce the substances in question.

38

The evidence afforded by the experiments of Professor Eugen Steinach (of the Biological Institute in Vienna) on rats and guinea-pigs, is incontrovertible. When still very young, their own testes or ovaries were removed, i.e., they were castrated or spayed. Then the reproductive masses of the opposite sex were implanted into their abdominal musculature. The reproductive elements of the implanted organs degenerated, but the other tissues proliferated[3].

So that later on, only that part of the graft which produces organochemical substances could function. If the grafts took successfully, the animals, though eunuchs, developed secondary sexual characteristics, not those, however, of their original sex, but of that of the implanted organs. The masculinized, originally female animals, acquired a more robust build, and attempted to tread normal females, etc. In the feminized, originally male animals, the nipples developed, they showed a feminine coyness, took the female part in coitus, etc. Indeed, feminized male rats even suckled one or two young ones with maternal tenderness!

Thus the presence of either testes or ovaries decides the development of the sexual characters, not only because of the production of egg-cells or sperm-cells, but also because of the specific organochemical substances which are poured by these organs into the circulation. These organochemical substances are responsible for the sexual stimulus by which our whole bodily development, and our psyche as well, is dominated. Especially these organochemical substances govern the appearance of one or other type of secondary sexual characters, as has been shown. Investigators have gone a step further and have inquired if they are not ultimately responsible for the appearance of the reproductive cells also, which is, after all, the most important point. Elsewhere too, new tissue-formation is often seen to be provoked by chemical stimuli, e.g., by toxins which are organochemical substances derived from bacteria and other micro-organisms.

We saw that organochemical substances derived from our own tissues might be active in the same way. We pointed out that if the thyroid gland is removed radically in childhood, sexual maturity will be retarded, or may be suppressed altogether. It cannot be doubted, after Steinach's experiments on animals, that the organic substances from testis and ovary have at least an equal influence in this direction.

This theory is corroborated by the fact that sexual maturity can be produced artificially at other periods of life, if one can suc-

3. At the age of puberty, also a striking proliferation of the interstitial tissue of the testis is noticed. For this reason, the interstitial portion has been called the "puberal gland".

ceed in starting the production of the respective organochemical substances.

Thus, Professor Steinach has succeeded in restoring fully the formation of reproductive cells in rats sterile from old age. He did this by artificially exciting the secretion of the respective organochemical substances. An obvious, though temporary, rejuvenation resulted. In male rats, the ligature and section of one sperm-duct was all that was needed. This caused the sperm-producing element in the corresponding testicle to atrophy, and the other element to hypertrophy. In female rats, however, implantation of a young ovary was necessary.

Such "rejuvenation treatment", as it is called, has been successful, though as yet only over a short period, in the treatment of impotence in men. It might possibly be also effective in curing frigidity in women.

These radical operations should, however, not be undertaken too lightly, for such a condition is sometimes Nature's method of ensuring mental repose.

Professor Steinach also succeeded in artificially producing a premature sexual maturity in very young animals. He was able to do this by any agency which would destroy the rudiments of the reproductive cells and cause proliferation of the other tissues. The following are such agencies: transplantation to some other site; X-radiation; heat; intoxication; and in males, ligature and section of both sperm-ducts. Unfortunately, if the reproductive masses are damaged on both sides, all formation of reproductive cells is henceforth impossible. I have not been able to ascertain whether this last experiment has been done unilaterally. If so, the premature sexual maturity might be accompanied by the production of reproductive cells. In this connection, the following case of a unilateral lesion, in which there occurred seminal nocturnal emissions in childhood, is very significant.

I refer to the case reported by Lacchi[4]. This case was a boy, aged nine, four feet seven inches high, with beard, erections, sexual appetite and sexual emissions. The left testicle was amputated for carcinoma, and within four months every one of the above phenomena disappeared. This disappearance is significant as a control-test.

The appearance of sexual phenomena is thus a profound modification of normal vegetative growth. This modification manifests

4. An analogous case is mentioned in the "Zeitschrift für Sexualwissenschaft", August 1921, page 167. A girl, aged six, with fully-developed breasts, had sarcoma of the ovary. This was extirpated. The phenomena of premature nubility disappeared. The patient became a child again.

40

itself first as a change in the composition of the body-fluids, and later by a new cell-formation — two processes which are hardly separable. Similarly, it is the sap of the tree which causes its fruit to grow.

We do not know at present exactly how these organochemical substances determine the direction of sexual desire. Theoretically one might suppose that these specific substances exert specific influences on the brain-cells. But this may be regarded as rather speculative and does not help us much.

The following hypothesis appears to me more probable- It is as we have just seen an essential condition of life for all animal organisms that the different organochemical toxins should balance and if necessary neutralise each other. In a hermaphrodite animal the corresponding toxin of the gonads might easily fulfil this condition. But since division of the sexes has taken place (vide chapter 40) copulation may be regarded as a rather imperfect means to the same end. While the exchange of juices in kissing and copulation is not very considerable, a mingling of cells does occur. In the process of fertilisation the cells concerned practically neutralise each other biochemically by chemiotaxis, so the next generation is for the time being undifferentiated. Thus from the very beginning only such individuals could properly procreate in whom this ancient impulse to find an antitoxin for its own toxin persisted unimpaired. Thus even today the toxin of the ovaries causes attraction towards the male, and the toxin of the testis an attraction towards the female, in the same way as during the consumption of food all plants and animals prefer those constituents of which they are at the moment in want[6]; and thus both the mutual attraction of the reproductive cells and the mutual attraction of the two sexes may ultimately depend on organochemical chemiotaxis.

Possibly, however, hereditary influences are concerned in producing equal numbers of males and females, as the Mendelian theory would indicate. In his hybridisation experiments in his garden, Mendel crossed white beans of pure stock with dark beans of pure stock. Later, white sheep of pure stock and black sheep of pure stock were crossed, and so with all sorts of obvious characters. In man, hereditary characters like haemophilia and colour blindness were tested in the same way and statistics kept. In these experiments with plants and animals, hybrids resulted which were crossed again with each other in various combinations and generations. After many experiments Mendel could predict in what ratio in any particular case the characteristics in question would appear. There are cases in which the respective characters are to be ex-

5. Several other authors have frequently pointed out the analogy between the copulation-impulse and the food-impulse.

41

pected in equal numbers. Possibly there is some similar basis for the ratio of the two sexes.

Appendix on Hermaphrodism

Besides the different types and gradations of hermaphridism mentioned at the end of the previous chapter, we must refer to that kind of hermaphrodism which occurs if the organochemical substances of both sexes are produced in the same individual.

The possibility of this type of bisexuality cannot be denied, for such cases have been produced experimentally. On simultaneously grafting testes and ovaries into animals previously castrated, Steinach obtained a bisexual type, a kind of artificial hermaphrodite, showing alternate periods of male and female tendencies. On microscopic examination these were found to coincide with alternating proliferation of (1) interstitial tissue of the testes and (2) of the tissues surrounding the egg-rudiments of the ovary. On the other hand, Kunt Sand found both tendencies occurring simultaneously in such experiments.

This hermaphroditic experiment is of special importance for the comprehension of sexual differentiation, because it brings us considerably nearer the solution of a difficult question. Men are known to exist who feel no sexual attraction towards women but rather a pronounced sexual craving towards men, i.e., towards their own sex, for which reason they are called homosexual. Similarly, there are homosexual women who are only attracted towards women. Since we know through Steinach's experiments that sexual attraction towards one or other of the sexes is largely determined by the presence of organochemical substances derived from either testis or ovary, the inference was drawn that such an individual peculiarity whenever it is congenital, is to be imputed to the presence of the wrong organochemical substances. A man need not possess an ovary, nor a woman a testis; it would be sufficient if the testis contained ovarian tissues and vice versa.

Steinach's above-mentioned experiment teaches that cases with such a hybrid gonad may be produced artificially, and at the end of the previous chapter we found that such hybrid cases occur naturally. Further observations at post-mortems and possibly during operations will have to elucidate how many cases of homosexuality are due to such hybrid gonads.

In the meantime these discoveries have already produced signal results. During the summer of 1916, Dr. Lichtenstern is said to have succeeded in rendering a pronouncedly homosexual man pronouncedly heterosexual, at the patient's own request by bilateral

42

castration and subsequent implantation of a normal testicle which was removed from another patient on account of cryptoschism (imperfect descent). The transformed homosexual has subsequently contracted a happy, though sterile, marriage.

Even should this type of operation prove successful, the majority of homosexual individuals will probably hesitate to have it performed on them. They are not unhappy on account of their peculiarity, but rather on account of our prejudices. It is we who are diseased and in need of cure. We must accept the fact that Nature has not endowed all people with the same sexual desires. Even the separation of the sexes is not absolute.

Chapter 5

SEX CHANGES IN MATURE MALE AND FEMALE

WHEN at puberty the primary energy of childhood has died down and the growth of all the organs of the body is almost complete, both sexes to their great astonishment feel a new impulse. This is a recurrence of growth-energy emanating from the two small reproducctive masses, which after their rapid development during the embryonic period, remain quiescent, as if they were destined to be rudimentary organs of no value. Now, however, there occurs suddenly a new stimulus to tissue-formation, and this setting free of unicellular organisms is the first beginning of the real sexual life, for hitherto the sexual life had only been of an infantile type.

During this period new life animates the testes and the ovaries. In the testes marked proliferation of the interstitial tissue occurs, whereby the organochemical substances referred to in the last chapter are elaborated, and from now onwards countless spermcells are formed and voided in large numbers at short intervals. In the ovaries, too, organochemical substances but of different kind are formed and from now onward semi-fluid egg-cells are matured and cast off though at much longer intervals. We have seen how the egg-cells have to force a laborious passage through the ovarian tissue. But how is the new cell-type formed in the male?

Now let us take the approach of sexual maturity. Caused by the specific action of the organochemical substances referred to in the preceding chapter, and accompanied by great local venous congestion, large numbers of newly formed sperm-cells make their appearance, and there occurs a profound local effect, and sometimes a profound general effect, psychical and physical, as well. As soon as conditions are favourable, the sperm-cells approach the egg-cells which are rich in food and towards which they are chemotactically attracted. By themselves they are incapable of separate existence as unicellular organisms. The next consequence comprises two categories of phenomena, increased tissue-formation and increased tissue-destruction.

All those influences which are apt to stimulate the sexual desire too much and which should, therefore, be avoided by persons who are easily aroused sexually, as we shall discuss more fully later on (chapted 32), are, curiously enough, exactly those which should be avoided in inflammations and conditions of pyrexia. Contraindicated in both cases are: any local mechanical pressure, increase in blood pressure, the consumption of spicy food and other stimulants, especially alcohol, all superfluous nourishment, especially of an albuminous nature, local heat, local massage, psychic exaltation. Conversely, those drugs which inhibit sexual excitation, as quinine, and salicylic-acid-preparations, are the most useful antipyretics.

Fever and heat are originally devices of nature which increase the energy of metabolism and so remove noxious influences. It is a pity that this remedy occasionally acts with too great a violence. Similarly, sexual life is an increase in energy, without which cessation and decay (vide chapter 66) would set in after the body has almost reached the end of development. It is most unfortunate that it so often appears with such unbridled violence. In the same way as relief is always experienced after the voiding of pus, so sexual desire is relieved every time the reproductive cells are cast forth. A certain analogy between the two cannot be denied.

We shall not, however, confine our parallel to the pathological point of view. Biologically considered, any kind of tissue-formation, even of a pathological nature, is the expression of certain growth-energy, which must be present to produce the tissue-formation at all. If we consider the various types of tissue-formation as they appear at various periods of life, we shall find an underlying definite scheme, since the diverse tissue-formations are an expression of a multifarious growth-energy pertaining to different periods of our life.

In youth the energy of growth is still at its height, and during this period it expresses itself in normal vegetative growth. As soon as this energy of growth becomes exhausted, it can manifest itself only in a different manner, namely, in the formation of unicellular sexual organisms. When with advancing age this form of energy, too, ceases, there occurs a typical, abnormal pathological tissue-formation only here and there, in the different body tissues. These are often without significance, and may pass unnoticed, though sometimes they are malignant and fatal.

Thus it is evident that the sexual cell-formation of sperm-cells and egg-cells occupies a position intermediate between normal growth which governs everything in childhood, and pathological tissue-formations as they appear in age. This defines the peculiar position of the sexual life in contrast to our normal vegetative existence, and throws a different light (vide chapter 40) on the history of sexual evolution.

When the reproductive cells have once become separated from the parent cells they must be discharged from the body. Even as regards this discharge, the reproductive cells occupy a position intermediate between increase of growth on the one hand and the tumours of age on the other.

In normal growth, only the superficial layer of cells of the epidermis or mucous membrane is spontaneously cast off, when worn out and degenerated. In more deeply situated tissues only the waste products are got rid of through the lymphatics or sometimes, even through special glandular ducts. All these processes occur naturally; external influences such as massage, etc., may help but are by no means indispensable.

In pathological tissue-formations, however, the surgeon's knife is nearly always required to remove the tumour.

In sexual cell-formation the casting-off is not so easy as in ordinary growth, but, normally, not as difficult as in pathological tissue-formations. We shall discuss this as it occurs in the two sexes in a little more detail.

At first, in both sexes, there is no need for external aid. Later on, however, the act of copulation is normally required for the emptying of the seminal vesicles in man and for the proper contraction of the uterus in woman. For the act of copulation, a partner is, however, necessary. We have here the curious phenomenon that two individuals are required for the natural performance of a physiological need. It is fortunate that, for other physiological functions, such as digestion and respiration, a partner is not required.

As in the removal of a pathological growth, an operation is necessary, so in this case, the woman will in time, after fertilisation has taken place, require the services of an accoucheur. At least his advice and assistance are often required during parturition and only too frequently operative interference is unavoidable.

Though our unnatural and far too sedentary mode of life, and our often very unsuitable clothing, may be in part responsible for the complication of parturition, in the history of human progress, we should not forget that even in the most primitive races, and in higher animals, birth is far from being a simple process. In the most normal cases the separation of the newly born from the umbilical cord is a sanguinary operation, which is unavoidable even in wild animals, who tear or bite it through.

It is certainly a great advance for us men, that our new found

46

cells are always of a microscopic size and that they have a point of exit ready at hand, while in woman the final process of separation is often very difficult. If in their marital relationship the two partners are grateful to each other for their mutual aid, the mother is possibly far more grateful to the accoucheur when everything has gone off well. And the solemn kiss given to the accoucheur, which used to be customary in high society, was no less heartfelt expression of gratitude and no less sacred than the parting kiss after marital intercourse.

Chapter 6

UNIQUE JOURNEY OF NEW SPERM-CELLS

WE SHALL now note how, after maturation and separation, the sperm-cells find an exit along a very convoluted duct-system. Unlike that of the female organism this path, though uninterrupted, is very complicated. This is not surprising in view of the fact that an embryonic renal system has been utilised. We must descend into the mysterious workshop of nature, in the cellar of our body, where we find two explosives which constantly convulse the world. It is not a death-dealing explosion, however, but a life-giving one. Let us carefully examine the structure of such a testicle.

When it reaches its final shape just before birth, it is not spherical, but ovoid, bean-shaped like a small kidney, but rather less flattened. The small organ is surrounded by a very resistant capsule of connective tissue, and internally it contains no fluid but only solid material. On dissection it is seen to be made of countless finely convoluted tubules which have been referred to and which under the microscope look like ordinary gland-ducts. Internally they are lined by a layer of cells which look like gland-cells but which are derived from the epithelial cells which were segregated in the embryo. To the naked eye these canals appear as thin threads, like a torn piece of crochet-work, all tightly packed into longish cones, which are separated from each other by firm connective-tissue septa. These septa are really prolongations of the external capsule which project between the cones and become thinner as they proceed. The whole scheme is really somewhat similar to that of the kidney. The softer tissue between the fine canals is the interstitial tissue which in all probability manufactures as its metabolic product, the above-mentioned typical organochemical substances governing sexual differentiation. The apices of these cones are directed towards a single point at the centre of the slightly concave side of the testicle corresponding to the point in the kidney where the efferent duct and the blood-vessels emerge, and to the spot in the bean where the embryo is situated.

These fine canals gradually amalgamate to form larger ones

(thus giving the cones their shape) and at the point where the cone-tips meet, and larger canals emerge, these larger canals, still strongly convoluted, form a thickening, the epididymus, at the hilum of the testis. In this way, the reniform shape is disguised, and the whole organ appears somewhat ovoid like the phalanx of a finger.

In the epididymis, the larger canals converge further to form a single duct which finally emerges at one pole of the testicle, suspending the latter lengthwise.

This duct which is firm-walled and unconvoluted is known as the *vas deferens*. As mentioned, it may be felt as a thickened cord through the skin of the scrotum, and seems as if it were the stalk by which the testicle remains suspended after its descent. In reality, it is the first part of the male genital canal. The sperm-duct runs upwards from the testicle along the groin, enters the abdominal cavity, describes a graceful curve at the side of the urinary bladder, and proceeds to the posterior aspect of its base. Here the two sperm-ducts converge and open with very fine apertures into the wide urethra. From this point onwards the urethra serves to convey both urine and semen.

Just before opening into the urethra each sperm-duct is provided with a lateral reservoir, the *seminal vesicle*. These are elongated and lie on each side against the posterior wall of the bladder.

When we use the terms *seminal canal* and *seminal vesicle*, we must remember that these are traditional names bound up with traditional errors. If one chooses names drawn from plant life, one would not say *semen* (seed) but rather *pollen*, for seed is the end result in the ripe fruit. In some races, however, and especially among the ancients, we find the view that the male supplies the seed and the female is simply the field in which it is sown. This is surely the height of male vanity. (vide chapter 50.)

This whole apparatus remains in its rudimentary latent condition till the age of puberty. Even the cells lining the minute canals remain inactive until puberty, since they are not glandular cells. We have shown in the previous chapter how, after puberty, sperm-cells are formed in millions by a new and unusual type of cell division. They are detached with a minimum of moisture and are simply pushed along by the newly formed cells behind them. In their further course in the epididymus, they are transported more actively by the ciliated epithelium which lines the tubes there.

Finally, the sperm-cells reach the two lateral appendages: the seminal vesicles. Many enter these and mix with the mucous secretion of their walls while others collect in the seminal-duct and only mix with the mucous secretion, when, at the right time, a strong contraction of the seminal vesicles and the seminal-duct occurs. The resulting mixture of mucus and sperm-cells is known as the semen, and is ejected into the urethra and thence out of the body.

Up till now the sperm-cells could only remain motionless like the egg-cells, but now there is enough space for them to move actively. A sperm-cell under the high power of the microscope appears like a longish dot (the part of the mother-cell cast off at the reduction division), provided with a curved hair-like tail (*flagellum* or *cilium*). The whole consists of almost fluid protoplasm. Have you seen frog-spawn in an early larval stage in an aquarium, when the black spot acquires a filiform tail and rushes about in the water? This bears a crude and highly magnified, but pretty accurate, resemblance to the movement of the sperm-cells, when a sufficient quantity of fluid medium enables them to become active.

Like a boat propelled by the spiral movements of a single oar at the stern, the small spot, the sperm-cell, is propelled forwards by the wavy motions of the flagellum at its hinder end. Every freely-moving cell is attracted by food and other useful chemical substances (positive chemotaxis) and repelled by poisons and other noxious influences which would coagulate protoplasm (negative chemotaxis). And so, as soon as the sperm-cell, which is almost devoid of deuteroplasm (yolk), enters the female genital organ, it is attracted by positive chemotaxis towards the egg-cell, which is of far greater size and contains much deuteroplasm.

A sperm-cell consists of little more than a nucleus and a flagellum, while an ovum, like any ordinary cell, has a large amount of deuteroplasm surrounding the nucleus. Under exceptional circumstances, in some lower animals, it is possible for an egg-cell to live and develop into an adult individual without conjugation with a sperm-cell (Parthenogenesis), but we know of no instance of a similar development of a sperm-cell without the aid of an egg-cell.

The sperm-cell and egg-cell differ greatly in size[1]. The latter, which is spherical, has a diameter of 17 millimetres and can just be seen with the naked eye, while the former, including the tail, is only .05 mm. long. The passage of the sperm-cell along the moist walls of the vagina and uterus is like a great ocean voyage. For these delicate creatures it is a fateful journey fraught with the danger of utter destruction. Of the 200 million sperm-cells discharged at a single ejaculation, only one survives if fertilisation ensues.

1. The total number of egg-cells present in the ovary of a woman is far smaller. Henle found in the ovary of a girl aged 18 years 36,000 egg-rudiments; Sappey in a girl aged 3 years found 400 thousand egg-rudiments, of which three or four hundred probably reach maturity and are cast off.

Even in the case of twins, at most only two egg-cells and two sperm-cells may survive. All the rest are destined by nature to perish in the maelstrom. This fecundity is Nature's device to ensure the continuance of the species.

Chapter 7

NUPTIAL FLIGHT OF NEW SPERM-CELLS

IN MIDSUMMER, many insects acquire the power of flight, and swarm out to pair. Vast numbers fail to be fertilised, and perish. In the same way these unicellular organisms swarm out, free and unhindered, each striving with all its might to be the parent of a new generation.

They are like a lot of factory hands in a big city, hardened by rough usage; deafened by the ceaseless noise; blunted by the endless monotony. They are all tied to their own trade and their own job. Only a few of them retain their original humanity and geniality. And yet these wheels in the industrial machine, and indeed all of us, sprang, long, long ago, from *all-round* men who lived a natural life, formed family groups to fight the battle of life for themselves, hunted or cultivated their food in the open air, acquired knowledge, not from books or newspapers but from their own experience of life, cured themselves when they were sick, and comforted themselves when they were sad or terrified.

This illustration from the history of the human race gives a clear picture of the evolutionary history of cell-life too. Our adult cells have long since forgotten that the primordial cells, from which in the course of evolution all higher species have developed, had to perform all functions, though in an elementary fashion, for themselves. In these unicellular organisms each cell had the power of changing its position, of ingesting food, of excreting waste-products, of growth, and division. If the two cells resulting from such a division became quite separated the division was equivalent to reproduction.

It is very different now. In our multicellular organisms, all the cells of which that gigantic cell-colony, our body, is composed, have long since lost this plurality of function, and become altered in various ways. They have become specialised to fulfil various special functions. The cells of the epidermis have become horny to form a covering, the skeleton has become hardened to form a support, the muscle-cells have become woven into elastic strands for the purpose of movement, the whole and all its parts are sur-

52

rounded and joined together by connective tissue. We have quite forgotten the autonomy and independence of the single cell; we can no longer realise it.

But now, when we see this new generation of unicellular organisms swarm out from the profoundest depths of our being, we are once more reminded of it. We are transported again to that primitive period, the period of unicellular organisms. There is a new generation of free-born single cells, consisting of almost fluid protoplasm, possessing the same embryonic character as the cells from which the whole course of our evolution began, as yet quite undifferentiated for special functions, a raw material still young and available for any purpose.

These cells, however, are too delicate and too feeble to be able to continue their existence independently. In the first rapture of the nuptial flight they pair at the earliest opportunity. So they double their energy and their useful elements by conjugating in couples.

But the fertilised egg-cell (*zygote*) at first still requires parental care, in order that a multicellular organism may develop by vegetative cell-division from the unicellular organism.

So the history of evolution continually manifests periodicity, an alternation of generations, first a sexual generation of unicellular organisms, then a vegetative generation of multicellular organisms. The life of these unicellular organisms is brief, but full of bliss; it is a nuptial flight. Then again follows a vegetative period of growth which naturally lasts far longer.

Man, however, has no simple structure of vascular bundles and no axillar defects like plants. The possibility of regeneration after wounding is very limited. We may be glad if our wounds even heal up. In man, it is solely the sexual reproductive cells which have undertaken the reproduction of the species. They can only do so by swarming out.

Chapter 8

HOW SEXUAL PLEASURE VITALIZES
OUR LIFE-ENERGY

FORMERLY, it was usually thought that the study of the sexual life had been completed when reproduction had been correctly explained. That is not so. Reproduction is only one of the phenomena of sexual life, fertilisation is once and for all an exceptional case, and can affect even in the most favourable circumstances only one or two, or at most five, of the countless sperm-cells. The stimulus of sexual pleasure in which all sperm-cells take such an active part is for every adult individual, day and night, a burning question, one of the chief factors of our life-energy. It will be the task of this work to discuss sexual life in this respect and to determine its chain of causality in all its details, so that we shall in future be able consciously to control this impulse better than at present.

In the previous chapters we have considered sexual life primarily as a tissue-formation; from now on it will appear more in its secretory aspect. In the next chapter we shall first discuss the anatomy of the excretory duct-system. In order to understand this better, we shall first make a few remarks concerning the abdominal cavity as a container of the excretory organs.

The abdominal cavity contains the three large excretory organs, the bladder in front, the rectum behind, and the genital canal in the middle. The latter, however, differs in the two sexes. In the female the whole genital canal, in the male only its middle portion, including the two seminal vesicles, occupies this portion. The beginning and the end of the male genital canal have migrated from the abdominal cavity, the testicles have passed outwards through the anterior wall and the urethra has pierced the lower wall.

These three excretory systems are evacuated towards the exterior by means of peristaltic (progressive) contractions of their membranous muscular walls. These muscular contractions in the interior of our bodies are imperceptible to us and therefore enter little into our consciousness. Our consciousness would therefore exert but little control over these three excretory functions, if the three organs were not contained in a common abdominal cavity with movable walls, as in a sack. Only the orifices in its lower wall remain open.

These movable walls consist of red muscle-fibres, which, since they can be directly observed on the body surface, are certainly under the command of our consciousness. They are the abdominal muscles which stretch from the ribs to the edge of the pelvis. When these abdominal muscles are contracted and the abdominal cavity is thereby energetically compressed, contraction will easily be caused in the three internal organs by the increased pressure. This action can, however, only be an indirect one, since the proper evacuative action of the said organs is peristaltic.

But how about the lower end where the floor of the pelvis has to be closed? The gluteal muscles are unable to close it since they are attached only to the exterior of the pelvis where they serve to extend the thigh. They overlap everything while we are standing erect. When we are sitting or crouching, however, that is, when they are not contracted, they lie lateral to the two ischial tuberosities, so that the lower pointed end of the pelvis becomes exposed. Thus four fixed points are easily palpable exteriorly, the ischia laterally, the coccyx posteriorly and the lower margin of the os pubis anteriorly. Here there is an acute angle in which the urethra may be felt as it bends upwards at this point. The small space between these four fixed points is the floor of the pelvis, and is completely filled by a special muscular layer, the perineal musculature. We must attach the greatest importance to this small group of muscles as the endings of the three excretory organs pass right through it.

This muscular layer does not lie in one plane but arches downwards in the same way as the diaphragm arches upwards. Corresponding to the sack-like form of the abdominal cavity this muscular layer is slightly lower in the middle. The two ischia laterally are somewhat lower than the coccyx at the back, and considerably lower than the pubic bone in front. It is this latter inclination of the floor of the pelvis which causes the upward direction of the penis during erection.

The floor of the abdomen like all other abdominal muscles consists of red muscle-tissue and can contract reflexly as well as voluntarily, very readily. Since, however, the mutual mobility of the three pelvic bones to which they are joined has been reduced to zero in the adult, these muscles can no longer be used for movement of the skeleton. They only serve, when necessary, effectively to close the three tubes, like three lock-gates.

In order to reach the exterior these ducts have to pass right through this muscular layer. We may say more correctly, perhaps, that the various muscle-fibres become deposited between the canals. If such a canal is half surrounded on either side, the end result is almost as satisfactory as if it had been surrounded by a proper sphincter muscle. When they contract, these muscles can greatly interfere with the free outlet of the ducts and may even close them completely, especially if they are employed simultaneously and the whole of the perineal region is thereby raised.

Every adult knows that the internal involuntary sphincter of the bladder is nearly always adequate to prevent the urine escaping. Only when it is in danger of being overpowered do we, in our apprehension, contract the external voluntary closing muscles.

The same holds good in the passing of faeces. One of my patients once had the external closing muscles completely torn owing to an extremely difficult labour. She, however, refused to have an operation to repair it until all possibility of giving birth to children had passed, as otherwise labour would each time be as difficult as before. This lady, has, however, suffered no inconvenience through it except in cases of threatening diarrhoea.

Chapter 9

THE MALE AND FEMALE SEX ORGANS

a) *The Female Genital Canal*

AS WE have seen in Chapter 3 the female genital canal is an embryonic elaboration of a rudimentary organ from the dim past, derived from the pronephros.

In the embryo the internal orifice of this canal was not overgrown by the reproductive masses as was the Wolffian body. Even in the adult body it is still situated at some distance from the ovary. It has a funnel-shaped enlargement for the better reception of the ripe ova as soon as they are cast off into the abdominal cavity. The moving protoplasmic threads, like huge cilia, which are situated on the edge of the funnel greatly assist the process.

Thus an egg will sometimes succeed in finding its way into the female genital canal. Whereas in man the two sperm-ducts have to take a circuitous route before they open into the urethra behind the bladder, the two egg-ducts (Fallopian tubes) in the female organism converge towards the mid-line and coalesce immediately behind the urinary bladder. Eggs are moved on in these ducts by the ciliated epithelium which lines the internal surfaces.

While in the male the two sperm-ducts on approaching each other are each provided with a separate seminal vesicle, the Fallopian Tubes form a single large reservoir[1], as soon as they meet, that is to say, after a short distance.

It is of considerable size and consists of red muscle, and is for that reason called *uterus* or *womb* instead of *vesicle*. Here, the egg, even if unfertilised, is kept for some time. It is then, together with the menstrual fluids, squeezed by peristaltic movements into the antechamber, i.e., the vagina, from whence it is able to reach the exterior.

1. In the female organism, urinary and genital canal are entirely separate, i.e., there is a separation in a coronal section in the male, in a sagittal section in the female. This corresponds to the obstetric dimensions of the pelvis, the male pelvis being more elliptic, the female on the other hand more circular. Only in some few mammals the uterus bicornis points towards a coalescence of the uterus out of two parts as though it were a paired organ.

Only if fertilisation takes place does it remain in this reservoir for several months. The fertilised egg-cell, and later on, the small embryo, surrounded by its special membranes, gradually embeds itself in the moist sero-mucous membrane of the uterus, by which it is then developed. After the third month of pregnancy, two stout blood vessels grow from the foetus towards the uterine wall and form the umbilical cord[2]. The much ramified ends of these vessels known as the *placento* or *afterbirth,* grow into and through the mucous membrane after the manner of a tumour. By this means an osmotic connection is established between the maternal and the foetal circulations.

The foetus remains *in situ* and grows for a further period of six months[3], until muscular contractions of the uterus occur in consequence of increasing tension, which finally lead to the expulsion of the foetus.

In the female genital tract the musculature of the cervix of the uterus is the involuntary internal sphincter whose contractions may often lead to serious obstetric complications. On other occasions, during an unwanted abortion, the embryo is only too easily allowed to escape. Contractions of this group of muscles often cause severe dysmenorrhoea.

The perineal muscle-layer with its external closing apparatus may also offer a protracted resistance during parturition, if a purely expectant attitude is adopted and no measures are taken against such an occurrence. It may, by spasmodic contractions, delay or prevent any attempt at gynaecological examination on the part of the physician. In some very rare cases it may indeed happen that owing to pain or fear, these muscles contract spasmodically[4], so as to render coitus impossible, or if this cramp occurs during coitus, the male member may thereby be seized so that the man cannot withdraw and venous congestion takes place in the glans. If the man remains quiet and above all makes no attempts at with-

2. The fact that later on the umbilical cord is spirally twisted is generally attributed to foetal movements and rotations, of which we are reminded by the growth of hair on the vertex. It is perhaps more correct to interpret the rotation of the foetus as a consequence of the torsion of the umbilical cord. A tree or any stem of a plant will grow twisted as soon as the different vascular bundles of which they are composed have a different co-efficient of growth. In the same way, surely, the arteries and veins which together form the stalk have a different co-efficient of growth.

3. These periods are, of course, only approximations. The average period of 280 days varies individually and according to external circumstances.

4. During a cramp, even the voluntary muscles are no longer under the control of the will. The opposite condition seen in elderly women who have had several children, where these muscles have ceased to function altogether, is perhaps preferable.

drawal, the cramp will generally pass off in most cases. As soon as it is found that the matter is becoming serious, one should immediately send for a doctor in order to prevent the glans from becoming gangrenous, for this may end fatally for the man. The physician will narcotise the female with chloroform inhalations or subcutaneous injections of morphia, to cause the cramp to pass. These cases generally happen in young girls.

The total length of the female genital canal is very short, like the female urethra. Neither ovaries nor Fallopian Tubes are much higher than the superior margin of the os pubis. They are really only the lateral appendages of the two upper corners of the uterus. The lower part of the uterus and its lowest point, the *os uteri*, protrude[5] a little into the vault of the vagina.

It is very remarkable how the uterus, which is normally so small, attains such huge dimensions during pregnancy; and even more remarkable how, once it is completely emptied, its muscular fibres contract uniformly, so that the increase in size which took nine months to develop, disappears almost entirely in six weeks.

The vagina is much corrugated. When these corrugations are distended during tamponade or other such procedures, it becomes obvious that the vagina is really balloon-shaped and can be distended to the size of a child's head. Thus the female genital canal is very well adapted for gestation. Its sensitiveness to pressure is not acute. Only when the uterus is suddenly shaken, the strain will produce an unpleasant sensation, like that of a strangulated hernia.

Even quite harmless procedures in the interior of the uterus may sometimes cause sudden death from shock. This is probably due to over-excitation of the sympathetic nervous system, small groups of nerve centres scattered in the abdominal cavity, and of which the *solar plexus* (*coeliac plexus*) is the largest. The mucous membrane lining the uterus is very subject to haemorrhages and to bacterial infections consequent on manipulation. This constitutes a serious danger to life since the uterine cavity is directly continuous with the abdominal cavity through the oviducts.

Per contra, the mucous membrane lining the vagina is very resistant to all external infections. The entrance to the vagina in woman[6] is carefully closed firstly by two small folds of mucous membrane, the *labia minora* or *nymphae*; secondly, two larger

5. Sometimes even very deeply. In a pathological case it may lead to prolapse of the vagina or even of the *cevix uteri*.

6. In other mammals only one pair of folds is found, which, like our eyelids and nostrils and lips, are lined internally with mucous membrane and externally with skin.

swelling folds of skin, the *labia majora*. We shall return to this structure which is known as the *vulva (pudenda)* later. So, looking at the female body from below, one sees not the vaginal opening but only the vulval slit which is continuous with the navel cleft. The latter contains the anal aperture, the former the vaginal and urethral apertures. These two openings are almost the same size in the female child, but in the adult the vaginal opening is much larger than the urethral.

Between urethra and os pubic there is just space for a small sascular protuberance, the clitoris. We shall see later how in the male these three structures, genital canal, urethra and vascular protuberance, have combined to form a single organ, which is of much larger size.

b) *The Male Genital Canal*

From the seminal vesicles a very short and narrow[7] canal leads downward on each side to the urethra, the posterior wall of which they pierce close together.

This point where the two seminal canals join the urethra is surrounded by an enlargement, the prostate, about the shape and size of a chestnut. It can be palpated through the anus, in the anterior wall of the rectum.

The function of this organ is unknown. It contains many microscopic unstriped muscle-fibres and many delicate glandular ducts, which open into the urethra, into which they pour a mucous secretion which seems to cause the special odour of semen. Certainly the contents of the seminal vesicles are odourless. It is on account of this secretory function that it is called the prostatic (presiding) gland, although the organ appears more like a rudimentary uterus, just as generally rudiments of the duct-system of the opposite sex are found in each sex. As in the female organism the two oviducts join behind the bladder to form a uterus, so in the male the prostate gland is situated at the posterior wall of the urethra just at the point where the two sperm-ducts join. The prostate is only of importance on account of its proneness to enlargements, tumours, calculi (similar to gall stones and renal calculi) and chronic inflammations, which often cause constriction of the urethra in elderly men, and render extensive operations necessary.

Immediately below the prostate, the male urethra pierces the perineal muscular layer in order to gain the exterior. This muscular

7. It is significant that the orifices of the two seminal ducts are so very narrow. Those sperm-cells which have not been stored in the seminal vesicles are subjected to a sphincter-like elastic resistance when they are ejected together with the complex contents of the seminal vesicles.

layer, however, is not as yielding as the anterior muscle-layer in the groin through which the testicles migrated. Moreover, in the male the opening in the muscular layer is not directed downwards (the shortest way) but slantingly forwards; thus the muscular action is more forcible in the male. As soon as it emerges from the pelvic floor the canal bends upwards along the external surface of the pubic bone (in the erect posture the inferior surface of the pubic bone). It is firmly united to the os pubis by connective tissue, and emerges finally on the anterior surface of the body, from which it hangs down for more than a finger's length immediately anterior to the scrotum which to a certain extent it hides.

When in the flaccid condition, looked at from the right, the male genital canal from the bladder onwards, describes a double curve like the letter **S** The os pubis is situated in the first curve. It is this external continuation which, as we shall see in the next chapter, has to function in copulation, and is therefore called penis or male organ. In the same way in woman the lower portion of the genital canal, i.e., vagina and vulva, are termed female copulatory organs. But since in the male the latter portion of the genital canal has to serve for the excretion of urine as well, we refer to the urethra when the canal itself is meant as if it only served for the urinary purpose; this even after puberty.

It is extraordinary that while the female canal has widened as much as possible, the male canal has lengthened as much as possible. Firstly the two sperm-ducts are enormously elongated within and without the abdominal cavity, owing to the descent of the testicles, and at the other end we have the very vascular prolongation at the outlet. Even the seminal vesicles are only elongated narrow structures.

It is extremely remarkable how the male genital canal is related to the abdominal cavity. As far as we are conscious of it, the physiological function of the sexual life has its starting point in the abdominal cavity, but the formation of sperm-cells, which is the most important function, takes place outside the abdominal cavity. It is only the secretory function which proceeds from the abdominal cavity, and it is of this function only that we are conscious. So it is not to be wondered at that up to the present the sexual function has been considered as entirely glandular.

Finally we must notice the peculiar way in which the male genital canal pursues its path through the abdominal cavity. From the testicles to the prostate it is paired and passes above the *os pubis*. From thence onward it is unpaired and passes below the *os pubis*. That makes in all three long canals, whose meeting point is situated at the neck of the bladder and which all three protrude for an equal distance outside the body. So it happens that the two sites of formation of the sperm-cells and the site of their ejection are quite close together. And yet this small journey of the sperm-cells touches all hearts and supplies the magic by which Nature rules the whole world, as Schiller says so succinctly in *"Die Weltweisen"* (*The Worldly Wise*).

Until the world is guided entirely by philosophy,
It will be driven by hunger and by love.

We shall discover in the further course of this book how this mystery is brought about.

Chapter 10

THE GENITAL CANAL IN THE SEX ACT

WITH reference to the female we saw in the preceding chapter that the lower portion of the genital canal simply becomes dilated to form a copulatory organ. This dilatation is regulated by corrugations and occlusory muscles. In the next few chapters we shall discuss the formation of the male copulatory organ in full detail. A certain essential prolongation we have already mentioned. We now come to the phenomena of congestion by means of which this otherwise most insignificant organ is temporarily enabled to serve as a copulatory organ.

Every organ receives an increase in blood supply when it is functioning actively, and conversely an increased blood supply is an indispensable condition for active functioning. This interdependence is a biological law of the first importance also in the sexual life. This most urgent of all functions requires a hyper-congestion. We shall now examine the anatomical mechanism by which the lower portion of the male genital tract is enabled to become hyper-congested.

It goes without saying that the wall of the urethra contains blood vessels, for there are no organs without them. At the point where the urethra pierces the muscular layer of the perineum, these blood vessels must naturally experience the pressure of this muscular layer. The blood in the arteries, which have muscular walls, will not be much affected by this, but the blood in the wide veins, which have flaccid walls, will be greatly congested by this pressure. So it is evident that in the evolution of higher animal orders a plexus of swollen and enlarged vessels was necessarily formed. The tissue is known as *cavernous* tissue and is also found as a vascular swelling on the heads of many fowls, e.g., the comb of cocks. The vascular congestion in the urethral wall commences at the point where the canal pierces the perineal muscles. Below the prostate and above the muscular layer lies a small portion of the urethra, and here there is no cavernous tissue, but from the muscular layer downwards the whole urethral wall is formed of such cavernous tissue. It is a prolongation and thickening of the urethral wall with its connective tissue and not of the skin. Only on the lower aspect (while pendulous this is the posterior aspect) of the penis, the urethral canal may be easily palpated in its entire length.

In the female, the same conditions prevail, though on a smaller scale. Here, too, the opening of the urethra with its vascular system is situated beyond the external occlusory muscles.

Here a similar congestive effect is produced but only on the anterior aspect of the urethra, as the vagina is situated at its posterior aspect. Thus immediately in front of the urethra, i.e., between urethra and os pubis, a cavernous *papilla* has formed about the size of a pea, in appearance somewhat like the glans penis. It does not, however, enclose the urethra. In the female mole, however, the urethra pierces the clitoris, as it does the penis in the male.

The local prolongation and thickening would in themselves be insignificant. It is, however, a typical vascular plexus, as even from childhood the penis is constantly changing its dimensions proportionately to the local blood pressure. During cold or after loss of blood it is very small; under the influence of blood congestion or skin stimuli it is, however, considerably larger. But only after puberty (every time some sexual stimulus occurs) this phenomenon reaches its height and becomes then of considerable biological significance, as it not only increases sexual desire, but also forces it upon our consciousness. We remarked a similar case concerning the descent of the testes. In such moments when sexual desire bursts into flame it appears as if all our energy had concentrated at this extreme point, in the same way as a Leyden jar seeks to discharge itself at its extremity.

We imagine that this phenomenon is the real starting point and origin of our sexual life. If this were so, then there would be but little sexual life in fishes, amphibia and birds, and the sexual life of the female would be specially insignificant. The actual importance of this phenomenon, however, we shall be able to discuss only in Part II. For the present we have to consider the anatomical reasons which enable this excessive blood congestion to take place.

The whole arrangement of the blood vessels in this organ greatly favours congestion. Nearly everywhere else in our body we find two veins to one artery. This is what we should expect, for blood flows quickly in the arteries but very sluggishly in the veins. But here on the superior aspect of the penis (anterior in the flaccid condition) there is only one vein to two arteries. This explains why even at a very tender age this organ is so prone to swellings and congestions. I have often seen a child born with an erected penis when too much pressure is exerted on the body to deliver an aftercoming head.

If, in the adult, congestion occurs in this vascular system in the originally soft connective tissue stroma of the cavernous bodies has become a strong network of very firm fibres and trabeculae[1], surrounded by a capsule of fairly strong connective tissue pierced transversely by blood vessels.

If in the adult congestion occurs in this vascular system in consequence of hyper-tension in the full seminal vesicles, or of some other even insignificant cause, i.e., if more arterial blood than usual flows in, causing an increase in local blood pressure, all the connective tissue fibres are rendered taut and many of the thin-walled veins are then almost completely constricted. The more blood that flows in at high pressure through the arteries, the more the venous return will be impeded. The whole organ will then become extremely hard and swell almost to bursting point.

This mechanism is considerably augmented and maintained by the perineal muscles, the external occlusory muscles, which, evolutionally, were probably the cause of the development of this cavernous tissue. This muscular layer impedes venous return to a certain extent by its normal muscle tone, but it does so far more when it contracts actively. As long as no congestion is present and the vascular system is relatively empty, this muscular layer cannot produce an erection, since it is not a proper sphincter muscle. If, however, slight congestion occurs, e.g., through a stimulation of the seminal vesicles, then this muscular layer can act very energetically[2].

When complete erection has occured in the male, another very striking phenomenon may occasionally be observed to take place at short intervals. This is a throbbing movement—a convulsion—which is not due to pulsations of the heart, for which it is far too infrequent, but is produced by the convulsive contraction of the perineal muscles. When erection occurs, one can produce these throbbing movements by a strong, voluntary contraction of these muscles.

During such throbbing movements only a very slight increase in circumference is experienced, together with a slight shortening of the penis. In mechanical parlance there is a tendency towards assuming a spherical shape.

1. In the dog and some other mammals a few of these trabeculae are cartilaginous.

2. The extent to which a complete male erection depends on the contraction of the external occlusory muscles can easily be observed on one's own sphincter ani.

Generally an erection is not of long duration. After a few minutes or more the blood pressure subsides and everything returns to its original condition, as though nothing had happened.

If, during the flaccid condition, the same abrupt muscular contractions are performed with a view to producing an erection artificially and of set purpose, failure will result, for the "*conditio sine qua non*", the congestive condition, is absent. And if one should try to produce a voluntary erection by mechanical compression, it would be extremely difficult to avoid compressing the arteries as well as the veins, thus favouring local anaemia, quite apart from the inhibiting action of pain.

The occurrence of an erection is thus not altogether under our control; it is a phenomenon by which we are often overtaken in the most awkward circumstances, and which may remain absent just when it is required. One should, however, only talk of impotence when in an adult erections do not occur at all. Thus in practice the question arises how consciously to control the first congestive condition of stimulation, both to cause and to prevent it. We can answer this only in Parts II and III.

It is fortunate that the external voluntary occlusive muscles, not being proper sphincters, are unable totally to cut off venous return, and can only aid in producing congestion. If it were possible to cut off the venous return altogether, gangrene would supervene, for the tissue would necessarily die if the blood supply were interrupted. This fact would, secondarily, endanger the individual's life itself.

The extent of the interference with the venous return and of the tension may be gathered from scars sometimes found in postmortems, which can only be explained on the assumption that during life the cavernous bodies must have become fractured internally, possibly through a fall or blow, like a stick of sealing wax.

There are exceptional cases on record of pathological erections (*priapism*). In such cases one should try all the measures suggested in Part III. In severe cases a physician should be consulted.

The volume of the penis in the erect condition is on an average four or five times as large as the original volume. During the greatest tension its length from the os pubis is about 1½ fingers length instead of 1 in the flaccid conditon, and the width about 2 fingers breadth instead of 1½. And yet this is only the visible external part. The internal part of the erection is curved round the os pubis and hidden between the thighs and behind the scrotum.

Such a condition of erection and throbbing produces in us a warm feeling of glow and pulsation. The skin of the penis, wherever it is movable, retains its normal yellowish-red flesh tint. For it is not a skin congestion but a congestion in the urethral wall. Only on the glans, where, as we shall see, the skin is transparent and close-fitting, the colour changes from pale red or livid to the deepest blue of venous blood, the latter especially round the margin of the glans.

Such a considerable swelling must, of course, have an influence on the position of the whole organ. If the investing membrane of the penis were not firm, then the whole organ would assume as far as possible a spherical shape during the period of maximum tension because that shape alone would equalise the tension at all points. But the membrane is tubular and can therefore only increase in length and thickness, and so must change its position. In the previous chapter we saw that the whole organ bends upwards at the external surface of the os pubis to which it is closely attached by connective tissue. This portion of the penis which is not visible externally can therefore not change its position. In order to yield as far as possible to the internal pressure the pendulous portion which is visible must alter its position so as to be in the same line as the fixed portion. It therefore raises itself up, and then the tension is as nearly as possible equal at all points. Hence the name erection, i.e., raising up.

Gravity, however, that is to say, the weight of such a large volume of blood, will have considerable modifying effect. In every attitude of the body the direction of erection will be the resultant of these two forces, blood pressure and gravity, and the effect of the convulsive contractions of the perineal muscles will be to compensate, or, on account of the throbbings, even to overcompensate the effect of gravity. When the body is vertical the penis will be much above the horizontal. If we eliminate the action of gravity in this direction by lying down on one side the penis will almost touch the abdominal wall. An infantile erection, however, with its small increase in blood pressure will have reached its maximum when the small penis makes an angle of 90 deg. with the abdominal wall. That is probably the extreme, as I once discovered. A mother had for some reason to take her son aged 5 or 6 out of bed while he was fast asleep. The above mentioned attitude was visible. She was greatly embarrassed by it and tried several times to press it down. This of course could only have increased the erection but it remained at the same angle which seems to be the maximum for children, though it is the minimum in the adult. The internal tension and the external increase in bulk are very slight in children.

Above we have advanced the hypothesis that during evolution of the species a vascular plexus developed owing to the congestive effect of the perineal muscles. We shall now inquire further why this vascular plexus grew forward along the os pubis. The tubular form of course is due to the fact that it is a prolongation of the urethra.

It is a matter of experience in mechanics that if a tube of complicated form is subjected to very high internal pressure, it will assume as far as possible its original shape, since every deviation from this form may reduce, but can never increase its capacity. Similarly, our joints will assume the semi-flexed attitude of their intra-uterine life, if they are subjected to high internal pressure by effusion of blood, pus, or serum.

Here, I think, the case is similar. In the foetal condition, curled up in the uterus with the legs pressed tightly together, the continuation of the urethra could not escape caudally, but could only grow along the abdominal wall[3].

During normal pregnancy, while the foetus lies head downwards owing to gravity, the penis can only grow downwards towards the head. Only when the child begins to walk does the penis begin to point towards the feet.

Later on, in adult life, every time congestion occurs, the tubular must assume as far as possible its original position, quite aside from the fact that it is fixed to the os pubis by connective tissue. In young children, in spite of the small increase in blood pressure, the erect position of the penis is easily assumed because recently that position was habitual. Thus, a childish erection has nothing sexual about it. The genitals of a child are really only foetal developments of an otherwise embryonic rudiment, so erections in children should not be considered as evidences of precocious sexuality, but merely as a return to a foetal position due to blood pressure. We shall further see, in Part V, that the childish sexual character does not develop on account of an internal sexual need, but simply because the child develops in a sexual world. This does not mean to imply that the formation of the sexual organochemical substances may not sometimes commence in the pre-puberal period.

Only after puberty, the spasmodic increase in blood pressure which we know as the sexual erection reaches its full development, together with the mature stimulus of the sexual organochemical substances and the associated mass-production of reproductive cells. As we have seen above, the male genital canal, when flaccid, assumed the form of an S lying on its side, thus —

3. In some animals, e.g., the bull, the penis, even in adult life, grows along the abdomen for some distance before becoming visible.

When erect and seen from the right. It has the form of the Greek letter

The path of the sperm-cells begins at the lower part of the letter, i.e., at the testes, travels upwards towards the abdominal cavity, enters it, describes a circle there (surrounding the os pubis) and finally travels upwards again at the external surface of the os pubis, where it finds exit. This remarkable phenomenon, erection, with its congestion and feeling of tension, has always stimulated man's emotions.

In all savage races, the first complete erection is always greeted with joy. Now, for the first time, the youth is considered fit to take his place as an adult and is permitted to take part in the chase and in battle. During initiation, he must prove his manhood by suffering without flinching all sorts of ordeals, e.g., tattooing, skin incisions, circumcision, introduction of rings into the nose or ear, knocking out of teeth, etc.

In our civilisation and with our clothing, there is no proper appreciation of this developmental phenomenon. It must, unfortunately, be concealed. This concealment spoils our character. Our tight-fitting clothes[4] give an oblique direction to the penis, which in fact diminishes its usefulness for copulation. Why should not our clothes be made a little looser and why do we not "dress" one day on the right side and the next on the left?

With us Christians those pagan celebrations of puberty are sublimated as Confirmation, when we are received as members worthy of reception into the Church. And why should we deny, or even proscribe, the sexual element in it? As regards stability of character and sexual life, the savage races can teach us a good deal.

4. The nipples of women are often deliberately rendered almost useless by close-fitting garments.

Chapter 11

THE GLANS AND THE PREPUCE
IN THE SEX ACT

WE HAVE not finished yet. On careful examination, we find that the male organ, the prolongation of the urethra, with its cavernous walls, is not a simple canal like a rubber tube, for at its end it bears a small head, the glans. This head is conical in shape, but oblique in the sense that only the inferior or posterior surface is not pointed. On this aspect, the urethra may be palpated as it pursues its straight course. The base of this head has a larger circumference than the penis at any other point and bulges considerably at the point of junction, like a circular swelling. This provision is very important for the movements in coitus firstly as an aid to massage, secondly in view of the external occlusory muscles of the vagina which grip it and prevent its slipping out too easily. In dogs and some related species, such an occurence is utterly impossible, as this edge is cartilaginous, so that forcible attempts at separation would probably tear the vulva.

The glans is covered by a very delicate transparent membrane, with the typical appearance of a mucous membrane, which merges insensibly into the mucous membrane of the urethra. Internally, the glans consists of the same cavernous tissue as the inferior or posterior surface of the penis, where the urethra may be palpated. It is therefore not so stony hard as the rest of the penis, even when swollen. This is very forunate, for otherwise the first attempt at copulation might often result in damage to the urethra and bladder, or perforation of the vaginal wall.

In the flaccid condition, however, the glans is not very noticeable, of small dimensions and not conspicuously different from the cylindrical portion of the penis. There is one more point to note. It is due to the nature of the cavernous tissue that the penis varies so greatly in size with the blood pressure. Sometimes, it is very large; at others, especially during excessive cold or after loss of blood, it may become extremely small. But how about the skin? Is it tight, almost to bursting, at one time, and at others almost inconveniently wrinkled? One need only think of the voluminous folds of a bellows or a camera. Nothing of this sort is found in the penis. Nature shames our machines with her simple devices.

Her solution of the problem is so simple that scarcely anybody has realised its difficulty. The skin lies nearly always smoothly disposed round the penis. The temporary surplus is taken up at either end. The skin of the scrotum can be wrinkled in the finest corrugations, like the most delicate crêpe paper, by minute muscular fibres, and during erection these fine wrinkles are to some extent smoothed out. As soon as the penis returns to its usual size, the scrotal wrinkles reappear. Sometimes, when the muscles are quite relaxed, the scrotum may hang lower than the penis. When the penis is fully erect, the scrotum disappears altogether, and the two testicles lie close against the penis. Thus the same portion of skin may be used for both organs.

At the other end of the penis, however, i.e., on the glans, the skin has lost its mobility, but as recompense we find, at the margin of the glans, just behind its projecting rim, a single large fold which is large enough to hide the whole glans. In this case, the fold of skin is a double one. Urine, after leaving the end of the urethra, must pass through this fold of skin (the prepuce) before it actually reaches the exterior.

In the erect position the glans is most exposed, and the fold of skin disappears almost entirely. In a very flaccid condition, however, due to cold, loss of blood, or age, the prepuce entirely surrounds the glans, as though to protect it.

In the female the clitoris is similarly supplied with a prepuce. The little protrusion known as the clitoris is not, however, quite covered by it. Here the foreskin is a very small fold of mucous membrane which hides about half the clitoris on its anterior (in the supine position the superior) aspect. On either side the fold merges into the two small folds of mucous membrane known as the nymphae. Covering all this are the labia majora which merge posteriorly into the buttocks so that in the adult they appear to be an anterior hirsute prolongation of them.

If we compare the two sexes in this respect we shall see that the female form with its freedom from protuberances is more closely related to the original type common to both sexes.

However, even in the female protuberances are sometimes found, especially prolongations of one or both of the nymphae. In exceptional cases, prolapse may bring about a prolongation of the female urethra. I once found extroversion of the urethra in a female to such an extent that it resembled an enormously elongated clitoris.

A great enlargement of the clitoris is said to be frequent in certain lands. This is a form of rivalry the male does not seem to appreciate, for in many tribes[1] there prevails the custom of shortening or amputating the clitoris by operation.

On the other hand there are tribes who by means of sucking or stings of insects aim at enlarging the clitoris as far as possible. Here and there attempts are made and with some success, artificially to lengthen the *labia majora* by pulling on them or suspending weights from them (cf. Hottentot aprons obtained by this means).

Generally, however, prolongations are reserved for the male sex. In the male, through natural selection the prolongation and swelling of the genital canal has become a normal phenomenon, because of its great advantages in the struggle for existence.

In the female on the other hand it has become a rare exception.

The enlargement of the male copulatory organ has gradually accomodated itself to the female dilatation, and vice versa.

Not only the mental characteristics, but physical conformations as well have become mutually adapted in man and woman. Matter has far more inertia than spirit and so bodily adaptation in prehistoric times has taken much longer.

1. For a small penis to occur in females it would be necessary for both clitoris and urethra to be greatly enlarged and to coalesce. This would be the female equivalent of hermaphrodite-formation in males.

Chapter 12

EFFECT OF CIRCUMCISION ON SEX HEALTH

THIS is an operation which is often required in males during early childhood in consequence of the smallness of the aperture in the above-mentioned fold of skin, which tends to impede the excretion of urine. Lack of hygiene is often the first cause.

As long as the contraction has not proceeded too far, one can always, before having recourse to an operation, thoroughly clean, disinfect and heal up the nearly closed space between prepuce and glans, by injecting a suitable fluid into the cavity. One should choose non-irritant and preferably astringent antiseptic lotions, e.g., lead water (Goulard's water) or a one per cent. solution of alum (one tablespoonful of alum to two pints of water). The injections are best performed with a bulbous syringe, having the canula slightly enlarged at its end. By introducing such a syringe between prepuce and glans and grasping the folds of skin round it with the hand, one can use the same liquid several times by injecting it between the prepuce and glans and letting it run back into the syringe. The action of the fluid may be reinforced by external massage. By this means, one may effectively clear the cavity: of course, one should avoid making fresh erosions.

Such local cleansing is all the more important because the collected dirt is liable to cause burning and itching, a fact which is possibly one of the most frequent causes of masturbation in children.

If the trouble has, however, gone too far, an operation will, in the end, be indispensable. The surgeon generally performs the operation as a real circumcision, by removing a circular portion, similar to the ritual circumcision among the Jews, for if the preputial ring is split lengthwise with the scissors, the desired widening of the lumen is at once obtained, but later on it will most likely grow together again in spite of any attempts to avoid it.

Circumcision is of great value as a surgical measure in pathological cases. It has a wide distribution ethnographically, as religious ceremony among several tribes and races. Frequently it is devoid of any religious significance and is employed mainly as a means of beautifying or improving nature. We have mentioned some of the ceremonies of puberty above.

The ordinary circumcision of boys as a rite of puberty is not contrary to nature, as nature herself exposes the glans as puberty approaches. It must have been a device originally to help nature a little. An entirely uncovered glans was considered a sign of fertility and in Genesis XVII the promise of a numerous progeny is bound up with ritual circumcision.

While performing circumcision according to rule, the rabbi endeavours to produce as large an erection of the small penis as possible, while murmuring prayers and formulae. This is a necessary proceeding, as otherwise he could not be sure where the glans commences. If by mischance a portion of it should be removed, death through haemorrhage would almost certainly ensue.

By drawing the prepuce towards him, he then cuts it off without damaging the glans. The latter he avoids by grasping the prepuce as close to the glans as possible with a forceps and by cutting along it. The glans is then further exposed and the whole bandaged, aseptically or better antiseptically, e.g., with *iodoform* gauze. In a few days' time the skin cut will have healed up.

There will be no loose fold of skin enveloping the glans. There will, however, be sufficient skin for an adult erection since only the outer portion of the foreskin which protrudes beyond the glans has been removed. The remainder will fold itself behind the margin of the glans.

The erection produced so soon after birth in all boys, and the permanent uncovering of the glans, whereby it is to a far greater extent exposed to touch, friction, and stimulus, together with a frugal and domesticated life, must have contributed very largely to the great increase and wide distribution of the Jews. In those days, when a high birthrate was a condition of existence on account of wars and as compensation for the high infantile mortality, they became by this means victorious in the struggle for existence. The prophecies linked up with circumcision have come true.

Circumcision entails other hygienic advantages of great importance in the struggle for existence. After this operation the collection of dirt in the preputial cavity is entirely impossible, for it no longer exists. It can therefore never become the site of venereal and other diseases which always menace the existence of the race. On the contrary the skin of the glans will now always be dry, a fact which ensures an adequate resistance against all harmful influences. May this serve as a warning for uncircumcised individuals

74

to endeavour to obtain by cleanliness the advantages they have missed through not having had this operation performed.

In order to show the importance of this point in the hygiene of the race, I shall, as a practicing physician, add a chapter on hygiene.

Chapter 13

MODERN METHODS OF SEX HYGIENE
AND SEX HEALTH

TO CONCLUDE these chapters dealing with the anatomy of the genital canal, I shall add a few remarks which refer more specially to the external orifices of the copulatory organs, keeping in view the micro-organisms to be found there.

It is a well known fact in bacteriology that all secretions are at first sterile, but later on when reaching the exterior are invaded by all kinds of micro-organisms, among which putrefactive bacteria are to be found. If no steps are taken against them they rapidly increase and betray their presence by evil smells. We should very soon be living in a poisonous atmosphere, and indeed our body would begin to decay before we had died, if we did not counteract this tendency as far as possible by the most punctilious cleanliness. Nature very energetically assists this process from the interior by always pushing out sterile secretions[1], which cause the other and already decaying secretions to be pushed further out.

This latter principle, the automatic cleansing by the *"vis-a-tergo"* at once elucidates the fact that people with a vigorous metabolism are much healthier and more active, while sluggish, torpid constitutions are vulnerable, unhealthy, and, when ill, are difficult to cure. Thus, by impeding the urine excretion, especially in paralysis of the bladder, decomposition of the stagnating urine, which is bound to occur sooner or later, may make the patient most seriously ill.

The same applies to the intestinal secretion, a mixture of all sorts of originally sterile glandular secretions, with the always non-sterile waste products of our food. Here the B. coli predominates, which regularly infects our wounds, as it is nearly always to be found on the door handles, etc., or the privy and is thus carried everywhere, as has been experimentally demonstrated.

The danger of auto-infection owing to insufficient *vis-a-tergo* applies least to the sperm secretion, because the urethra is thor-

1. Similar to the secretion of sperm-cells.

oughly cleaned several times daily through urine excretion[2]. This does not mean to imply that a correct and regular exercise of the function such as is proper to married people is not also a hygienic desideratum in this respect. One should remember the remark made above that the contents of the seminal vesicles are always odorless, but acquire an unpleasant smell when passing the prostate gland. In the female genital canal the cervix is usually the limit of self cleansing.

While this process of automatic cleansing is very useful, it still remains our duty to remove the secreted substances from the exterior by thorough washing. This applies to the whole surface of our skin with its countless microscopic sweat and sebaceous glands. If the ablutions are not performed regularly every day it soon becomes very difficult to make good the omission.

The thorough cleansing of a neglected skin surface is not at all easy. Firstly, a layer of air adheres to the skin, which on simple immersion shows itself in the presence of countless little bubbles. Secondly, the skin is impregnated with the fat produced by the sebaceous glands, and this is always difficult to remove. The best methods are soapy water, hot water, lysol water, e.g., 0.5% solution, i.e., $\frac{1}{2}$ tablespoon of lysol to two pints of water or alcohol[3]. One should always aim at removing the last traces of soap with an excess of clean water or with a little alcohol, since every remainder of soap is injurious on account of its caustic action, especially in tender regions.

Finally, it is very difficult to dry the skin again once it is wet, as it is hygroscopic; one should think of the *hair-hygroscope* in this connection. If the skin is not properly dried, then all ablutions only tend to favour decay and decomposition, especially on the folds of the skin. Where two portions of skin lie in close contact, they become increasingly moist under normal body temperature and evaporation from the skin. One can easily convince oneself of the truth of this in summer by sleeping for a few minutes with the face on the back of the hand or on the arm. Both surfaces will soon become moist. One should not dress after a bath until all folds have become thoroughly dry again. Sometimes one may assist this process a little with powder, because then the surfaces cannot

2. This natural aseptic irrigation, comparable to the best surgical irrigation, is absent in the female. On the contrary, the female genital canal becomes much wider towards its external opening, so that the female easily suffers from *fluor albus* after even the most harmless infections, whereas the male genital canal will suppurate only after a virulent gonorrheal infection.

3. However injurious alcohol may be, when taken internally, it is of the greatest value from the hygienic point of view, and also in inflammatory processes, especially in moist skin eruptions, where one aims at repelling the leucocytes.

lie in intimate contact with each other. In most cases the dust derived from the towels and our clothing is sufficient for this purpose, a fact which should console us for wearing out our clothing. As, in contrast to the skin, the mucous membranes should remain moist, we should aim at keeping these dust particles out of our respiratory organs; especially at night, when we go to bed, we should avoid raising dust with our clothing, which we would then breathe throughout the night. I have often seen midwives grossly injure the lungs of newly born children immediately after birth by wielding their powder puff in the inguinal region.

As long as it is only the secretion which is decomposing, thorough washing may still be sufficient. In time, however, the decomposition increases in extent and attacks the underlying skin, especially in moist situations, e.g., one should recall the feet, where the skin may decay between the toes until the physician may find the whole sole macerated and decayed, and with a smell as of carrion. It may happen thus in all folds of the body. Ablutions alone are no longer sufficient, and the skin has first of all to be thoroughly disinfected. The above mentioned solution of lysol which is not very poisonous, is eminently suited for this purpose. For smaller surfaces of skin the poisonous *sublimate* may be used, e.g., a tablet of one gram (15 grains) to two litres (4 pints) of water, or if the smell is very pronounced, one should use formalin, e.g., 10 gm. (one small tablespoonful) dissolved in half a litre (one pint) of water. The latter solution is painful, however, if the skin is sore or has even minute excoriations and tears. For injections, far more dilute solutions should be used.

All that has been said applies to the whole skin surface, but most particuarly to the lower part of our body, where besides the small glands of the skin and mucous membrane, the large excretory organs have their orifices. Here are found the most pungent odours; one need only think of musk, castoreum, hyraceum, amber, civet in the animal kingdom. Similar malodourous substances are not wanting in our own male and female genital organs. They are found especially where small wrinkles most easily produce a stagnation of secretions, i.e., in the vulva, the prostate and, last though not least, in the preputial cavity.

It is difficult to reach the prostate, and to this is probably due the fact that in advanced age operations are ᴜ ᴀfen required. For vulva and vagina, injections of water, or preferably mildly astringent or disinfecting solutions, are required. This is especially important after menstruation, even in young girls. By this means not only all auto-intoxications but also later ᴏᴌ all external infections may be counteracted. With reference to the preputial cavity I will once more recall the anatomical structure.

One is only too inclined to consider the preputial cavity as lined with mucous membrane. We have, however, shown above that the glans is covered with skin, and that the foreskin is a real fold of skin, as the name indicates. In contrast to the mucous membranes, these two surfaces should be kept dry as possible because the danger of infectious diseases is considerably reduced, as the skin becomes firmer and more resistant the drier it is kept.

It may easily happen that one may be exposed to the danger of infection. We live in a society where danger of infection threatens us from all sides: in hotels, in strange beds, strange w.c.'s. It is not even necessary to leave one's family for that. How many infants are infected by servant girls and midwives, and vice versa, parents by children, etc.

In the most faithful marriage and with the highest moral standards, cleanliness and sexual hygiene should be strictly practiced, so that it may not be said to our detriment that the children of darkness are more sensible than the children of light. It might finally ensue that in extra-marital relations, hygiene would be more insured than in marriage. One does not find venereal disease only among prostitutes and drunkards, where it is always present. We physicians often see behind the scenes how frequently venereal disease is brought into the marriage as a *dot* or is later on brought in by husband or wife. The evil has so often scaled the walls of the old fortress, marriage, where one thought oneself safe.

If one or both partners are ill with venereal disease, sexual abstinence becomes a duty, but for how long? Even the most experienced doctor is unable to answer this. In such desperate cases the physician will order the use of contraceptives (condoms) as a protection, in order to act in accordance with his responsibility. They act better than the prepuce, which is Nature's safeguard. It will also be his sacred duty to teach the uses of antiseptic precautions to the two partners.

Everybody should be educated on hygienic lines from childhood onward. Then he will spontaneously avoid the unclean. And if he should get into danger, he will not go under helplessly. A careful conscientious education during childhood is the first step towards self-control, with which we shall deal in Parts II and III, and towards ideal love, with which we shall deal in Parts IV and V.

Part II.

SEX HEALTH AND THE PERFECT SEX ACT

Physiology and Practice by Married Lovers

Chapter 14

Introductory:

SCIENTIFIC DUTY OF AUTHOR NOT TO WITHHOLD ANYTHING OF SERVICE

AFTER having discussed the anatomy of the sexual apparatus in full detail, we shall now proceed to demonstrate the physiological functions of the sexual life.

Here we shall deal from a more individual point of view with the further progress of the newly formed cells, i.e., the manner in which they are excreted from our body[1].

We cannot, however, fully understand this secretory function until we study it in comparison with the other two secretory functions of the lower pole of the body, the intestinal function and even more the secretion of urine. Only thus can we fully appreciate the whole inter-relation; and difficult questions concerning one function may find a surprising solution by analogy with one of the other functions.

The close relationship between these three excretory processes has up to now been very little considered.

The connection between the three above-mentioned functions is obvious. Not only do the three organs lie close together, but they are supplied by related blood vessels, innervated by related nerve trunks and affected by the same external influences. Stimuli, drugs and poisons which affect one of these organs generally influence the other two to a greater or less extent in the same sense. The secretory character of the three organs is identical, and it is one and the same layer of muscle, the resistance of which has to be overcome by all three. Birds and fishes have only one orifice for the three secretions. Only mammals are more highly differentiated. Thus in man the male has two apertures, the female three.

The urinary secretion and the secretion of semen are indeed most closely related to each other. In the male they share a single common outlet, the prolongation of the urethra. Up to this point the embryonic excretory duct of a true embryonic kidney, the Wolffian body, serves as a genital canal. In the same way, the female

1. For the race the formation of the single cells is the main point. Individually, however, we are chiefly concerned with the secretory function. This is a physiological reason, in addition to the anatomical one, why testes and ovaries have always been considered as glands, whereas they are in reality tumours, connected with an excretory duct system.

genital canal is strictly speaking only the excretory system of a rudimentary pronephros.

I must at the outset ask the reader's indulgence when discussing the intimate details of any one of the functions, which, if we employ the comparative method, are highly important on account of their analogy with the other functions, but in themselves are not very savoury . . .

In the end this will be worth while, and if we pursue the comparative method the reader will have an additional gain. It is a touchstone for self-knowledge. Anyone who is annoyed by these physiological details, need not read any further; he must realise that he is scientifically not sufficiently emancipated to be able to study such difficult questions successfully. Let him choose something easier.

It was the duty of the author of this work not to withhold anything that could be of service to the reader. He begs that any obscurities or errors may be pointed out to him, so that he may avoid them in the future.

Chapter 15

THE THREE HUMAN EXCRETORY PRODUCTS

BEFORE making in the next three chapters a comparative study of the excretory function in the three different cases, we must state here at once, that although the excretory mechanism is the same, the excreted material is entirely different in the three cases. We shall, at the same time, enquire in every instance how far we have to do with a glandular secretion.

Firstly, the intestinal contents. The intestinal contents consist of a mixture of waste products and glandular secretions. The gut contains all gaseous, liquid and solid waste products of the food we have taken in, substances that have not been absorbed, but are simply expelled after passing through the alimentary canal. The lower portion of the intestine moreover contains large quantities of the bacteria which have been of service in the process of digestion. Further, the gut contains the whole of the secretory products of all the digestive glands, from the microscopic gastric and intestinal glands to the large glands, such as the liver and pancreas. Next to the food-residue, the products of this glandular secretion are quantitatively very considerable. This is clearly shown by the fact that at birth, faeces are passed, although the newly-born child has never yet taken any food, unless perhaps it has swallowed a little of the "waters" (liquor amnii). Finally we find in the gut as well as in the other excretions, numerous dead epithelial cells and much mucus; both derived from all the mucous membranes of the gut and of the gland-ducts.

Owing to the admixture of food-residue, the evacuations of the gut are called excretions instead of secretions. This distinction is, however, not as important as appears at first, for if only wholly digestible food-materials are taken in, such as rice, sugar, butter, roast-beef, etc., the food residue almost entirely disappears. The color is derived from the bile. As soon as the supply of bile is cut off, the faeces become colourless.

The odour is that of putrefactive processes, and may, therefore, be made almost to vanish by the daily consumption of Yoghurt (a bacterial preparation of milk first introduced from Bulgaria). But the smell of any substances accidentally mixed with the food, such as sulphureted hydrogen compounds after the ingestion of sulphur or onion, remains unaltered.

The volume of the faeces is more or less proportional to the food residue, but depends even more on the water content, which is sometimes very small, but may at times be excessively great, so that the intestinal contents may become quite liquid[1].

1. In taking a medical history it is usually wise to inquire into the consistency rather than the volume, the latter being very often wrongly estimated by the patient, and necessitating a further examination, a task one would rather dispense with for one's own sake as well as the patient's.

Under the influence of some drugs, e.g., Epsom salts, and some diseases, e.g., cholera, the excretion of water by the intestine may considerably exceed that by the kidneys. The excretion of the contents of the bowel is dependent above all on the volume of the contents. Here, as in the other two excretions, the mechanical pressure produced by over-distension stimulates contractions in the muscular walls, at the same time the irritability of the intestine may be either morbidly increased or diminished.

Secondly, the urine. The urine is a typical glandular excretion, a waste product of the glandular cells of the kidneys. Since, however, the cells of the kidneys are very well supplied and nourished with blood, the urine also contains the main portion of the liquid waste products of all our tissues and organs in so far as they are introduced into the circulation by means of the lymphatic system[2].

These products of metabolism are in the first instance those of the muscular tissues, which perform our mechanical work. It is therefore hardly to be wondered at that the smell of the urine, when no food is taken that might influence it, is rather like bouillon, even if no meat has been eaten.

If, for example, small traces of oil of turpentine are swallowed or even only inhaled, the urine will assume a pleasant odour of violets. In ancient Rome, the ladies of the demi-monde did this on purpose, and they took a little belladonna (hence the name) as well, so that the pupils of the eyes should become as large as possible.

The production of urine varies in quantity with the rate of metabolism, and especially with the blood pressure. The blood pressure and the secretion of urine can be artificially increased by all kinds of stimulants, for instance through the consumption of strong irritant drugs like alcohol, hops, cantharides (Spanish fly), oil of turpentine, balsam and many ethereal oils and condiments.

The production of urine is indispensable for the continuation of life, on account of its vital importance in purifying the blood.

Finally we come to the sexual secretion. As the bladder periodically expresses the urine by means of muscular contraction of its walls, so likewise, by energetic contractions of their muscular walls, the seminal vesicles and ducts of the adult discharge periodically a few drops of mucous liquid—the semen—a turbid viscous fluid like a thick gruel, which soon becomes more liquid when exposed to the air.

This is neither a solid substance as in the gut, nor a watery solution, like the urine. It has the typical character of an emulsion. Just as milk is an emulsion of microscopic globules of fat swimming in a colourless menstruum and blood an emulsion of microscopic red corpuscles swimming in a colourless menstruum, so the semen is an emulsion of microscopic sperm-cells swimming in a colourless menstruum, mixed with a quantity of mucus derived from the mucous membrane of the seminal vesicles. Besides this mucus the semen contains a few crystals and a number of dead and de-

2. Solid substances are at first not contained in the urine. The gaseous end-products of our metabolism are excreted by the lungs.

generated epithelial cells derived from the genital canal. The colour of the semen is between that of milk and that of water, and the smell is stale and something like decomposing leeks. Further, the reaction of the semen is neutral and it is salty like tears or blood-serum.

The innumerable young vigorous new-formed cells derived from the testes form by far the most important part of the semen, though quantitatively only a small percentage of it. Thus it is not so much a case of glandular secretion as of a quite peculiar new-formation, as we have already pointed out in Chapter 2. As in the case of the secretion of urine, the energy with which the secretion is ejected does not depend so much on the composition as on the quantity, i.e., the overdistension stimulates the muscles to contract. Here again we have to consider the varying sensitiveness of the organs to irritation, and the degree of irritation to which they are subjected.

Thus there are cases in which the apparently normal secretion contains no sperm-cells (azoöspermia)[3]. This often happens after recovery from gonorrhea, if the two narrow sperm-ducts are completely closed by the contraction of the scar-tissue in the process of healing; also after operative procedures, for instance vasectomy, i.e., the intentional interruption of the continuity of the two sperm-ducts. If this occlusion or interruption of continuity takes place in adult life, when the seminal vesicles are already accustomed to secrete mucus, this secretion of mucus without admixture of sperm-cells can go on as before, and indeed with all its normal attendant manifestations of congestion, erection, desire, voluptuous sensation and satisfaction. If, however, the two testicles have been removed, epecially in childhood, then not only will the ejaculation contain no sperm-cells, but the organochemical matter mentioned in Chapter 4 which gives rise to the normal irritability of the adult nervous system will be absent from the blood-stream. Such an individual is not only definitely impotent but is also defective in other respects.

Unlike the production of urine, the function of semen-production is not in itself an essential condition for the preservation of life. All of us have lived through childhood without producing semen, so an adult can remain alive with little or no production of semen, especially in advanced years. But when once the seminal vesicles become distended, they will empty themselves as in the case of the bladder, either with or without our conscious consent.

The female genital apparatus is more economical, both as re-

3. A symptom that has nothing in common with impotence. One can only speak of impotence when erections are lacking, for instance in paralysis of the external occlusory muscles.

gards the number of cells expelled and the periodicity. At menstruation, generally only a single unfertilised ovum, something like an abortion, is expelled together with a large amount of blood and mucus derived from the excretory tract, and with a number of dead and degenerated epithelial cells. At the beginning and the end of menstruation, mucus preponderates, during its middle period, blood. In the seminal secretion of the male, pinkish traces of blood may also occasionally be found, but they are of no importance. In the same way, in catarrh of the mucous membranes of the bladder and bowels, the mucus may be more or less tinged with blood, especially in infants and young children. It is not improbable that originally in carnivorous animals this greater amount of blood in the female secretion had a certain significance as a sexual lure in the struggle for existence. It also made the sexual act easier at that time when this discharge of blood was still a principal factor at the rutting period.

Apart from this sexual secretion, a small drop of mucus derived from the genital canal may be excreted, by the woman from the mouth of the uterus, and by the man from the orifice of the urethra, during sexual excitement; this is of no special importance as long as the drop is as clear as water. It is often merely an expression of voluptuous feeling. If this drop of mucus in the man or of vaginal discharge in the woman is turbid and milky or purulent, it means in the man certainly gonorrhea, in the woman possibly gonorrhea, but in most cases only leucorrhea, or "fluors albus", which the French politely call "fleurs blanches" instead of "flueurs blanches".

Such a catarrhal discharge from the female genital tract may be comparatively harmless, containing only putrefactive bacteria, but it may also contain pathogenic germs, even those of a contagious disease, for instance gonorrhea. So it is much easier to make a mistake in the diagnosis of this disease in the female than in the male. The latter notices it early because milky and purulent drops escape from his meatus (hence the name gonorrhea = flow of semen which was given to it in error). These drops leave starchlike traces on the linen in drying. Violent pain and burning on micturition and on erection induce him to consult a doctor. Actually, each day's delay makes this disease of the mucous membrane more difficult and more tedious to cure. For this reason even a very slight infection in which the discharge is at first hardly noticeable, and only turbid, like soapy water, may often give rise to the most unfortunate results. In the woman this disease is as we have said, generally unrecognised in its initial stages, and for this reason it is a prolific source of innumerable genital abdominal diseases and of sterility[4].

While man only gets a urethral discharge by infection with virulent gonococci, woman, probably on account of the width of her genital tract, is much more prone to fluor albus on the slightest provocation, the vulva and vagina being so easily accessible to even the mildest infection. Morover, the possibility is greater because most women and girls omit external and internal cleansing after each menstrual period, so that the resistance of the mucous membrane is soon lowered.

In conclusion, if we consider these secretions which were formerly regarded as waste matter, it is not surprising to find that the microscopic cells, which are by no means waste matter, but on the contrary new-formations, have only recently been recognised as important—like pearls in a mass of mud.

It was not till 1677, in the days of the famous microscopist Leuuwenhoek, that a Dutch student at Leyden, named Lodewyk van Ham, discovered the sperm-cells, which he called spermatozoa. Swammerdam, who died in 1685, rightly conjectured that contact of an egg-cell with these spermatozoa gave rise to fertilisation. The human ovum was not discovered till 1827, by C. E. von Baer, and only in 1850 did duBarry succeed in actually observng the penetration of a rabbit-ovum by a sperm-cell.

4. Luetic (syphilitic) infection, on the contrary, often causes a series of miscarriages.

Chapter 16

DIGESTION OF FOOD AND SEX HEALTH

SOME readers may be shocked to find that we mention that function which is so repulsive to us, because it is concerned with the waste matter of the body, in the same breath as the genital function, which is to lead us to the highest idealism. Science, however, must not be swayed by sentimental considerations of sympathy and antipathy, which have already led us astray far too long. Those of us who are well brought up are only too prone to make a mystery of the one function because the accompanying sensations are so pleasant, and of the other because they are so disagreeable, but this is not right. Science should not make a mystery of anything; on the contrary, it should elucidate everything. Its noblest task is to discover the interconnections between all phenomena.

I consider the intestinal function first, because it offers us the best opportunity for studying the conscious control of our bodily functions. The years in which we had to learn control of our bladder now lie far behind us, but the law of constancy obliges us in advancing years to pay ever more attention to the bowel excretion. Micturition is a trivial matter, especially for the male; it can easily be done anywhere: whereas the activity of the bowel requires far more trouble, self-control, and muscular effort, to produce either a positive or negative result.

It is, therefore, not surprising that the bowel-excretion does not give rise to the emotional and congestive manifestations which are so typical of the seminal secretion; but intestinal colic may sometimes cause as violent phenomena as those of sexual secretion, particularly of the female, and even loss of blood.

It is the peculiar construction of the organ that makes intestinal excretion such an important factor in learning self-control.

We are confronted with the question how it can ever be possible to control such a function. To begin with, we must make a fundamental change in our conceptions of voluntary and involuntary muscles. This distinction is not absolute, but relative. The greater development of the transversely-striped muscles, as compared with

90

the unstriped membranous muscle fibres, is accounted for by the fact that in the embryo the former develop in full activity, as is evidenced by the mother's feeling foetal movements, while the unstriped muscles function very little or not at all during intra-uterine life and are therefore less differentiated from the connective tissue.

Moreover the unstriped muscles work involuntarily because they lie so deep in the interior of our body, that they are outside the sphere of our consciousness. But even this difference is only relative. All our "voluntary" muscles were in the early stages of extra-uterine life just as helpless and involuntary as our "involuntary" muscles still are. Anybody who has watched little children knows what a lot of effort it costs them to develop all these groups of muscles one at a time into voluntary ones. They learn to do this by experience. At first the various groups of muscles are moved involuntarily as if by accident, and the child observes the sensation of the contraction of the muscles involved as *cause,* and the external phenomena of movement as *effect,* and repeats the same movements in endless variation as a game, till it finally gains voluntary control of the muscle groups concerned. Now that we are grown up we have quite forgotten these exercises and can no longer remember how our hearts beat fast and our heads grew hot from the exertion. What endless trouble it cost us to learn to walk! As grown-ups we can get only a faint idea of it, for instance, if we learn to swim or to cycle.

This training of our skeletal muscles is always only partially successful, and even that only in the case of those muscles which we can observe and which we use frequently. The various groups of muscles in our back, for instance, almost always remain involuntary, however old we grow. And even with the best training, how relative this control is. Artists, e.g., famous pianists and violinists, and many skilled craftsmen achieve far more. And if at any time spasmodic contractions occur, the best trained muscles are no longer under our control.

All the involuntary unstriped muscles too, which we have laboriously exercised from birth, e.g., those involved in urination, are fairly under the control of our consciousness, though we still notice a certain incompleteness of control; whereas we have studied the control of the skeletal muscles from such an early age and so diligently, that we imagine that they are subject to our "will" and "order" without further consideration of cause and effect.

Yet the whole process follows the same course in both cases, though less smoothly in that of the unstriped muscles on account of their less complete differentiation. We have always begun, consciously or unconsciously, by learning cause and effect, and then later, whenever the same situation recurred, we have applied our experience. Thus we are enabled to make use of this chain of causes and effects in any way we like, by adapting ourselves to it. Here "to rule is to serve", as the greatest rulers of ancient days knew so well.

This is the great lesson of life at which we have all laboured since our birth, and unconsciously even before it. The progress a child makes in this respect is almost incredible, particularly in the first year of life; all the movements of its little hands and feet are

91

at first absolutely aimless, but soon have a definite purpose. After endless repetition and estimation of every cause and effect, the child learns at last to control all its movements both as regards time and place, allowing for the law of gravitation and what it has learnt by its sense of touch. Learning control of our transversely striped muscles was, so to speak, our preparatory school; we no longer think of that when we are grown up; but now begins the higher education, which teaches us to become ever more and more conscious of our involuntary muscles and at last to bring them under conscious control. The reader has already been given the solution of this problem: we need only continue by the same method.

I will use all the details of the exercise of the intestinal functions as an example to demonstrate how we can attain the highest point of mental superiority; for there is no other bodily function which so clearly demonstrates this principle. We shall not grudge the trouble, however small and unimportant many of the details may seem to be.

Theoretically, it is a question of making the unconscious conscious; practically, an involuntary function is elevated into a voluntary one; this is the corner-stone of all self-control and the basis of all higher conduct.

Generally speaking, particularly in the new-born child, and also in states of unconsciousness, reflex peristaltic movements of the intestinal wall occur whenever it is stimulated by distension. As soon as these peristaltic contractions have extended sufficiently far downwards for the occlusory muscles to feel the pressure, the latter contract even more strongly so as to occlude the exit of the bowel completely. This is also reflex action, i.e., movements without the participation of our consciousness.

This antagonism, this battle, may remain undecided for some time — as long as the two opposing forces are evenly balanced. We can interfere voluntarily with this process either by augmenting the pressure by means of the abdominal muscles or by using the perineal muscles to support the internal occlusory muscles. In this way we are able either to maintain or to disturb the balance—whichever we wish. We often do much to bring about the positive result, e.g. we inhibit the contraction of the external occlusory muscles when we pass flatus. In the same way an accoucheur particularly warns a woman in labor not to hold back when the waters break; he does this in the hope that the escaping waters may bring the foetus a good way along the birth canal, and the child may even actually be born. Thus it is possible voluntarily to influence the involuntary muscles.

But most people have no idea of this antagonism, and even we doctors, however well trained in physiology we may be, do not always remember it, but even without this knowledge we are all sooner or later reminded of this function by feelings of pressure and tension. The mental image of this function occurs to us; by reflex action we gradually and unconsciously adapt our respiration and our musculature—certainly less markedly than if we did it consciously,

92

but nevertheless often not less efficiently. Unconsciously and for more frequent and lengthy periods, we close the upper openings of our body in order to hold our breath, as if we wanted to see if the impulse really existed. Such gentle but oft repeated impulses are often more efficacious in stimulating peristalsis than a single conscious pressure with the abdominal muscles. A small gas bubble is easily set in motion, and when the internal balance has once been disturbed, it is not so easily restored.

The proper function is even more effectively elicited if these preliminaries are assisted mentally, for instance if we concentrate on the thought: "I must and will go to the w. c. at once"; even if we are not at the moment thinking about a contraction of the muscles. In this way our will power can work wonders, but only where there already exists a chain of cause and effects — never as "deus ex machina" (without a physiological basis) as was formerly believed.

The psychological augmentation of the function can be greatly increased by suggestion, as we shall show in Chapter 35; for instance, if we take bread pellets in the belief that they are laxatives, as is told of Maria Theresa. In such a case, our psyche is completely engrossed by the expected function. The more free we are at such times from other impressions, the more effective is the stimulus. So in hypnotism all our energies are concentrated on one point.

We cannot impress too strongly upon the reader, that this function or indeed any cell function should not be disturbed by undue haste. If an impulse to go to stool occurs and is assisted by our voluntary muscles, if we go to that place where we are accustomed to go every day, preferably at a fixed hour, to ease ourselves in solitude and comfort, — the only place where we are allowed to give a moment's rest to our occlusory muscles; we feel this cool sensation (just as a cold water douche is more efficacious than a lukewarm one); finally the moment comes for increased abdominal pressure; then almost always the miracle happens that our involuntary muscles contract exactly at the moment we desire!

This regularity of time and place works wonders—indeed some people can only perform this function in their own homes. This is the force of habit.

The desire to pass flatus or urine may be the first signal that the internal balance is disturbed. But it is better not to respond to this call too soon, just as in parturition it is of no advantage if the forewaters escape too early.

If we carefully observe the influences that are at work, we can earlier voluntarily stimulate the chain of causes and effects, and direct them into the proper channels. Waking up and stretching oneself after a night's rest, getting out of bed, washing and dressing oneself—all these bodily movements, with the deeper breathing consequent on them, are powerful adjuvants. Even more efficacious still are the more energetic and purposive movements, especially of the abdominal muscles, e.g., abrupt contractions of the diaphragm, powerful massage of the abdominal wall, compression of the abdominal cavity with the bent knees while lying on the back, etc. In this way it is possible to simulate the involuntary muscles of the bowel to contract with absolute mathematical precision. With practice it is possible, even in difficult cases, to render the involuntary musculature of the bowel obedient to our commands, though this training takes longer than in the case of the voluntary muscles, because of the greater differentiation of the latter.

The more attentively we study the physiological conditions, the more easily we shall succeed in setting the chain of cause and effect in motion, and ensure the desired result. We shall have to consider the choice of foods in connection with this function[1].

For this reason some people are very fond of brown bread as a mechanical stimulant to the bowel, others of gingerbread, figs or dates; for this reason, too, many people like vegetables and fresh fruit to ensure a large water and gas content for a longer time during digestion.

I have had hypochondriacal patients whose only interest in life was to choose such foods as would prevent constipation, and even discussed the subject at table; these were poor unfortunates who produced nothing else in the world. But if we want to have complete control we must begin much earlier. Even in choosing an occupation, we must see to it that it is not entirely a sedentary one if we are already inclined to constipation. We must continually remind children not to neglect this function.

Everybody must recognise the importance of the advice given by the doctor to pregnant women to take suitable exercise, advice which favourably influences the movements of the unborn child.

Much of what has been indicated here is always carried out unconsciously in the absence of knowledge, but to attain complete victory, especially in difficult cases, we must conform as far as possible to the physiological chain of causes and effects.

1. Our food takes about two days to pass through the whole length of the alimentary canal. If we go to stool once a day, say in the morning, the excreta passed will not be the result of the midday meal of yesterday, but that of the day before. Laxatives, and in sensitive persons, all sorts of influences can expedite the process. Gasses act as pioneers and clear the way.

Chapter 17

URINARY SECRETION AND ITS LESSONS
FOR SEX HEALTH

A S DURING the development of the foetus (see chapter 3) our two kidneys represent only an improved form of the two embryonic Wolffian bodies, so also both the excretory systems are quite similar, and the mechanism of the urinary and seminal secretions almost identical. I therefore beg the reader to consider this chapter not only as concerning the urinary secretion, but also with respect to the seminal secretion as well; a distinct economy, as otherwise it would have had to be printed and read twice over.

We are all familiar with the distressing spectacle of a child who has not had a timely opportunity to urinate. He becomes more and more uneasy and fidgety, squeezes his legs together, as though that will help his occlusory musculature; he twists and turns in all directions in the effort to relieve his pain and trouble. It is quite impossible for him to fix his interest on anything whatever; the more acute the antagonism grows within him, the more excitable and nervous he becomes; and how congested is his troubled little face! At last all his nerve centres are overwrought, all the muscle-groups of his body twist in clonic spasms, and so we see the trembling, convulsive picture of a maximal hypertension. He bursts into profuse perspiration until at last, perhaps quite unexpectedly, often because the occlusory muscles have relaxed their energy for an instant, the expulsory musculature wins the day and the urine flows unhindered. The bladder is relieved; only the child's clothing is wetted.

The true significance of this finale as the climax of the peristaltic-secretory function of the whole excretory apparatus only appears convincing when we study it by the comparative method with the seminal secretion, because here, on account of the small volume of the fluid to be voided, the whole secretory function is only manifested in this finale.

With this normal scheme of the urinary secretion in view we should, however, be far from the truth if we imagined that the sensation of desire to urinate is always proportional to the amount of urine actually in the bladder. In the first place we can voluntarily increase the impulse when we submit the bladder to increased mechanical pressure through contraction of the abdominal musculature. Even a distension of the lower bowel may mechanically increase the pressure on the bladder and cause a precipitate desire to urinate.

Besides which, the irritability of the bladder-wall may be artificially increased by the employment of the substances which we have already mentioned.

We mentioned them then because they increase the amount of urine, and we refer to them again here, because at the same time they may render the bladder-wall excessively irritable and congested. In serious cases the irritability of the bladder-wall may be greatly increased, if through the ingestion of irritating drugs or through chill or infection, etc., a regular catarrh of the mucous membrane has been set up. In such a case the smallest traces of urine in the bladder may occasion the most powerful and painful contractions of the bladder-wall, as if it were greatly distended. Just as in conjunctivitis, a tear-drop in the eye may be as intensely painful as if grains of sand had blown in.

And if one devotes special attention to the desire to urinate this impulse is felt sooner and more powerfully; for instance when a schoolboy holds up his hand in class to ask permission to leave the room, all the other boys suddenly feel the same desire. The same happens if one accidentally sees someone else urinating, or even suddenly thinks of this function.

In all these cases it is the imagination that acts as an irritant.

If then, in practical life, we seriously ask ourselves the question: is the impulse that I feel at this moment only the result of an accidental stimulus, or is it really the voice of Nature telling me not to neglect this important function, how can we obtain an answer?

It is not always an easy matter to settle this problem. With a little observation and experience we shall be able in most cases to decide what influences are active in any particular instance. Furthermore, there is frequently *a posteriori* a very good criterion already in existence, which may serve as precedent. When a real over-distension takes place, if we do not obey the impulse with physiological regularity, it will burden us increasingly until finally the secretion ceases. If, however, the stimulus is only accidental, then the impulse may perhaps be momentarily much more powerful and peremptory than usual, but never with this regular periodicity; and if we do not yield to it, then in a short time the impulse decreases, far sooner and more permanently than if we had yielded to it immediately.

We can also formulate the same principle in the positive sense: after a suitable satisfaction, we experience an appropriate period of rest; after over-stimulation, if we yield, the impulse will always disturb us more capriciously and no longer allow us to rest.

With all these causes of artificial over-stimulation, a regular, suitable satisfaction, together with a regular and frugal diet can work wonders. Strength of will, exercise and self-control prepare the way. And the more earnestly we look upon life, the more shall we avoid both dangers: excess and insufficiency. We must control our reflexes, but this control should never be abused, and the function deliberately repressed.

96

If, however, one attempts too great a repression of this function, then after a few periods of rest, the impulse is felt again still more imperiously until finally a period of morbid exhaustion sets in, and the impulse really considerably diminishes; and one is as pleased with his victory as the peasant, who wanted to cure his horses of the bad habit of eating was at first with his success. But one should never forget that such attempts to circumvent Nature lay the foundation of paralytic conditions, and cause much suffering later on.

To suppress the function permanently is impossible. Finally the internal tension must become overpowering, and the occlusory muscles are forced to give way. The product of secretion then flows out, voluntarily or involuntarily, but flow it must. As long as we are able to think for ourselves, we must see to it that no injury ensues from it, either for ourselves or for others. And for this reason Part III is devoted to the problems of self-control.

Chapter 18

THE PRODUCTION OF SEMEN.
THE SEMINAL APPARATUS

NOW that we have thoroughly discussed the other two secretory functions, we come to the real object of our study: the seminal secretion, apparently the least important of the three secretory functions which are localised at the lower pole of our body, but really the most important by reason of its ultimate effects and the phenomena which accompany it. But the reader who has had the patience to study the other two secretions, has now gained a correct insight into this function.

If, however, a thorough description of the seminal secretion is still required, read the last chapter over again carefully; but read *semen* instead of *urine, seminal vesicles* instead of *urinary bladder,* and *seminal ducts* instead of *ureters.* The seminal secretion with all the normal and abnormal influences which act as stimuli, follows the same scheme as the urinary secretion.

Just as in the urinary bladder, the antagonism is only caused by the volume, the distension; it makes no difference whether the semen contains a great number of sperm-cells, or none at all. So we see how erroneous were the old ideas that the spermatozoa could excite erection by the liveliness of their own movements. This is so far from being the case, that this independent movement does not occur until they can move in a thin fluid menstruum. The following explanation will make clear why we have two seminal vesicles but only one urinary bladder. In the period of embryonic life when the anterior abdominal wall was still quite open, not only the primordial kidneys, but also their excretory canals were two separate ducts leading to the genital eminence. But later, when the abdominal wall was closed almost to the umbilicus, simultaneously with the formation of the umbilical cord, a single unpaired urinary bladder composed of a single cavity, and consequently a single unpaired urethra, was formed.

Functionally, however, there is no essential difference; as a general rule both the seminal vesicles contract simultaneously[1] and separately only under the influence of very slight stimuli.

Because the semen is ejaculated from *two* seminal vesicles, it may be imagined that it will be ejected with greater ease and force. This, however, is not the case, as the two excretory ducts of the seminal vesicles, and especially their openings into the urethra, are so extremely fine, because really they are only embryonic excretory canals, that even the most powerful contractions of the seminal vesicles are scarcely able to force the semen into the urethra.

It is very significant that these two apertures should be so extremely small, much smaller than the two seminal ducts. Because the two seminal vesicles are only laterally attached to their ducts it may happen (in contradistinction to the urinary apparatus, in which both the ureters discharge into the bladder itself), that sperm-cells simply *pass* by the seminal vesicle without entering it. In this manner it might only too easily happen that semen would escape with urine unnoticed, without exercising its fertilising function, as is sometimes the case in serious paralytic conditions (spermator-rhea—seminal emission without erection). But the extreme fineness of the two apertures in itself causes a resistance as elastic as the best occlusory muscle. So the antagonism in connection with the secretion of semen is unmistakable, even for those sperm-cells which have not penetrated into the seminal vesicles.

The problem of the ejaculation of the semen is rendered very much more difficult, because on account of the small volume of these organs and their concealed situation, the utility of abdominal compression must be inconsiderable. Instead of this Nature employs a far more efficacious method, so that when finally the antagonism has reached a spasmodic culminating point, it can accomplish the final evacuation in a surprising manner, which will be fully discussed in Chapter 21.

Our seminal apparatus, however, had developed but little since the beginning of the embryonic period; but in this case congestion is paramount. For this reason erection is such a typical phenomenon of the sexual life.

1. Although the seminal vesicles lie closely pressed against the bladder, one on either side, the urinary bladder and the seminal vesicles never function simultaneously, any more than at the upper pole of the body swallowing and breathing take place simultaneously. This last does not happen, because when swallowing food, the epiglottis bends downward and so bridges over the windpipe at the opportune moment. And in the same way each time that the seminal vesicles with their occlusory muscles are stimulated, the erection thus occasioned immediately constricts the urethra to such an extent that the voiding of urine is almost impossible. If that were not so, and if the urine were voided along with the semen, as is the case in serious conditions of impotence, the semen would always be washed away with the urine without being able to cause fertilisation.

The periodicity of the secretory manifestations is, as we have already explained in Chapter 15, dependent on the volume of the substance to be voided; the greater the volume, the shorter the periods between the excretions.

In this respect it is worth while comparing once again the seminal secretion of the male and the egg secretion of the female organism. If the quantity to be excreted by the male is small, it is surely reduced to a minimum in woman: only one solitary almost microscopic egg-cell.

In conclusion, as we must go a little more closely into the details of periodicity in both sexes, I will make a few practical remarks on the subject.

The age at which the sexual secretion begins to appear, is termed in both sexes the age of puberty. In girls the first traces of menstruation generally appear at from 13 to 15; in tropical races this happens much earlier, but in Germany and Holland frequently much later, especially in the country. This occurrence is repeated regularly at intervals of from 3 to 5 weeks; in anaemic girls fortunately less frequently and less profusely.

In the youth at from 14 to 16 years of age, the first traces of emissions occur during sleep, and these are repeated once or more each week as long as he remains sexually abstinent, antagonism reaching consciousness by means of erections. As far as no external, more accidental, influences make themselves felt, the erection-curve runs more or less parallel with the emission curve. As often as the seminal vesicles and canals have emptied themselves or when this has occurred say twice at a relatively short interval, it may happen that under influence of the recent experience, erection will recur with redoubled strength; but if one does not give way to it, there at once sets in for a shorter or longer time, a relatively, if not completely, calm period, until the seminal vesicles are gradually once more subjected to high pressure.

It also happens in the males of the lower animals that when copulation and masturbation are impossible, the seminal fluid is finally spontaneously ejected, especially during unsuccessful attempts at mating.

It is still less commonly known that it may happen exceptionally in the female organism that the typical feeling of sexual satisfaction, with its congestive pulsations, is very distinctly experienced, either during sleep or in a half-dreaming state at night; in the daytime this only occurs as the result of a powerful extra-genital stimulus; e.g., a very passionate kiss.

There is absolutely no cause to worry about our nocturnal emissions, as long as they only happen in sleep, even if they are ac-
100

companied by vivid dreams. At most, if they occur too frequently, they leave a psychic depression as a symptom of fatigue. For the sexual function occasions in both sexes a deep agitation of the nervous system, which may be manifested in the most varied ways, particularly in the psychic sphere.

Woman arrives at the end of her functionally active sexual life at about 50 years of age, after the secretion has gradually become less frequent and profuse. Amongst tropical races, where puberty commences earlier, old age also sets in earlier. This time of life is known as the climacterium. We should not be surprised that in the female, although youthful and active in other respects, this function ceases at an early age, if we consider how difficult it is for the egg to force its way through the ovarian tissue, and how this difficulty must increase with advancing years, as the ovarian tissue loses its elasticity and becomes harder and firmer. But for copulation the climacterium (or change of life) is no hindrance; on the contrary it removes all danger of pregnancy. It is only with very advanced old age that the possibility of copulation is lessened and finally excluded, because the mucous folds become too stiff, and vulva and vagina appear to be too constricted.

In man, however, even when he is old, the sperm-cells which are constantly forming afresh can be so easily excreted that this secretion only becomes gradually limited with most advanced age, and no limit can be assigned. But what otherwise would be the most effectual stimulus to erection will then be found useless. At any rate sooner or later relative impotence may set in through diminished power of response to stimuli.

When a married person has regularly practiced sexual intercourse, and this is suddenly interrupted by the death, illness or absence of the partner and not resumed, there often elapses a considerable interval before nocturnal emissions reappear; a striking proof of how powerful the impulse must have been before the spontaneous emission occurred.

If one is troubled with too frequent nocturnal emissions, e.g., if they occur every night, he should consult a physician who can no doubt prescribe hygienic measures without resorting to drugs. Emissions only seriously threaten the health if they occur in the daytime: and it is worse, if they occur, as for instance in advanced age, without erection, just as the urine may drip away through paralysis of the occlusory muscle (sphincter).

Chapter 19

FALSE POPULAR NOTIONS OF SEX THAT IMPERIL THE YOUNG

THE monthly sexual secretion of woman has been rather euphemistically called her monthly purification, because in former times it was thought that her blood would be thereby freed from impurities; just as during the puerperium it is termed a purification when the entire open uterine surface cleanses itself. We might with just as much reason call nocturnal emissions a purification, because substances are then excreted which should actually be got rid of. But we are so little accustomed to thinking physiologically, that we take more notice of the external soiling than the internal cleansing.

This soiling occurs so much more easily in young men because there is no wearing of a diaper to help as with girls. This symptom is manifested in the young man quite unexpectedly and at irregular intervals, and any unaccustomed clothing of the parts which could be employed, would only aggravate matters through friction and excite the production of secretion.

I now come to a rather painful question, and I should not have touched on it at all if I had not been so frequently consulted about it in my practice.

Young fellows tell each other that seminal emissions are very harmful; they even think that it is a proof that prostitution is indispensable for them, for a man does not want to "wet the bed" like a baby. This idea scarcely ever fails to convince our young men; yet it is quite erroneous, if only we have the courage to look the facts in the face.

An involuntary escape of urine or faeces is a fearful thing, because the bed or clothing is spoilt at once, though these excreta disturb no one when laid in the proper place. With the seminal secretion, however, the reverse is the case. Here normal sexual intercourse can have the most far-reaching and often terrible results; while the involuntary secretion of these few drops causes far less disturbance than, for instance, when through energetic muscular exercise all our sweat and sebaceous glands start secre-

102

ting at once. And for this reason we are often obliged to change our linen, and to wash the whole of the body thoroughly, including its lower part. In winter if it is too cold to do this in the bedroom, we should at least rub the entire surface of the skin with a rough towel on rising. If we are also in the habit of going early each morning to stool, we can satisfy all hygienic requirements with a single wash-down. If necessary, we can then change all our clothes, or change day-shirt and night-shirt regularly every night and morning, which is a good habit from childhood and occasions no special expense.

Where is now your necessity for prostitution? Go and preach that to your young companions who perhaps admire your worldly wisdom, take them to a house of ill-fame and in one night ruin their health and their youth and perhaps all their lives... but don't prate any more to me about hygiene and cleanliness!

The worthy author of "The Elements of Social Science" goes one step farther. He expresses the opinion that not only are nocturnal emissions injurious, but that they are related to spermatorrhea, which we have already referred to as a symptom of paralysis; whereas in reality nocturnal emissions, which occur with erection during sleep, furnish the best proof of manly vigour, whereby in time of need Nature comes to our assistance with sweet dreams. It is not at all a morbid manifestation, but a natural safety-valve which allows these organs to remain quiescent for long periods without affecting the function, until the happy time when the desired suitable life-partner may be found.

It is idiotic to make such a fuss about this trifling uncleanliness. If we are so particular, we must admit that Nature is never clean, for all living cells contain fluid albumen. If in the springtime for instance we peel a little twig, the inner bark is quite wet. Everything that we call life makes us unclean. For life is really the absorption of clean elements and the expulsion of unclean ones. *Life* and *cleanliness* are material opposites; we cannot eat out of clean dishes.

Especially in the sexual province exaggerated desire for cleanliness may awaken the worst suspicions. Woe to the maiden whose linen is found spotless when it should be soiled! And to the young man too, who thereby reveals that he has gone astray.

Here the same principle applies that obtains for every surgeon and every workman, — it is not becoming dirty that is blameworthy, but remaining dirty. Hygiene does not demand of us that we should remain clean, but that we should continually renew our cleanliness. And cleanliness is a virtue because it must be renewed every day. Our whole life is a fight against dirt, a struggle for life.

In times when man had not become so dualistic, this was better understood than at present, and people were often cleaner than we are, in the disposal of the faeces for instance. Only thus is it comprehensible how among savage races the crudest surgical operations, some of which we hardly dare attempt with all the refinement of our modern science, succeed splendidly. This is because they run fewer risks with *bacillus coli* and similar germs.

Through an erroneous idea of what cleanliness really is, much harm has been done, especially in the sexual sphere. Reproaches have been hurled a hundred times against young men for such harmless soiling of linen, and they have thus been driven to self-abuse and concealment of the result. But it is only now that we realise how far we have wandered from Nature.

Mothers have had more tact in these matters. If their daughters have been a little alarmed by the first spot of menstrual blood, they have comforted and consoled them, glad that they had now arrived at womanhood. The first seminal stain should also be welcomed as a sign that the youth is now adult. It is the pollen of the flower that unfolds full of hope. He should then be comforted by the thought, as we said in Chapter 2, that the sexual life is not only a secretory function, but a creative new-formation, which should be honoured and not dragged in the mire, and that some day it should bring him the joy of founding a healthy and happy family. Each renewed emission will then serve to remind him of this lofty ideal.

How many men there are whose lives are darkened by despair, and who might have been happily rescued if their mothers had spoken thus with them at first.

Chapter 20

THE PHYSIOLOGY OF ERECTION
AND EJACULATION

ERECTION is the most prominent manifestation of the sexual life, but it can occur only if, firstly, a certain degree of congestion, and, secondly, a certain degree of irritability of the central nervous system, are present, two preliminary conditions which mutually support each other very effectively.

What causes the congestion? In order to answer this question we need only refer once more to our parallel between the urinary and seminal secretions.

We have not forgotten the case of the child with such a strong desire to make water, who was denied the opportunity; here we see so plainly the secretory antagonism with all its accompanying symptoms, so congestive and then so spasmodic!

I beg the reader carefully to recall this familiar picture of a child suffering; it is a picture of suffering mankind, wrestling with its bodily needs. Especially is it a picture of sexual suffering with its congestive excitement; and I can only imagine one other picture that can equal it: that is the ecstasy of voluptuousness, when at last the natural desire can be gratified[1].

If we can appreciate this picture, we immediately have the answer to the question how it is possible for such an apparently insignificant function as the voiding of semen to excite so much congestion. As we have seen in the last chapter but one, the embryonic origin gives the predisposition; but sometimes the resistance occasions such marked congestion as to prevent ejaculation. For unfortunately the secretion of semen is a function which always meets with strong resistance. Remember that this thick, viscous mucous emulsion must be forced through two capillary tubes in order to reach the urethra. What resistance! Is it then surprising that all the symptoms of congestion, which appear only exception-

1. As a contrast to these two pictures of youth, let us think of the senile symptoms occurring in advanced age, when, as a consequence of paralysis of the antagonistic resistance, semen escapes unnoticed and unrestrained. Here voluptuous sensations are out of the question.

ally in the secretion of urine, should regularly accompany the secretion of semen? Such colossal resistance which can never once be abated! So in this case the impulse must be increased to its extreme limits before so great a resistance can be overcome. The seminal secretion dominates the entire circulation of our blood; it makes us blush only to think of it.

And furthermore a man ought to think himself lucky to get off with a simple congestion; it is much worse for women, for in their sexual life they suffer from repeated haemorrhages, first in the tissues of the ovary, then in menstruation, and then a great deal at child-birth.

Every child who has an excessive desire to urinate shows the congestion principally in his face, and accompanying symptom of the cerebral congestion caused by the psychic strain on the will; for a congestion always occurs locally where an organ is strained to the extreme.

With the seminal secretion it is essentially the powerful local resistance that calls forth local congestion, through which, as we explained in Chapter 10, a maximum erection occurs, as soon as the external occlusory muscles are drawn into the antagonism by sympathy.

In some exceptional cases an erection occurs when urine is voided. I remember the case of an infant only a couple of months old, that is, too young for any psychic influence or training to be concerned. His parents paid great attention to hygienic questions and had kept him always scrupulously clean and not too tightly clothed. "I always know," said his mother, "when he wants to urinate." How can you know that?" I asked. "I can see it," was the answer, "when his little member swells. Then I hold him over the chamber till he passes urine." So in the case of this inexperienced little boy, the normal muscular antagonism that accompanies a desire to urinate is sufficient to act as a local stimulus and occasions an erection, although only a childish one.

So we see that erection, viewed theoretically, is not by any means confined to the sexual life. As we have already shown in Chapter 10, it is ultimately a function of the external occlusory musculature, as soon as this is sympathetically affected by the antagonism of one of the three excretory systems. Every adult male knows how strong an erection may be produced in the course of the night by an overcharged intestine or bladder; and how frequently, when waking in the morning, erection, perhaps accompanied by erotic dreams, is a warning to empty the bladder. In advanced years a man is often proud of his virile powers, and they suddenly disappear just as he wants to utilise them. And then the attempt to approach

106

the object of his desire banishes for an instant the impulse to urinate, and the whole illusion disappears. This mockery, and, when it happens frequently, this misery, might be spared, if one properly understood the facts of the case.

And erections in childhood show us more unmistakably than anything else that erections may occur without any pressure of semen. At this age there is no pressure of semen at all. That at this age it is only a childish erection, depends not only on absence of any distension of the seminal vesicles, but also on the fact that the spongy connective tissue is not yet very rigid, and that the appropriate organochemical substances have not yet increased the irritability of the nervous system. But still it is an erection.

Both stimuli often act together: the urinary and seminal pressures. That this never leads to an unwelcome mixing of both secretions, depends on the fact that in man each of these two functions precludes the other (see chapter 18). This is not so in woman. I remember one case of a grown up young girl of good family who was rather stupid. She was always trying to escape from her parents' home to have intercourse with young fellows. This led her also to masturbate and wet the bed. In youths the contrary is often observed, they cease wetting the bed on reaching the age of puberty.

An erection is more rarely produced by intestinal antagonism; but I have seen such cases produced by sudden expulsion of intestinal gases.

But in the first bloom of life, the sexual impulse is so overpowering that we really get the impression that erection is exclusively a sexual function. In this period of our lives it is really the sexual impulse that acts as the causal factor in the vast majority of cases. This should not surprise us. Ultimately it seems to depend on the lumen of the excretory canal, whether or not the antagonism shall assume the spasmodic character which is essential for the production of erection. The frequency of erection is in inverse proportion to the lumen of the excretory canal. So all the above-cited experiences bear witness, and we are now able to see why in this respect the pressure of the semen has the lion's share, if not the monopoly.

From this principle it will also be evident why the erective function must occupy so much more modest a place in the female. The female genital canal is typically characterised not by narrowing, but by widening. The female urethra is also less complicated and wider than in man. Only the intestinal canal is of the same diameter in both sexes.

So far we have only dealt with the increase in the force of the blood stream, as it is occasioned by the muscular antagonism. So as to avoid as far as possible complicating the question, I have not yet touched on the active role played by the central nervous system, a role which is so important not only in the spiritual side of love, but also in the more material mechanism of erection. For the production of an erection, a strongly reacting central nervous system is required to serve as the connecting-link of the reflex.

The principle is sufficiently familiar. When, prompted by a stimulating sensation, our muscles begin to move, this takes place with the rapidity of lightning, yet the process is not at all simple. In most cases in order to produce this action the message must go a long way round, just as when we send a telegram; first to the central office, and then on to the destination. In this way a sensation is transmitted over the sensory nerves to the central nervous system (brain or spinal cord) and then back to the group of muscles involved, which then contract.

In and for itself alone this digression would have no significance, but on this complicated circuit not only can a stimulus influence many side-lines and become combined with other mental pictures, but it may also, no matter how weak it was at first, be immensely strengthened. For all nerve cells, like all the other cells, have the power of storing up energy. In mechanical work as a rule the newly formed energy is instantly used up, because an immediate result is demanded. But cell-life never acts in such haste. Here, by the absorption of nutriment, energy is slowly but unceasingly stored up. So too in the cells of the central nervous system, as soon as the cells are set in action, e.g., when a group of muscles is to be brought into reflex action, either when a group of skeletal muscles must carry out bodily movements, or smooth muscles must move the intestines, or the blood pressure must be regulated by increased heart action or arterial contraction.

So to a great degree it depends upon the normal sensibility and on the reserve of energy in our central nervous system, how rapidly, correctly, and powerfully we are accustomed to react to all influences, and how smoothly all our functions can be performed.

It is also an indispensable condition for the production of a powerful erection that our central nervous system should possess great sensibility and a store of energy.

As has been abundantly proved by Steinach's experiments (see chapter 4), it is the organochemical substances secreted by our testes or ovaries which produce this increased sensibility at puberty. If, however, through advancing years, this sensibility is greatly reduced and the seminal tension not so imperious, it is then almost entirely during sleep (see chapters 35 and 36) that the mental energies may be concentrated without disturbing influences, and that an erection may occur. In this connection we understand still better why in the bloom of our sexual life, it is precisely in our sleep that we are overtaken by emissions, and why it is in the intoxication of love that sexual passion can rise to such heights.

Owing to the changeable character of our central nervous system it often happens that the most trifling causes may lead to the most powerful excitement, and also the most trivial stimulus cause the strongest erection. Now we may better understand why our whole nervous system and especially all our sexual impulses are continually so capricious, so changeable and so uncertain.

And now it will be clear to us how, in this complicated circuit all kinds of side influences can effect us, either accelerating or inhibiting, especially the psychic influences to which we have already referred, when we stated that the special alarm-signal, the erection, which should theoretically only be the result of an overfilled reservoir, may be aroused at other times by other stimuli, such as a mental image.

It is still more important that the nerve-paths that we have described, represent a link between the spiritual and the material life, by means of which the most beautiful interchange can take place. One thing in the sexual province is most surprising, and that is that while the congestive stimulus at the lower pole of the body awakens the soul, through the spiritual sphere this passion may be turned into love.

The higher the stage at which we stand in the history of the evolution of the species, the more complicated these nerve-paths become; and so we have ultimately arrived at the point where we feel spiritual love to be something far more precious than its physical basis.

Because our brain possesses such a number of complicated nerve-paths, the mental energy can if necessary be diverted into quite other channels, particularly into paths which calm and soothe the sexual excitement. Every stimulus in other sections of the brain, or in other portions of the body, and every congestion in other brain centres or other parts of the body is capable of exerting a restraining influence on our sexual impulse. This constitutes one of the most important factors in self-control.

Chapter 21

THE ERECTION AND CLIMAX IN THE SEX ACT

SO far we have studied the causes of erection, and how it is called forth through muscular antagonism, congestion and nervous impulses; we shall now enquire further into the significance of this phenomenon.

An erection occurring during defecation is of no consequence, when urinating it may be injurious; for it has not developed any further in connection with these two functions. It has developed into the curious and striking complications with which we are all acquainted, only in connection with the seminal secretion.

It is a game of ebb and flow in our circulation which of itself fills us with pleasure and delight. But erection is of quite special significance for the seminal secretion: it shows us in the simplest possible manner how we can be freed from the tension of the secretion; it spurs us distinctly on to massage, and thereby arouses in this organ, which has hitherto experienced only a desire to urinate, an entirely new impulse.

I speak of this by analogy with other swellings. The tension and redness of inflammation, the pain and tension of a bruise, the pimple and itching produced by an insect sting, are all related cases, in which tension and swelling almost invariably drive us to massage.

Now we begin to perceive how it is possible that the sexual stimulus can be so raised to the climax of passion and delight, and is far more impulsive than any of our other bodily needs. The more we yield to these acute massage-motives, the more passionate their character is seen to be. If we just think of a tiny swelling caused by an insect sting, when we start to rub it the irritation becomes more and more intense, until we have scratched it open and fluid exudes. So also the seminal pressure, with its accompanying resistance, its congestive erection and massage-motives, excites our circulation and respiration and our whole being far more intensely than any other cause.

We are especially excited by the convulsive movements we have already referred to (chapter 10) and it is these convulsions which fill us with pleasure; for each one brings us a step nearer to climax, or tends to do so. They give us some idea how supremely happy the final convulsion will make us in the act of copulation if we can only reach this point.

If, however, one fine day, tired of struggling, we want to permit the secretory catastrophe, simply because we wish to give up further resistance, we shall soon see that it is not so simple a matter as it was with urination.

Now try just for once to evacuate the seminal vesicles voluntarily. These organs are much too small for that, and lie too deep; and besides, the resistance is much too great, even when they are overdistended. Even if prizes were to be won by it, the man is not yet born who could evacuate his semen to order, no matter how much strength he may exert in the attempt. The first condition necessary for the evacuation is erection; but in order finally to expel the semen, the erection alone does not suffice; even the convulsive movements to which we have referred cannot alone effect this.

Because during adult life seminal secretion and erection are always coincident, it has always been teleologically understood that erection facilitates ejection. But such is not the case! Quite the contrary. The erection even increases resistance, because as a true function of the external occlusory muscles, the calibre of the urethra can only be diminished by the congestive swelling thus produced. Just try for once to pass urine during a strong erection!

Now we come to a fatal incongruency. The more the erection drives us to massage, the worse the state of things becomes, for all massage and especially the massage of coition, increases the erection and thus carries the resistance to its culminating point. Only the magic wand of Nature is needed to give relief when the acme of despair has been reached. Well, Nature accomplishes this miracle.

A similar thing happens at the climax of the procreative act. The erection which has spasmodically increased, suddenly becomes an excretory function, because the spasm of the excessive erection driven to its extreme point by the movements of coitus is diverted to the ejaculation-centre situated a little higher in the spinal cord. Then the resistance of the external occlusory muscles is immediately relieved as well as the intensity of the erection, while the strength of emission is doubled. With a few convulsive movements all is over.

This commotion is so sudden and powerful that one really feels the relief and pleasure as if it came from the spinal cord itself.

However, it is not in our power to press out the few drops of thick semen. Here it is only the diverted reflex that can save us.

It is especially during our sleep, when resistance is absent, that the whole thing can happen so gently that we scarcely dream of it and do not wake at all. In rare and exceptional cases, e.g., if it takes too long to satisfy the wife, in the act of coitus, on account of semi-anaesthesia and total exhaustion of resistance, it can happen so automatically that we scarcely notice it. Normally, however, it is typical that the more erection is reflexly increased through lively movements in coitus, the nearer one comes to the moment when the excitement, increased to the point of madness, becomes an excretory function.

Then there is no more delay, no gradual diminution of resistance, no curve of fatigue which heralds defeat, but just as in the above-mentioned instances of diverted reflexes we have this sudden paradox: the greater the spasmodic resistance, the stronger is the sudden ejaculation. Then the semen will be thrown as high up the vagina as possible. Similarly in the wife the analogous erection of the clitoris and mutual massage movements have caused meanwhile the most voluptuous sensations, the same catastrophe happens in her case. The erection was needed to successfully call forth this manifestation. Although, or perhaps because, it betokens an increased resistance, it possesses such great value for this catastrophic secretory function. The more tightly Cupid's bow is drawn, the more deeply the arrow sinks into the heart.

Chapter 22

THE ROLE OF HUSBAND AND WIFE
IN THE SEX ACT

IT is far more distinctly recognisable in woman than in man, that the reproductive cells originate from a tumour, in this case, the ovary. Here there is no such system of excretory ducts as in a glandular function. Only after the egg-cell has reached the neighboring excretory system of the rudimentary pronephros do the same purely secretory processes take place as in man.

While in man the first escape of sperm-cells from the cell aggregation does not produce the least sensation or excitement, and sexual excitement is only felt after the seminal canals and vesicles have been subjected to considerable pressure; in the female organism on the contrary, a deep-seated stimulus must be produced, though perhaps an unconscious one, every time an egg-cell forces its way out of the ovarian tissue, like a tiny abscess (see chapter 3). This occasions discomfort and spasmodic pains, which are simply attributed to the troubles of menstruation. Furthermore, in the two egg-ducts and the uterine cavity the same secretory character as in man finds its expression, because the ovum mixes with the mucus, and later with mucus and blood from the genital passages. The uterine wall is far more muscular that the walls of the seminal vesicles; and on this account the monthly expulsion of the sexual discharge, composed of this mixture, may occasion the most severe spasmodic contractions.

It therefore results that in woman, no less than in man, the entire genital sphere works in a state of labile equilibrium, with muscular contractions and congestions; an ebb and flow manifested in man on a considerable scale by erections, but in woman on a smaller scale by the less striking erection of her clitoris. It is, however, a moot question in which of the two sexes the influences and stimuli are the more powerful and intimate!

The females of the lower animals give expression to these acute sensations of tension and pain by their peculiar cries; the cow for instance by a loud cry indistinguishable from her lowing when she wants to be milked.

But it is coitus which in woman, as in man, causes the deepest and most agreeable emotions. In both sexes this occurrence forms not only the climax of erection, but also the climax of the secretory function.

In extensive falling of the womb (*prolapsus uteri*) in which the mouth of the womb becomes visible, it has actually been observed under the influence of artificially induced sexual excitement, that a drop of mucus is first pressed out of this organ and then, on cessation of the uterine contractions, is aspirated again inwards. We thus see that at the critical moment a violent contraction of the uterus takes place, analogous to that of the seminal vesicles in the male.

This outward and inward movement of the drop of mucus, although certainly very efficacious in facilitating conception, is, however, not absolutely indispensable; for the sperm-cells are active enough to find their way up alone, even if they have only been deposited at the entrance to the vagina. It is not infrequent that a young girl is rendered pregnant, although she was not at all aware of having experienced proper coitus.

This condemns the so-called Spanish method as unreliable, a mode of copulating which is often used in Spain with the object of avoiding pregnancy, and officially tolerated by the Catholic church, because according to Aristotle the "*virtus attractiva*" of the womb is sufficiently powerful to lead to conception if the semen is deposited anywhere in the vagina (Sanchez: "*De sacramento matrimonii*"). This mode of copulating consists of the following: just before the ejaculation the partners change their positions, so that instead of the woman's legs being spread apart, she holds them close together, and the man's are outside hers. Now if the woman squeezes her thighs close together it is impossible for the man to penetrate far inside.

And still more convincing are the cases, not at all infrequent, in which a woman finds herself pregnant although penetration into the vagina was quite impossible, either on account of the narrowness of the vagina or for some other reason.

In this connection it is most important to enquire whether in normal coitus the amount of fluid secreted by the female canal at the orgasm is not much greater than one would be inclined to think from the above-mentioned experiment. Reports of trials made with "Karezza", in which a much longer time of enjoyment is allowed the female partner, seem to me to bear this out.

Karezza, also called *Zugessant's discovery*, is a mode of copulation in which both partners lie so still in mental ecstasy, that there is no ejaculation at all; so that they can have intercourse in this way as often and as long as they like. Those who have practised it describe it as a continuous revelling in voluptuous sensation, just as in their courting days, though at that time they had never been able to have enough of it. But this practice is scarcely reliable enough to be classed as a preventive method; only the man can, when ultimately his feelings overpower him, use the so-called French method, and withdraw before it is too late; or he may, as a guarantee against surprise, wear a sheath.

114

In any case the sperm-cells generally find a sufficiency of mois-ture within the walls of the vagina after sexual intercourse to enable them to swarm up, attracted also by the favourable thermic and chemotactic conditions. So it is easy to understand why the chances of impregnation are greatest when both partners experience the orgasm at the same moment.

And then if fertilisation really takes place it becomes apparent how much secretion the uterus may contain—far more than the seminal vesicles. Some nine months later, through overdistension, the muscular wall of this container is stimulated to contractions compared with which all the secretory activities of the male are but child's play.

The question, "To what extent in the sexual life of woman can the orgasm appear as abruptly as in man?" is, with many married couples, an extremely delicate one. We men always seem to think that there can be only *one* right mode of intercourse that gives satis-faction, and that is the method we are in the habit of practicing personally. We then expect the impossible from our wives; yet the excretory canal of the pronephros is quite different from that of the primordial kidney.

In the female organism the clitoris too has only a limited power of erection, consequently the orgasm never takes on the impetuous and violent character that it does with us men. And there is another difference too. Internally, instead of two tiny seminal vesicles, the woman possesses a large muscular organ of thick red muscle, the *uterus*. So it is not surprising that it takes much longer for her to reach the climax; but when once she reaches the conges-tive condition, and the nervous centre which actuates her uterine contractions is set in motion, her excitement will not be so easily calmed as that of man, who sinks immediately after he has reached the climax into a sort of impotence.

I am fully aware that there are certain women who reach their culminating point just as abruptly as men, and this may be ac-companied by an internal sensation of pulsation; but in the ma-jority of women the curve of voluptuous sensation follows another and more symmetrical course. If we make a graph of both curves we shall find that man's rises sharply to fall again, like the out-line of the steeple of a church, while that of woman is a long and gradual curve like the indented roof of a cathedral, with wavy lines due to peristalsis. I therefore think it much better to give two different names to these manifestations in the two sexes, and to speak of the man's *culminating point* and the woman's *sexual ecstasy*.

A very profound difference in the sexes is here concerned, and

115

in the ultimate consequences of the act of the coitus the essential differences may well be observed: as soon as the rapidly accomplished act is completed, the man is finished and is not personally concerned any further; but the woman now begins to feel first the anxiety of uncertainty, and later a world of maternal solicitude and devotion[1].

It is highly interesting to note in this connection that, as ethnography teaches us, in every case where there is a question of functional power, woman shows more staying capacity, while man is capable of a greater momentary effort. In the scheme of reproduction the sexual division of labour goes back to the hermaphroditic period; it is indeed the oldest division of labour in the world, and analogously in the history of man, the first economic division of labour was made when the man went hunting or fighting, while the woman stayed at home to keep things in order. So from the earliest times our sexual organisation has been the ruling factor in every detail of our lives. Indeed even before birth we see a picture of the sexual life in miniature, how manfully the sperm-cell marches forward, while the egg-cell stays quietly at home.

1. The Art of Sexual Love is essentially a readjustment of the sexual differences of man and wife to the end of reaching a mutual climax at the same time.

Chapter 23

PRACTICAL BENEFITS OF SEXUAL RELATIONS BETWEEN MARRIED LOVERS

THE adaptation of the whole mechanism of erection is so excellent, that we should now like to say a little about it from a theoretical standpoint.

In the period of enlightenment which followed on the theological middle ages, people turned their attention once more to the study of nature, and they were especially delighted with the adaptation of various phenomena. But to the leaders of this movement, such as Bernardin de St. Pierre and Süssmilch it was soon apparent that this method places us at the mercy of a boundless imagination. Darwin was the first to formulate a new principle — that adaptation ensured the survival of the fittest. But even this does not by any means remove the danger of subjectivity.

Meanwhile in the field of mechanics and physics another method has been shown by experience to be most successful, namely the investigation of the chain of causality. But at first it was not possible for them to apply this method to living Nature with its endless complications, because they sought adaptation in everything. It was only later that men began to investigate free from prejudice, and to recognise imperfections in Nature itself. So we no longer regard adaptation as an invariable thing, but only secondary and auxiliary, because as a working hypothesis it can often point out the way by which we can trace the causal connection.

Yet, whether we speak of adaptation or non-adaptation, we must never forget that these are only phrases — and so must only be taken as relative.

Although not introduced pedantically every time, this prudent mental reservation must always be thought of when in this work I speak of adaptation or non-adaptation; phrases which would otherwise be rash and presumptuous. It is not possible for us men to regard all things in their mutual relationships, because in Nature two sort of phenomena occur, which are diametrically opposed to each other — construction and destruction, progression and retrogression, which, however are interdependent.

If we term the connection of natural phenomena "adaptation", that is really a figure of speech, as though we were speaking of human actions consequent on human considerations; and it would seem as though we had dared theologically to take the stand that we had some insight into the purposes which have ruled in creation since the beginning of all things. But in the study of Nature it is not permissible to speak literally of Nature's purpose. In Nature we can only recognise cause and effect, or more correctly speaking, really only a constant occurrence of phenomena side by side and one after the other, from which we may guess with more or less success, the probabilities of the future series of events.

Only in our brain as the highest power of cell-life, our imagination often conjures up pictures of future acts, which then predispose us to the committal of these acts. Our brain can also keep a certain future purpose in view; and we term our acts, adapted, especially when they are adapted to the fulfilment of this premeditated purpose, and still more commonly if they agree with what we have in view.

In Nature also we observe phenomena, which surprise us, because if we men had so arranged things ourselves according to our own plans, they could not have been better or more expedient.

This impression is so irresistible that anthropomorphically also we speak of adaptation. And this mode of expression is really so brief and practical that I have already used it frequently; only it must be rightly understood.

In Nature we call everything adapted that is well organised, and almost everything in Nature is thoroughly well organised. In living Nature especially, the conditions of existence are so complicated that everything that is not fairly well adapted is not at all capable of existence; it ceases to live, or it reproduces its kind less extensively (Darwin) than better organised individuals.

And the evolution of organs through exercise (Lamarck) implies a process of adaptation. Thus cell-life really develops as a beautiful whole, with a wealth of adaptations. To trace these out will always be one of the most delightful and pleasurable tasks of Nature-study. And so we continue to employ this picturesque phrase, though really we can only find a chain of causes and effects.

Such modes of expression only become dangerous if we allow ourselves to be led by them into too great a generalisation of the idea of adaptation if, for instance, we wish to establish a systematic view of life on this conception of adaptation, for only too often that runs counter to experience.

I have gone so exhaustively into the subject of the adaptation of the mechanism of erection, only because I must refer in so many other places to shortcomings, errors and non-adaptations of the sexual organisation.

If then we finally enquire why we consider the mechanism of erection so well adapted to its aim, the answer must be that we have in mind the guarantee of the desired result, for through it we are so absolutely driven to coitus, and cannot effect coitus without it, whereby reproduction of the species is the better guaranteed. For fertilisation is the principal factor in the preservation of the species.

But the answer may be extended to all useful results, such as: increase in blood pressure, intensification of our vital energy and the joy of living! For all these things are also factors which afford effective help in the struggle for existence. Above all, however, one should be careful not to imagine that the one excludes, or ought to exclude the other.

It is, however, literally correct to speak of the purpose of our sexual life, as far as we mean thereby our human deeds, which should always be well thought out. And here also it is true that we scarcely ever have only one purpose in mind; the action only ripens when several motives work together. Thus we are led to copulation through our sexual impulse, i.e., through the above-described antagonism; or by the wish to render each other mutually

118

happy, or in the hope of producing children. And all these motives do not by any means exclude each other; and ultimately we use Nature to attain our own ends.

We do not desire to limit ourselves in this work to the question of the reproduction of the species, as though that were the only purpose of the sexual life. This has already been done too often. On the contrary we now want to study first of all the primary effects of sexual excitement: lust and love, both motives that have been scientifically far too neglected up to the present, and which are yet of vital importance for our life's happiness and conduct. By this restriction the book may lose in completeness, but even within these bounds there is abundant material.

If we enquire the purpose of our sexual life even with this reservation, we scarcely dare give an answer, on account of the vastness of the subject. One might just as well enquire after the purpose of life itself. Life is a search for self-expression, and sexuality is only a more intense expression of life. We will not worry further with the question: what is the purpose of life? As in all problems, the sexual life must have a purpose of its own, so that it may become as pure, as strong and as beautiful as possible.

Chapter 24

NORMALLY FUNCTIONING SEXUAL LIFE AS HEALTH STIMULANT

IN the last chapter we refuted a very common error of the past, when people always used to enquire the purpose of Nature, and were then often led to form the most outrageous hypotheses. Now we shall cast a glance at the old medical ideas of the past, of those days when our colleagues still wore peruques and birettas.

First and foremost there were the learned, speculative philosophers, who, according to the particular school to which they belonged, endeavoured by one method or another to remove the "morbid matter"[1], or if they could not manage this, to divert it to other portions of the body, preferably the surface of the arm or leg, where it could not do so much damage.

This they effected by the employment of counter-irritants or derivants, for the diversion of the humours, relics of which may still be seen in the popular use of *setons, moxas,* and *blisters.* And when all this failed, they flew to blood-letting, a method by which they thought they could actually see the morbid matter flowing into the basin, which a member of the family usually had the honour of holding.

Was this all useless? Many of these methods certainly brought relief or cure. If you doubt it, ask your grandparents or great-aunts! When I was a young man I knew old people who heaved many a sigh as they remembered the good old times: "Ah, yes," said they, "folks don't do these things nowadays, but they always used to do such a lot of good!" But times change; our patients expect quite other derivants for their relief from us: watering place after watering place, operation after operation. These do good too, only they are rather more troublesome and expensive. In reality it was not a removal of "morbid matter", but an inflammatory process that was concerned.

In regard to the four cardinal symptoms of inflammation: *rubor, calor, dolor, tumors* (redness, heat, pain and swelling), these symptoms of congestion would be favourably influenced by this method, and if in such cases it was possible to excite symptoms of congestion in some other part of the body, then the redness, heat, pain and swelling in the morbid part were relieved.

We can now understand the success in their own day of our historic predecessors, as well as the fact that nearly all of these methods have fallen into disuse. We know now that the congestive conditions are not so much dependent on the quantity of blood as on the innervation of the vessels. At present we possess

1. We may here remark for the benefit of the layman that in a great many diseases there is no question of "morbid matter". Many ailments are only functional derangements of the activity of the organ, e.g., a *hypertrophy,* i.e., *excescive,* or *atrophy,* i.e., *defective,* development of one or more organs.

much more effective methods of controlling these vessels, and increasing or regulating the blood pressure, and of relieving freely moving part the edges, and from the less mobile part the middle portion, will be then known, we have all the modern methods of electro- mechano- and balneo-therapy, as well as many antipyretic and sedative drugs for internal administration which were not then dreamt of.

Above all, we are now much better acquainted with *etiology*, the *causes* of disease, and consequently with the principles of antisepsis. And therefore modern medicine lays more stress on prevention than on cure.

We strive first of all to prevent disease (prophylaxis), and then if disease occurs, to lead to a cure by the use of hygienic methods.

We do not want first to fall sick and then to allow ourselves to be tortured. On hygienic grounds we are led to regard the rush of blood to the sexual organs and their erection every time as a physiological derivant against all other congestive influences; while, finally, nocturnal emissions, and above all normal copulation, act as soothing as blood-letting. The latter is also accompanied by a feeling of faintness, which was formerly interpreted as a sign that enough blood had been removed. It is just this soothing relief of tension which does us so much good, in contrast to the irritating effect of masturbation.

Medical science is often shamed by Nature, which so frequently does things more simply and better than we can by artificial methods. But unfortunately not less devoid of danger, for one can also give way too passionately to sexual pleasures, just as some people in former times had become so used to bleeding that it no longer had the slightest effect on them.

We may remark in passing that we find an analogous relief of tension to that formerly obtained by bleeding, not only as a result of exercise of the sexual functions, but of the other two secretory functions.

For instance we may feel greatly relieved after a thorough urinary or intestinal evacuation, and if congestion or inflammation has been present, the increased blood pressure of the affected part will more or less disappear as a result of the evacuation. In the seminal secretion the evacuation takes a secondary place; the innervation of the vessels is more strongly influenced.

On the other hand we can now better realise why asceticism and denial of the sexual life are commonly compared to a stagnant pool; while normally functioning sexual life stimulates us ever afresh, like a running brook always fresh and clear, because through it the blood pressure varies healthily each time, and so the blood is constantly refreshed.

While not every girl unhappy in love dies of wasting disease, it cannot be denied that a starved sexual life may lead to all sorts of illness, dyscrasias and scrofula, or at least may act as a predisposing cause of these.

We physicians see this only too often. On one occasion at least I had experimental proof given me. I remember the case of a young fellow of good pious family, whose medical attendant I was. He was terribly scrofulous and was persuaded by some of his friends to try sexual intercourse as a remedy. He did so, and the experiment was so strikingly successful that his parents who knew nothing of the matter, were agreeably surprised at his appearance, as they told me themselves. Unfortunately he had sought the remedy in the most dangerous way in prostitution, with the consequence that he got acute gonorrhea. He came to me for treatment, and he told me the whole story in self-extenuation. He recognised too late that in this case the remedy was worse than the disease, as vivisection is more useful to science than to the animal experimented on.

Chapter 25

IMPORTANCE OF MASSAGE
IN IDEAL SEXUAL LIFE

SINCE the time we have referred to, medical science has progressed in other directions as well. Once upon a time the "humoral" pathologists thought that metabolism took place in the body fluids, the "solid" pathologists in the body-tissues; some thought the heart, others the liver, to be the source of our bodily heat. But we know now that the real units that compose our body (see chapter 7) are the cells, which have been built up like the stones of a great house into a composite structure. Real metabolism, especially oxidation, occurs in every separate cell, while the circulation of the blood serves as a means of transportation.

As we have frequently observed, the circulation of the blood is very actively augmented by sexual stimuli, whereby all chemical processes in the cells are immensely increased. The process of oxidation is specially stimulated by it, as we shall further explain in the next chapter; but before doing so, we must settle a difficult question which is often overlooked, although it merits special attention in this connection.

Just as in public traffic the heavy vehicles cannot stop at every single house, so our blood-vessels cannot bathe every single cell. To repair this omission, the individual cells are bathed by the lymph, which acts as a connecting link between the cell and the blood. This lymph is not subservient to the circulation, but is subject to variations of pressure which ultimately determine the intensity of our metabolism.

These variations of pressure are of two kinds: osmotic or mechanical. The osmotic variations of pressure are caused chemically by the amount of salt, sugar, etc., contained in our food. These substances possess a high osmotic coefficient. The mechanical variations of pressure, on the other hand, are caused by every mechanical movement of our body — either active or passive.

The production of these mechanical variations of pressure we call massage. Artificial massage has long been known as one of the most powerful of remedial measures to stimulate metabolism after a blow or fracture, in order to restore the function of the injured organ, for though continuous pressure is very injurious, rapid alternation of pressure and non-pressure is very healing, and for this reason massage always works wonders when one of our limbs has become stiff through immobilisation or constriction. Also when the tissues are infiltrated with lymph, pus or blood, not only can this fluid be dispersed by massage, but ultimate resorption greatly facilitated. Furthermore, atrophied muscles become better nourished as a result of massage.

Because massage is constantly indicated for an ever-increasing variety of cases (savage races have successfully used massage from the earliest times), the opinion has recently gained ground that it is not a special method of healing, but one of the principles of life.

We can best realise this if we notice how strongly the formation of our bodily organs is governed by it even in the embryo. Just a few examples.

How do the rounded curves of our body originate? They are thus rounded because we develop in the rounded interior of the womb, and this is rounded because the waters, like all fluids, exercise an equal pressure on every part of the uterine wall.

These few examples suffice to show to some extent the fundamental importance of massage. With every movement of the body, changes of pressure occur, and the more energetic our movements, the more will every part of our body be subjected to or relieved from pressure, which constitutes ideal massage. And from this it follows that just those muscles and organs which have most exercise, develop the most strength. All growth, all muscular education, all individual development rest on this principle.

And now we come to the application of this principle to our problems. When I speak of massage in regard to the sexual life, I do not mean only the caresses and embraces usual to lovers, or the moment of the act of copulation itself (see chapter 21) as the climax of passion, but above all the energetic stimulation of all our vital functions in this beautiful period of our lives.

Who does not know tedious people of no importance who contrive to do everything with a minimum expenditure of energy? They do everything so that it just suffices, but always with the minimum of self-massage. These people are predisposed to anaemia and scrofula; physically and mentally they are cripples. We can best realize this by gymnastics in a room with dumb-bells, or still better without any apparatus. If we do this with slack muscles, we shall produce no energy; but if we do it energetically, and with our muscles as tense as possible, then we shall feel ourselves revivified and our strength permanently increased.

Of course, in the economic field it is always a good idea to produce a maximum effect with a minimum expenditure of force; but in the working of living Nature the matter is not so simple.

A young, healthy, and observant child will soon notice how well he feels after strenuous muscular effort, and so he will unconsciously render all his bodily movements as easy and powerful and bold as possible, which looks so attractive,

124

especially in the young child. It provides him with a store of energy and permanent health for the future.

But this surprising joy of living is generally lacking in the hobbledehoy period. The fire of early youth, when everything had the charm of novelty, has died out. For as soon as love awakes in the young man, a new life awakes in him also. Now he wants to display his strength, and takes a pride in his powers. He wants to win his chosen one, to be admired and honoured by her. He is zealous in his efforts to meet her again, perhaps gets up early in the morning so that he may see her once again before going to work. In all his actions he wants to surpass his companions. He wants to strike out in the world so that he can found a family with her. He spares no pains.

So through the ardour of the sexual life not only our circulation, but also our physiological massage is set in motion, so that the increased energy of our circulation really benefits all the cells of our body, and the metabolism is stimulated in every individual cell.

The same thing applies to our breathing.

In the fresh air we breathe deeply and slowly, so that our lungs are not only thoroughly ventilated, but thoroughly massaged. If however, we are breathing in a heavy, dusty atmosphere, our breathing becomes quicker but more superficial, and the natural massage is therefore decreased, especially at the apices of the lungs, because these lie furthest from the diaphragm, so that in the course of time there is a tendency to necrosis (disintegration of tissue), and particularly a pre-disposition to tuberculosis.

In contrast to this, let us think of the influence of sexual excitement with its breathing deepened from pleasure and delight, like a fire that burns with heightened glow, and we shall see how powerfully this new stimulus intervenes as a massage-stimulus of our physical and psychical life. And each time that engaged couples can embrace, or married couples have the joy of falling in each others' arms, these are only the concluding chords of this ecstasy of love.

Everybody who has experienced this, knows its vitalising effect. With the young girl this develops more internally, and therefore more intimately and lastingly. Although her inner impulses lie more deeply hidden, and she herself may not recognise their existence, they work all the more surely in her on that account. The improved massage does not fail in its blessed effect, and its climax is crowned in a happy marriage.

In conclusion I must touch on one other question in this connection — a most delicate one, because on this point every man has his own opinion, often quite unfounded and so all the more obstinate.

I was often asked as a practitioner whether intercourse during

125

pregnancy is not an abomination. This question is not so important as it may appear, because in the early months one is not certain about the pregnancy, and in the latter months all intercourse is excluded by the increased tenderness. There still remains the intermediate period, if the wife still feels fresh and well. If then both partners want to have intercourse (and this desire is quite normal), let them be guided by the general principle: "Live as hygienically and reasonably during pregnancy as at any other time."

By referring to what we have said above, the reader will easily see that this is good advice, not only for the mother, but also for the development of the foetus.

Why should not the child of a merry young mother be as lively and strong in all his bodily movements as she? Not only because the energetic mother will play and romp with him later on. Oh no! Long before birth, whilst they both belong so intimately to each other, every little step, every abrupt movement of the mother's, finds its echo in the body and soul of the little child; so why should not her sexual impulses and movements also have their influence?

In the later months of pregnancy the child will produce a lively local massage with his own energetic movements; for the better development of his own little body, and to prepare the mother for her most trying moment. And who is not reminded by this, of the often marvellous cures of Thure-Brandt massage of the internal organs?

Chapter 26

INCREASED ENERGY THROUGH
IDEAL SEXUAL LIFE

IF we enumerate once more all the sexual stimuli which are produced by secretory antagonism: congestive symptoms, deeper breathing, increased massage, the excitement of our entire nervous system, then we obtain a combined impression of increased activity of all our vital functions, that is to say, an increased vital energy, which is indeed difficult to measure, weigh or count, but which ultimately culminate in increased oxidation.

It is not simply figuratively, but empirically that we speak of warm love and glowing passion. Sexual stimulus excites an agreeable warmth, which glows in our faces. We may imagine on the one side a fire on the hearth that burns with a lively flame whenever it is stirred up, and on the other one that has nearly gone out because it has been left unattended.

Fortunately the increased oxidation and the consequent increased heat-production caused by a sexual stimulus never reaches the pathological degree which we call fever; although when there are dramatic complications one might well speak of feverish excitement.

And yet this increase in the total amount of bodily heat is greater than we should imagine, if we know from the study of physiology how very constant our body temperature is; although here only the internal temperature and not the temperature of the entire body is meant.

And on this account the thermometer does not assist us much in our judgment of the total bodily heat. It is unfortunate that Pettenkofer of Munich never tried the experiment in his air-bells for the estimation of oxidation, of comparing the oxygen consumption and carbon dioxide production of two couples, the one at the height of love's ecstasy, and the other asexual, "cold right through to the heart", although he often tried the experiment with two people at a time, one active and hard at work and the other at rest. And the difference was enormous!

Empirically, the rise in our total body-temperature caused by sexual stimulus is not recognisable. The sexual life excites in us an ardour almost surpassing the fire of early youth. Even the birds

127

acquire a brightly coloured plumage at mating time, and many insects also, when they swarm out to breed. And for this reason we are always glad to see rosy cheeks on our young folks; not because we are so fond of red, but because it denotes a warm temperament. When we are old we are pale, and in death, white and cold.

Of course, we may also be excited by many other motives, and all these may appear along with the sexual ardour. The one motive does not exclude the other; on the contrary, they mutually increase each other. But at the same time the sexual stimulus is one of the mightiest of all, because it resides in our inmost being and continually awakens afresh.

For not only does the glow of love burn within us every time the sexual impulse wells up in our own being, but, because we live in a world full of lovers, also each time we see a person of the opposite sex or a pair of lovers. We already anticipated these feelings when we were children. Even our daily work seems lighter when we are working with the other sex. Just as when the light shines it illuminates all things, even the most insignificant, so the sexual life sheds warmth and colour on all around us, even the most ordinary things. And the love we observe amongst animals awakens the same feelings in us; and every flower speaks to us of love. The soul sensitive to love is like the clear mirror of a pool which reflects the sun not only once, but sparkles a thousandfold with the rippling of its waters.

The strength of the sexual life is so great that it is not a deficiency that we have to fear, but an excess! For sometimes this impulse may dominate us to such an extent that it threatens the whole happiness of our lives with disaster. For this reason we always stand in need of self-control; and to this subject we shall devote the whole of the third part of this work.

Just one more observation. The principle "nothing is made for nothing" also holds good in the sexual sphere. Just as we can produce fire by rubbing two articles together, but must rub very vigourously, so also we cannot obtain the increased warmth and energy without effort. We have repeatedly seen, and we shall see further in the next chapter, what numerous hindrances and difficulties the sexual life has to contend with, a resistance which must be overcome both in the material and psychical sense. This is the hardest task of life for adults; for one must be adult in order to be sexually mature. Only now we can thoroughly understand how greatly the sexual life may increase our energy: sexual energy is proportional to sexual resistance.

Chapter 27

HOW TO OVERCOME PHYSICAL HINDRANCES TO THE PRACTICE OF THE IDEAL SEX ACT BY MARRIED LOVERS

WE have constantly mentioned all kinds of strong obstacles in the case of the seminal secretion, in contradistinction to the secretion of urine. The late beginning of this function, the viscous consistence of the secreted product, the minute orifice of the seminal canal, the spasmodic increase of the muscular antagonism, and finally the accessory stasis of the circulation. All these internal resistances excite us to the highest degree and drive us either to despair or to the height of ecstasy.

There is also a further great difficulty, because to perform this function correctly we need a partner[1].

A whole army of difficulties must be surmounted before we can find a person who will put up with our little ways; and what a lot we have to go through before we have reached the point where we can make each other quite happy!

But even at the last moment when happiness seems to be in sight, we find that Nature has placed a hindrance in our way, which although very small is very confusing. According to our views, the genital organs of man and woman are very badly placed. We have already seen (chapter 9) that the genital canal in the male has its opening in the front part of the body, while in the female it is quite underneath. That is not convenient. Besides which, in woman not only is the entrance to the canal hidden between her thighs, but it is further closed by two pairs of lips, like double folding doors.

Connection can therefore not take place unless the two partners assume a very unusual position. And for this reason no absolutely *correct* position for the accomplishment of the act exists. On the contrary, in various nations and races all sorts of possible and almost impossible positions are found either usually or exceptionally: standing, lying, or sitting, facing each other, or both

1. We shall treat of psychic hindrances, such as frigidity of the woman, or her dislike of everything sexual, in Chapter 57.

facing the same way. But always in a forced position of the body. Only one thing is constant, and that is that the woman must open her legs as far as possible[2], so that her genital fold shall become a genital orifice. Nor must the woman lie with her head and shoulders too high, nor too deep in pillows, but rather with a cushion under her loins.

It is therefore perfectly clear that such difficulties occurring at the last moment are highly adapted to increase the excitement and the passion to madness and thus precipitate the climax.

There is another category of hindrance of a more accidental nature though more difficult to overcome, to which one may be exposed. I refer to the resistance offered by all possible forms of narrowing of the orifice of the female genital canal. The vaginal entrance is often only a trifle underdeveloped, an infantile stage of development that soon corrects itself. Sometimes, too, the entrance is more or less obstructed by a small mucous membrane, a slight arrest of development, similar to the tongue-tie so often seen in new-born children. Sometimes there is a more resistant cartilaginous growth which can only be removed by operation. In very rare cases the orifice, or the entire vagina may be absent, and then one has to be content with caresses or other methods of sexual satisfaction.

The slighter variations generally disappear of themselves during childhood, if only the child is kept clean, especially in these parts. Otherwise they are overcome by the use of cleansing injections, which the adult maiden should always practice after each menstrual period. If this practice is neglected, however, everything goes wrong at the first attempts at connection. So the adaptation of the organs to each other, which we mentioned in Chapter 11, should be constantly maintained by each new generation, and constantly improved.

In very serious cases, of course, a doctor should be consulted; but usually it is easy to distend the soft parts by gradual and gentle stretching. But this should be done with great care, otherwise tiny cracks may be produced which in healing form scars, so that the constriction of the orifice becomes even worse, just as happens with the boys' prepuce (see chapter 12). This wound-cicatrisation with constriction of the orifice explains many stupid stories concerning girls who have become pregnant and then at the time of delivery it was seen that they had no proper entrance at all to their

2. Hence the idea that it is very immodest for a woman to spread her legs apart in public; rather should she walk about in a long dress as if she had no legs at all! Many useful activities and healthful exercises have been kept from her for ages, e.g., horse-riding, as though it were impossible for her, whereas it really presents no difficulty.

genital canal; for after their rape, as the wounded surface healed, the orifice grew firmly together.

I have dealt with these constrictions of the vaginal entrance in such a detailed manner because from pure ignorance they make so many marriages a torture, when they give rise to tiny tears and abrasions in the mucous membrane at coitus. Although these abrasions and tears may be extremely minute, if they are not given rest and opportunity to heal, they will through repeated connection never remain uninfected; and in the course of time may become so fearfully painful that at each new attempt at intercourse screams of despair will break the silence of the night. Consequently this defect, so insignificant at first, may not only mar the inauguration of connubial bliss, but the terrible pain that ensues as a result of their neglect may cause an aversion to sexual intercourse and a hatred of the husband which will not entirely disapper even after surgical intervention has remedied the evil.

Spasmodic contraction of the occlusory muscles which are situated around the orifice of the vagina (see chapter 9) may render connection painful or impossible, and in rare cases interfere with withdrawal after the act is concluded. So we see that there are pitfalls here.

But even without any mechanical obstructions the woman may suffer from hyperaesthesia (excessive sensitiveness) of this organ which makes it impossible for her to allow her husband to approach her. If this nervous affection develops only as a secondary symptom, as a result of the above mentioned local suffering, local treatment is indicated and generally successful. If, however, it originates in neuroses which proceed from the central nervous system, as is often the case in hysteria, then the condition is much more serious and not always curable.

I do not want to leave the subject of these painful hindrances without again referring (see chapter 4) to the most painful of all which we encounter as the normal consequence of sexual intercourse: I mean the martyrdom of child-birth. Among savage races normal parturition occurs just like any other normal physiological function; if, however, malformation of the pelvis presents an insurmountable obstacle, the mother and child both die, and the deviation is not reproduced.

However, with our ever-increasing civilisation and the greater perfection of our means of assisting parturition, this natural selection tends to disappear; and, furthermore, owing to our unnatural manner of sitting, especially during long hours at school, not only the normal development of our internal sexual organs, but also that of the bony pelvis is still more fundamentally spoilt. This has increased to such a degree that a painless delivery is an exception[3], indeed, for many centuries now, the pains of child-birth have become proverbial. The words of the Bible, that the pains of child-birth are a punishment for our sins, have not prevented us from committing the sin of unnatural education. And so the birth of a new human life, this most joyous of all events in living creation, has become a hellish martyrdom for the mother; and the best developed children[4] can scarcely ever be born alive.

The pain which we once caused our mothers should make it a point of honour with us to suppress this horror for the future. It is unjustifiable, calmly to continue with this cruelty and degeneration of the race. As this has developed through carelessness in the course of generations, we could with care bring about a great improvement in the course of a few generations. And yet systematic efforts to attain this object are not always made. Only lately the training of our youth, especially of our girls, begins to be a little more rational, and at least the beginning of natural selection can be seen when those women who have survived unusually difficult confinements take care of themselves through the use of preventives that they do not fall again into this desperate condition. In this way they will not further reproduce their own defective tendencies.

The more unprejudiced our study of the sexual life, the more must the obstacles mentioned in this chapter yield to the light of science.

So far we have only mentioned material obstacles in the woman, but there may also be some on the man's side. I refer here only to impotence.

The female organism is always capable of cohabitation, the male only during erection. On account of the congestive effect of all skin stimuli and mental pictures which take effect through reflexes from the brain, the man can to some extent control this unconscious function. Indeed it is easier for him to cause an erection than to terminate a spontaneously occurring one.

However, he does not always succeed. There are many men who never get an erection (absolute impotence), and cohabitation is

3. Indeed we can entirely relieve the most painful stage of parturition by intervention under chloroform. This is not sufficiently practiced, but with such palliatives the cause of the trouble is not removed, but only maintained and rendered graver for the future through the abolition of natural selection. Twilight sleep through scopolamine is far too dangerous and only relative insensibility is produced so that the pain is forgotten; this is a poor consolation.

4. The greater mortality of little boys compared with girls must be in the main attributed to the difficult births of the boys, as on the average boys are somewhat bigger than girls.

impossible very often because the erection does not occur at the right time or because it does not last long enough (relative impotence). In all these cases both partners are disappointed; and while the wife can with some astuteness hide her frigidity, no evasion is possible for the husband, and the more worried about it he becomes, the less likely he is to succeed.

On the wedding night especially, relative impotence is a common occurrence, and is then mostly caused only by the unusual nature of the situation. Generally it is, like the tightness of the bride, a proof of chastity; one does not so soon master the technique of copulation, and easily gets lost in the rosette of folds forming the vulva[5].

The performance of even the simplest functions requires some practice. How long, for instance, it takes for the young mother to get the newborn babe to take the breast for the first time.

This is an appropriate place to refer to a quite mistaken idea that it is necessary for the first attempt to be made on the wedding night. This over-haste may spoil everything, even all future married happiness. Especially if the couple have not confided enough in each other during their engagement, a too abrupt approach of the bridegroom may shock the bride, and even wound her feelings very deeply. It is indeed quite overpowering to think that they are facing each other now without the least restraint. External caresses, if impulsive enough, will be quite sufficient on this occasion to produce the desired satisfaction for both parties. The next time one can go a little farther, and then they both experience the real climax of the pleasures of love, and their love will only then become an ideal love for life.

Even if the relative impotence lasts more or less during the honeymoon, there is no cause for anxiety. The remedy is simple enough. A period of abstinence mutually planned and honestly kept will almost always suffice, and the period of abstinence will scarcely ever be observed to its end. As the result of habitual masturbation, there may sometimes be relative impotence on the husband's part or frigidity on the bride's, but these generally disappear of themselves in time, if only calm and patience are exercised, and the old habits are not resumed.

Relative impotence due to advancing years (see chapter 60), constitutional disorders, mental strain owing to worry and care, or resistance on the wife's part, etc., is very frequently complained

5. When a doctor is going to examine a woman, he finds it easier to introduce his instruments if he begins the introduction on the posterior side, as here there are only *two* folds, and in their neighbourhood the sensibility or liability to pain is minimal.

of. These are cases in which the physician can more readily console than cure.

Absolute permanent impotence right from the commencement of married life is rare, because the young man in such a case must be aware of his defect, and should not have married without making his fiancée acquainted with the facts, and coming to an understanding with her. Then at any rate a physician could be consulted as to whether he could do anything by improvement of the general health. Fortunately, the most passionate of wives can be sexually satisfied without regular copulation, an act for which many women are not at all adapted.

Only in the most unusual cases would one be inclined to effect a testicular transplantation or other rejuvenating treatment by Professor Steinach's system (see chapter 4). Such a serious undertaking is especially not indicated if the trouble is a symptom of approaching age, or a premonitory symptom of a constitutional affection. In such cases the impotence is a sign from Nature that mental and bodily rest is necessary.

In desperate cases of frigidity in woman, similar operations may be undertaken for the transplantation of ovaries. But what should we say, if after the husband's having been very disappointed over his wife's coldness, the operation should have such a marvellous effect that in spite of all his efforts he now finds himself unable to give her all the pleasure she wants!

Chapter 28

SOCIAL RESTRICTIONS ON
SEXUAL INTERCOURSE

IN addition to the internal resistances and physical obstacles
to which we have referred, there are also a number of economic
obstacles which must be removed, and through which in many
affectionate people passion is stimulated to its utmost degree.

The more traditionally the institution of marriage is organised,
the more is the free choice of a partner systematically restricted.
Even in prehistoric times it was considered incestuous to cohabit
with very near relations, while intercourse with persons too widely
different from oneself was naturally out of the question. So from
the earliest times sexual intercourse has been naturally limited by
exogamy and endogamy; although these limits varied extremely
in different races and tribes. Later, the economic conditions which
tended furthur to widen the differences between different races
produced a far more appreciable limitation of the possibilities of
marriage, and now as the reverse side of prostitution, innumerable
affectionate people must remain single. Yes, even in married life
there are still many conditions which, if the marriage is monogam-
ous, exclude sexual intercourse, for instance, the menstrual periods
and the time just before and after a confinement.

Besides which, there are special categories of people who are
wantonly condemned to celibacy, such as priests, officials and women
teachers; while others from an exalted ideal, look upon sexual
abstinence as something exceptionally praiseworthy. In the course
of time, abstinence before and even in marriage has become a
categorical commandment. The production of illegitimate children
was regarded even in historical times, especially among the upper
classes, as something not at all unusual or dishonourable; but it has
now become an increasing cause of despair.

In consequence of all these categoric obstacles the sexual impulse, especially in the most respectable classes, may increase to
madness and become an uncontrollable passion so that ultimately
one renders oneself unhappy or brings others to misery. A passion
thus terribly roused often leads to desperation and suicide. J. J.

Rousseau and Fourier long ago remarked that we should not despise the passions, as such, but rather the fact that we men had neglected to direct them into the right paths. When a river is dammed through icepacks, it may overflow and ruin everything around, this self-same river that originally had watered and fertilised and rendered lovely the whole region.

When we have come to a proper understanding of this whole chain of cause and effect, then we also know precisely in which direction we must seek salvation, in order to prevent this immeasurably increased passion from leading to such despair in future. The ascetic ideal, however useful and necessary it may be for early youth, and old age, has always made things worse for the vigorous adult and will certainly continue to do so. Throughout the centuries of our era, man has sought in vain to enforce this solution.

Suppose we were to give up further striving after the impossible? Suppose that at last we consented to be so reasonable as to learn from Nature? Suppose we could at last all begin to work together earnestly so that every individual who has reached manhood and who longs for love could listen to the demands of Nature and bring his love to expression without anxiety or remorse? This should henceforth be the aim of all sexual reform! Instead of a destroying fire, passion would then be converted into the friendly sunshine of our lives.

Falling into the other extreme, the question has been asked: whether through unlimited indulgence the sexual life would not entirely lose its passionate character. It has been asked: if from puberty the exercise of the sexual function were always enjoined as a duty, would this function then not be rendered as free from passion as, for instance, the secretion of urine now is? It is a fact that in the Middle Ages there were some would-be saints who actually gave themselves up to unbridled intercourse in the hope of killing the lusts of the flesh.

This is a desperate measure, and one fore-doomed to failure, as everyone knows who has read the foregoing chapter attentively. All these irritating obstacles which lie in the way of the seminal secretion cannot be removed, and will always cause this function to retain its passionate character. And if we try to carry that method so far that it paralyses the function by exhaustion, then indeed the remedy would be worse than the disease.

But, as human beings, we are not satisfied with a merely animal appeasing of lust. We claim higher ideals, and before these are attained a great deal of self-control and self-denial must be exercised.

136

The greatest difficulty however lies in the following. As we expect it to afford us satisfaction, it should be not only a suitable and permissible satisfaction, but since the material foundation of this function is a regularly recurring urge, the satisfaction must also take place regularly and periodically if we are to obtain the full benefit of it.

A solitary experimental connection is for a normal adult rather tantalising and an aggravation of the evil. On that account it often happens that serious symptoms due to abstinence may be observed in persons who, as we know full well, have coitus now and again.

We might represent the passion-curve by a zig-zag line which falls suddenly after each act of sexual intercourse and often sinks below zero, but rapidly rises again. Through impure sexual intercourse, the curve falls from disgust so far below zero that one wishes to change the object of one's passion with every new rise of the curve. In pure, more ideal love, however, the curve approaches more and more to a constant straight line; even in marriage, both parties should reflect that after every connection their mutual love should blossom afresh; every time a fresh bud that bursts into a more lovely flower than before.

Everyone does not realise this in his own case. He who longs in vain for relief, always thinks that satisfaction on one occasion would save him, he does not demand more for the time being. So with Faust, who pawned his soul to the Devil for one single moment's pleasure!

Yes, then one has really "gone to the devil"! And so many a man is attracted like a moth to the candle flame, in the hope of salvation.

The problem is almost insoluble, because even in our cool climate we are sexually ripe at an age when the body has still scarcely reached its full development, and certainly not its full powers of resistance, and in addition the economic condition of the individual, owing to the complicated nature of our social conditions, will not be at its best for many years. And yet even in these early years of the transitory period, the impulse makes itself felt so categorically and so imperiously!

The task for the parent and teacher is hardest of all in these transitory years, when they seek to direct the love-life into the right path. No stereotyped generalisations and traditional commonplaces are of any use here; each case must be studied individually; and we should never condemn another because he has acted differently from ourselves. In every case education in love should be ideal, not simply negative, and still less impure.

Chapter 29

THE FOUR CATEGORIES OF HUMAN SEXUAL SATISFACTION

IF we want in the waking state to experience all the pleasures of love and passion, with the highest altruistic ecstasy, this is best attained in a licit union of two lovers who mutually love and respect each other, as should occur in an ideal marriage.

And we must once more observe that other function, so that we can understand how much higher this ideal of ethical and physiological satisfaction stands than all others.

What does a loving mother do when her little darling has a strong desire to urinate and weeps because he cannot do so? To relieve the cramps and pains the mother lays hot wet compresses on his little body, gently rubs and massages the abdomen, and does not leave off until the crisis is over and the little one is relieved.

Now we understand better why in the sexual life natural cohabitation between man and woman is the gentlest and best of all methods of relieving the tension, not in sleep but in the intoxication of love.

Ordinary, regular intercourse, as it occurs in a happy marriage, disturbs us the least and calms us the most effectually.

It is most astonishing to reflect how Nature has so arranged this procedure that it falls to the lot of both partners to be operator and subject at the same time. After all the preliminary difficulties and obstacles, Nature at last surprises us with the simplicity and easy solution of this problem, because such a beautiful result is obtained with so little trouble, and even with organs which were already useful for other ends. Thus is actually realised the classical "tuto, cito, jucundo"[1], which medical science in the olden times accepted as its ideal.

This mutual satisfaction of the two sexes, this *heterosexual* mode of satisfaction, is in every respect as well adapted to its end as if it had been prepared for us by a loving mother.

But we do not want to rush on too fast with the realisation of this ideal of our age. Before we have reached the point where all these conditions are ful-

1. The remedy should be "sure, quick and agreeable".

filled in a happy marriage, we may possibly be for a long time at the mercy of our mother Nature who so often subjects us to a severe trial. Yet at last she takes pity on us. For long before our marriage, the above-named conditions are often fulfilled while we are lying asleep alone and quiet in our beds. That is her time to bring us secret relief[2].

During sleep the sexual excitement does not easily attain the excessive degree which frequently occurs during the daytime. The antagonistic resistance is not so powerful, and above all the manifold complications of our consciousness are almost entirely absent. Everything occurs so gently that sleep is not disturbed at all; at most one experiences agreeable dreams. A little congestion can scarcely be avoided in this congestive function, but everything takes place in the best way possible.

With masturbation, the voluntary touching of one's own body in solitude, however, the opposite is the case. For then one is awake; the brain and spinal cord are stimulated and irritated to the highest degree; there is no peaceful rest, no mutual warmth, none of the intoxication of love. One performs this delicate biological function roughly, and becomes so accustomed to crude means, that later in marriage, one scarcely feels any satisfaction from the gentler physiological procedures.

For it is a fixed law that every mode of satisfaction that has become a habit, makes us less susceptible to other modes with other associations. Love, the one essential condition, is lacking and with it all holiness. Of course, the secretion may be evoked by means of this brutal act, as by an artificial operative procedure, but it is by no means the beautiful natural function. Before dealing further with the subject of masturbation, we must define the term more precisely. By *masturbation*, which is also called *onanism, self-pollution*, ect., we mean any kind of manipulation destined to provoke sexual excitement in oneself. From the ethical standpoint, the solitude and secretiveness of it are typical.

The name comes from *manus* — the hand, and *stuprum* — unchastity, and means sexual impropriety with the hand, or by any other means of massage.

The popular name *onanism* comes quite wrongly from the biblical mention of Onan (Genesis 38-9), for in this verse a voluntary interruption of the procreative act was referred to (coitus interruptus[3]), an act that was considered so shameful in Onan because he thus sinned against the law of Moses. (Deuteronomy, 25:5-10).

This erroneous interpretation of the story of Onan has led public opinion into error not only in regard to masturbation but also to *coitus interruptus*, as though in each case we were speaking of a mortal sin. Through this fatal error countless people have been led to despair, and instances are not rare where it has led to suicide, sometimes of the most horrible nature, in the hope of escaping from the torments of hell fire.

This psychological anxiety has done more harm through the centuries than any physiological damage due to coitus interruptus, and yet well-intentioned but erroneous authorities still frighten young people who practice masturbation, by quoting the story of Onan.

A name that has led to so much error and despair should no longer be maintained. In practice, we doctors employ many different names for masturbation, because it may assume so many different forms. In children it is generally only

2. Regarding female erotic dreams, see Chapter 18.

3. As a common and still much used preventive method, *coitus interruptus* is often termed *the French method;* but a method was known at the Renaissance in Italy, which was probably identical, and was at that time known in France as *the Italian method.* Goethe refers to it in his translation of the *Life of Cellini* (who lived in the 16th century), Book 3. Chapter 7.

a bad habit due to improper training; in adolescents obstinancy, brutality, sometimes even vice, or a morbid symptom; in old men frequently a sign of dementia.

A special sub-division is *mutual masturbation,* when the same crude act is practiced on another person, generally of the same sex (homosexual), a phenomenon ethically quite different, because it is not practiced in solitude. If the ordinary masturbator is frequently shamefaced and shy of other people, mutual masturbation leads on the contrary to shamelessness. It is the preparatory school to the brothel, especially when practiced on a large scale as often happens in boarding school and barracks. But we shall only speak of ordinary masturbation in the remainder of this chapter.

As a basis for a rational hygiene, it is of the highest importance to study and compare these two alternatives of youth: masturbation or nocturnal emissions.

We have referred to the distinction between violent masturbation and nocturnal emissions occurring during sleep. This distinction however, is not always so categorical; emissions are sometimes found less salutary; the fatigue or exhaustion due to masturbation may vary within very wide limits. On account of their practical importance, I will now be rather more explicit.

With an emission it may happen that we were indeed more or less stupefied by sleep, but that at the actual moment the whole experience was very closely related to masturbation. And conversely, after long continued abstinence we may while half asleep, masturbate so gently and involuntarily that it takes place like a spontaneous emission, without shock or nervous tension.

But no matter how soundly we sleep, we may feel exhausted and depressed on awaking in the morning after a nocturnal emission. This is often taken to prove that such emissions are harmful, and that prostitution and other such indulgences are much better for young folks.

I do not object to the observation, but I do to the conclusions. All that has been demonstrated is that one feels miserable on awakening while still under the influence of the emission. The causal nexus may however lie elsewhere. Perhaps too much was eaten or drunk the night before, for instance sweet drinks like chocolate, punch, champagne, etc., which cause extreme heat in the night; or perhaps one lay in a constrained position, e.g., on the back, with venous stasis in the cerebellum or spinal cord. In all these cases one may have had a troubled sleep and uneasy dreams, which might well be the cause of the emissions. Therefore, before drawing such unhygienic conclusions in the name of hygiene, one should carefully look for all causes which may have produced such uncomfortable sensations, whether with or without emissions, so as to avoid them in future.

I have not said that masturbation always has serious consequences. The consequences only become grave when one is the slave of the habit, just as with alcohol; for one can never tell beforehand how much one may be predisposed to them. *Principiis obsta!* From the very beginning we should be on our guard.

It is also true of masturbation that the younger one begins it, the worse the consequences may be. Also, the more violently the emission is induced, the worse it is; and really it should never be a deliberate excitement of the sexual impulse, but at most a final yielding, if the degree and duration of the excitement have become overpowering.

I go a step farther, for Nature is never absolute in her laws. Just as emissions may depress us, so masturbation may sometimes protect us from something worse. It is above all in the sexual sphere that we sometimes meet with the most intricate complications and insoluble conflicts of duty. As compared with prostitution and seduction, masturbation appears to be the lesser evil.

140

If one finds himself in such a position that he does not feel ethically quite sure of what he ought to do and after examining his conscience he thinks there is an urgent reason to masturbate, he can then best guard against self-deception by making a rule to allow 24 hours to elapse between the intention and the deed.

This then follows the same rule as the death penalty once did; for the difference between murder and execution often lay in the fact that in the latter case a certain time was always allowed to elapse between sentence and execution. Like that old Roman, who when his slaves made him angry, cried out: "Oh! what a thrashing I would give you if I were not so angry!" But after all everyone feels that it would be better if thrashings and the death sentence were abolished altogether.

In Chapter 65 we consider the two different methods of treating habitual masturbation.

It is frequently stated that masturbation is much more common in females than in males, but this is difficult to prove because this act leaves no visible traces. At most the experienced physician may sometimes notice that one side of the trousers is more worn than the other on account of the rubbing of the nails of the right hand. Then again, girls are less scolded than boys for a little sleepiness or a dreamy look which is often the consequence of masturbation.

One only knows the beauty of sexual intercourse, the ecstasy of love, when one can experience this impulse with a loved one who meets it with an equal passion.

This spiritual rapture may be the principal factor, and it is not necessarily man and woman who feel themselves drawn together; a youth may be charmed by another youth, and how often there is a passionate attachment between two young girls.

There are males who feel themselves attracted sexually only to members of their own sex, and also women who can only have passionate intercourse with their own sex[4].

This, however, must always remain an exception, because only the minority of people are so constituted[5] and persons who are not so predisposed will not lightly renounce the magic charm of the opposite sex with its physiological advantages in the procreative act. And for this reason the over-zealous activities of the moralists and legislators who jealously strive to preserve the monopoly of heterosexuality may be considered quite superfluous. From a material point of view, there is not a solitary method of homosexual satisfaction which possesses the slightest advantage over the ordinary heterosexual intercourse, which can quite well stand competition; and survival in the sense of Darwin's theory by means of descen-

4. The opinions expressed in the last part of this chapter sound surprising and perhaps shocking to us British, emancipated in our views of sex though we may think ourselves. We must remember that in many Continental countries, not only is homosexuality regarded much more lightly by public opinion, but the law considers it a matter of personal taste and leaves it quite unpunished, except where the protection of minors or the maintenance of public decency is concerned. This is the case in Holland, where Dr. Rutgers lives and writes. (Translator's note.)

5. This inclination seems only to develop so thoroughly exclusively when the material reasons for it are present (see chapter 4).

dants is of course quite impossible. It goes without saying that every case of the sexual seduction of children should be punishable, even when this is heterosexual and therefore doubly dangerous. Otherwise, however, from a legal standpoint, every adult should decide for himself in what manner he finds his own sexual satisfaction; on condition that he does no injury to anyone else and creates no public scandal by it.

Meanwhile public opinion, mingled with fanaticism, considers that homosexual inclinations are terribly immoral, whereas we see every day before our eyes what an endless amount of immorality and misery are caused by heterosexuality. Although inferior and depraved persons sometimes commit homosexual acts with seduction, prostitution, violence, etc., unfortunately these shocking things come forth out of the realms of darkness still oftener in the heterosexual sphere; and the climax of cruelty and horror, lust-murder, has, so far as I am aware, been observed as exclusively of heterosexual origin.

And then there is always the fantastic idea that homosexuality only knows the pederastic mode of satisfaction, that is to say the anal instead of the vaginal method. This is of course a custom that is most repulsive to us, but it was very highly prized in antiquity, and at the present time is still held in high honour in many parts of the world. In the oriental view of life, this act was perhaps considered animistically as contributing strength of mind, besides which it has often been intended as a symbol of the most intimate love-union, and felt to be the highest expression of passion. Further in many cases it is only an obsession arising sporadically and originating from childhood, when we watched the mating of animals with astonished eyes, without really understanding them.

But we must not generalise. In regard to all female homosexuals, who are probably in the majority, these theories are not applicable ,and we learn from the experience of homosexual men that this *modus vivendi* does not offer so many advantages after all as has been stated.

There is hardly an organ of the body or a method that might not be employed as a means of stimulus and satisfaction, and that will not be used on occasion. Indeed, even in heterosexual intercourse, anal connection is by no means unknown as a preventive method; so it cannot be regarded exclusively as a characteristic of homosexuality.

Frederick the Great said that every man shuld be happy in his own way. And if vaginal connection, which has been found the most suitable simply because it is the only method which can not only give pleasure but can also fecundate, will always occupy its favoured position, that does not prove that where this method is not possible other harmless methods cannot provide the same delights if only the love stimulus is sufficiently strong.

The essential thing in the sexual function is the contact. Which of the poles of the body it is that feel drawn to each other is unimportant. Psychical rapture is not dependent on such insignificant details.

Part III.

MODERN METHODS OF SEXUAL CONTROL
that Make for a Healthier and Happier
Sex Life

Chapter 30

Introductory:

SEXUAL CONTROL ENRICHES OUR LOVE LIFE

THE muscular antagonism which we have considered in Part II was only the material substratum of the question; psychically this same conflict takes place within us as a mental struggle, a struggle which sometimes robs us adults both day and night of our rest and peace of mind, and subjects us to the most rigourous test: shall I conquer, or shall I fail? Like Hercules at the cross-roads.

There is, unfortunately, scarcely any function so little under our voluntary control as the sexual one, which plays so important a part in determining the happiness or misery of our lives, and even the welfare or suffering of future generations.

We deceive ourselves greatly when we men call ourselves conscious beings in contrast to the animals; we have still to strive, before we can be such in reality.

This is especially difficult for us in the sexual province, because the sexual impulse originated in the most primitive times, when we were still but very slightly differentiated from the lower animals. In this respect only the urge of hunger surpasses the sexual impulse; and there are some moments when the sexual impulse is the mightier. Only in this province we are less frank than the animals.

Sexual self-control is not sufficiently esteemed by public opinion, because it is looked upon as something negative. But we forget how greatly, in a positive sense, sexual self-control deepens and widens our love-life. The more self-control we have at our command, the more richly and beautifully will our sexual life blossom out; and this is true not only for individuals but also for the community.

In contrast to an asceticism that would deprive our lives of all happiness, happy and kindly men think that we should be allowed a little tolerance, so that life shall not be a weary waste. A little tolerance for the "jeunesse dorée" after their fashion and for the masses after their fashion; for after all, we only live once. But the new generation is not satisfied with such rubbish; it abhors the

145

brothel with its body-and-soul-destroying disease, and its lack of real satisfaction: it detests alcohol which enervates us, and frivolity with its contamination.

The rising generation demands a solution of the question founded on sound principles; with its full consciousness it requires finer pleasures. Not tolerance, but idealism.

The oscillation between an unyielding stoicism on the one hand and an enervating epicureanism on the other, has undermined the joy of living far too long. The history of the evolution of mankind shows us a better way. Only with gentler manners could love-making be romantic (see chapter 46); in earlier times when sheer animal desire led to marriage, jealousy, revenge and murder seemed indispensable to self-preservation.

Even now, without a certain amount of self-control, all friendly intercourse between the two sexes which had not marriage as its avowed object would have to be discouraged as dangerous and morally inadmissable, as soon as it had taken on the slightest sexual complexion; for it would thus always be a temptation of Satan, as many pious folks actually term it. Indeed, when we entirely lose our self-control, we fall from our present domesticated or civilised state (see chapter 11) back to the animal state. But with conscious self-control we become the lords of creation.

How is it that nowadays a girl, even if young and pretty, can go home or make long journeys alone, or fill public offices? This is all only possible because assaults on respectable girls have become quite an exceptional occurrence.

Only in the mutual certainty that the bounds of propriety will in no wise be overstepped, should two persons in sympathy with each other permit the maximum of tender intimacy, such as is generally allowed to engaged couples even in the most respectable families.

And if we imagine this principle not limited to engaged couples, but extended to society at large, how much more Arcadian rapture would this earthly life afford us!

With this ideal before us, let us now study the question of self-control in sexual matters.

We would like definitely to decide, in each case with full knowledge of cause and effect, what is good and what is evil, what is permissible and what is not permissible, and we will then willingly renounce much that at first sight appears so tempting, but which really debases us, the gain for us will be so much the greater. We want to help each other in seeking new standards, and if in our opinion one of our fellows falls into error, we must not narrow-mindedly condemn him (or her) but must strive all the more to help him into a better path for the future.

We must not be surprised that in the sexual province in particular, the problem of self-control plays such a very prominent part. Contrary to the old Latin saying that most people need spurs and a very few the bridle, in sexual matters the opposite is the case, most people need the bridle and very few the spurs.

Of course, there are times when the Latin proverb applies to

146

sexual matters. Doctors sometimes come across people with slug-gish constitutions whom they would like to inspire with a little more sexual impulse, a little more energy, so as to keep the flame of life burning more brightly.

Thus when we speak in this section of sexual self-control, we mean first of all the bridle; but we must not forget that now and again the spurs may be needed to stimulate the sexual energy. Both may be of equal importance in making our lives a thing of beauty, and scientifically considered they are but the two sides of the same problem. Both are included when we define sexual self-control as the conscious mastery of this function.

This third part of our work possesses still further importance, for it deals with a question of the conduct of our lives. Nothing in the whole world is so hard to master as our sexual impulse; and when we have once obtained an insight into the means of govern-ing it, then we have *a fortiori* discovered the right way to become the masters of ourselves.

Chapter 31

CONTROL OF THE PRODUCTION OF SEMEN

WHEN we speak of sexual self-control, what is really meant? What must we control? First of all, we must devote our attention to the material basis of our sexual life, i.e., to the new-formation of the reproductive cells. But in order that all influences may be brought out as clearly as possible, I shall begin by dealing with the male sexual life, and for the time being only speak of the production of the semen. The same applies in principle to the female organism as to the male (as we have shown *in extenso* in Part II), only in woman it is less frequently apparent.

The essential constituent of the seminal fluid is the microscopic sperm-cells, harvest of an embryonic tumour, which we have already dealt with in Chapter 3. What laws and regulations govern the release of these cells from the period of puberty onwards, whether this function proceeds continuously and regularly of itself, or is associated with daily, monthly or yearly periods, or whether it is more or less influenced by our absorption of food or by voluptuous impressions—we must withhold the answer to all these questions for the present.

But our attention has been drawn of recent years to the enormous importance of some organochemical substances which are at work in our blood stream; especially such of them as originate in the testes or ovaries. As has been experimentally proved, these substances are of decisive importance not only for the production of reproductive cells but also for the arousing of the sexual instinct and for the direction of the impulse (see chapter 4).

Normally this chemical factor remains so far quite beyond our influence.[1] Only in the most desperate pathological cases the question may arise whether it is not preferable, in persons with deep-seated hereditary taint, to deprive them of their capacity for reproduction by operative section of the sperm-ducts (vasectomy)[2] or egg-ducts (salpingectomy). Vice versa many cases of defective

1. In the next chapter when dealing with secretory stimulants we shall refer to the effects of a meat diet, which is perhaps here partly responsible.

2. After this the sperm-cells can no longer be expelled, and the production of the reproductive cells soon ceases; just as in the female organism the production of ova always stops as soon as an increased resistance in the tissue of the ovary prevents the escape of the ova. This occurs easily in virulent suppuration. After the section of the seminal duct the interstitial tissue of the testis is produced in far greater quantity, whereby (at any rate at first) sexual desire and potency are increased. In castration, i.e., the removal of both testes or both ovaries, on the contrary the production of these important organochemical substances would cease, and the physical and mental condition of the patient would become permanently defective.

sexuality which now receive no care or treatment might possibly be cured by operations for the transplanting of normal "glands", or similar procedures.

I mention this in respect of many cases of nervous depression, melancholy, mental deficiency and loss of vital energy. But one should be most cautious with such operative interventions, because the symptoms mentioned are frequently only the secondary indications of deeper mischief, that is to say Nature's healing method, to ensure the necessary rest.

Amongst ordinary pharmaceutical drugs there are some which have an effect on the sexual system. Quinine and salicylic preparations, and also alcohol in excessive doses[3], not only weaken the sexual impulse, but appear also from their toxic effect on the protoplasm to be able to inhibit the production of healthy reproductive cells.

Here we have a warning that we should always be most cautious in the use of such powerful poisons, and if possible leave them alone altogether, so as not to undermine the vital energy.

Healthy reproductive cells are best guaranteed by all-round health and strength, combined with a good heredity.

The other components of the semen, which form quantitatively by far the greater part of the contents of the seminal vesicles, such as mucous, epithelial cells, cystalline substances and water, are all typical secretions of the mucous membrane which lines the vesicles and other excretory passages; and it is also not improbable that the quantity of their production depends largely on the same causes that influence other mucous membranes. Just as all mucous secretions are perceptibly stimulated by such powerfully exciting substances as alcohol, hops, cantharides (Spanish fly), spirits of turpentine, balsams and many essential oils and spices, it is not at all unlikely that the same drugs influence the production of these constituents of the seminal fluid to a marked degree, and increase it. We cannot be certain about this; but it is known that some of these drugs are very poisonous, and may cause cystitis, and even acute nephritis with haemorrhage from the kidney.

As we see, medical science stands abashed in these fundamental questions.

The constituents and quantity of our urinary secretion has been laboriously studied for centuries; and these we can pretty well control, if we only pay strict attention to our diet and avoid irritating spices. And our intestinal functions can be regulated to the nicest degree by means of modern hygiene.

3. Chemotactically all unicellular organisms are repelled by alcohol, probably on account of its coagulating effect on their albumen. This is also fraught with consequences for the successful combination of the fecundating cells in conception; children conceived or begotten by drunken parents often prove defective in mind or body.

Very often the contrary seems to occur; because under the influence of stimulating quantities of alcohol many an unwanted child is bred.

But here, where the vital question of sexual production is concerned, we are still in complete ignorance.

If we desire to judge of the normal or abnormal production of semen, we should work out methods of chemical and microscopic examination such as are usual with the urine, and with the counting of the red and white corpuscles in the blood. A substance can only be properly and scientifically studied if it can be measured, counted and weighed.

If only one half of the time that has been wasted for centuries past in dissertations and theories had been spent in actual investigation of cause and effect, who knows what progress might already have been made towards voluntary control of this function, such as we have long since learned to exercise over so many other originally involuntary ones.

It is certain that we should have organized our food and dress more appropriately long ago; we should then no longer force our children at the critical time of puberty to remain sitting so many hours per day in positions which render their circulation stagnant, but we should see that they alternated their hours of study with suitable energetic muscular exercise.

The connection between sexual and social abuses would not then remain so long unheeded; we should zealously do our best to render it possible for every adult to realise an appropriate fulfillment of his sexual ideal; the sexual life would then become ennobled; love would be the highest virtue. But just as the astrologers have sought in vain to read the course of all earthly events from the starry skies, so men have always attempted to subdue the sexual from the spiritual side, instead of beginning from the material foundation.

And we might approach a little nearer to a solution of this problem by enquiring a little more closely into premature and retarded development in plants, animals and men. In Chapter 40, dealing with sexual evolution, we shall refer to this more in detail.

Chapter 32

STRENGTHENING THE SEX VIRILITY OF MAN.
DIET AND SEX CONTROL

IN THE previous chapter, in which we treated of the formation of the sexual *substance*, the result was an "ignoramus" (we do not know); and now that the question is whether we can govern the *secretion* of this substance, the state of things is much worse, for we must confess we cannot ("non possumus").

The sexual urge, which can cause us such torture, is not called forth by the semen as such, this emulsion being of itself almost without influence, but from tension in the seminal vessels and ducts, which forces itself on our consciousness by the congestive manifestation which we term erection.

What do we expect to accomplish by self-control? No matter how loudly we may declare in our pride that we can control everything by our consciousness, our science, and our strength of will, the formation of semen goes on steadily, constantly increasing, and the seminal secretion will always be and remain a periodic function. Although the formation of semen is not a *conditio sine qua non* of our life (such as the secretion of urine, for instance) yet because its amount continually increases, its expulsion finally becomes as imperative as that of the urine, although its volume is far less.

Both these secretory functions go on whether we wish it or not; if not in our waking hours, then during our sleep, these substances are secreted. The question is then not "are you sexual or not sexual?", but only "in what paths does your sexuality run?" The product of the sexual secretion surprises us, either sunken in dreams or in the intoxication of love; voluntarily called forth, or repressed as strongly as possible, it springs forth however much we should like to prevent it. We can school ourselves to avoid every kind of sexual activity, to abstain from masturbation or copulation, but it does not lie in our power to stop the secretion. Herein lies our "non possumus".

As regards the urinary secretion we can always postpone the evacuation of the bladder for some little time by strong contractions of our voluntary external occlusory muscles; but if we try to do the same thing with our spermatic secretion we should only increase the erection. Will power and mental superiority are powerless here.

So if it does not lie in our power to regulate the tension in our seminal vesicles and ducts at our pleasure, well and good, let us at least not voluntarily permit tension and congestion to be increased by accidental influences; we should carefully avoid all such as produce the effect. If we are temperate and discreet in these matters we can really achieve much success. We will now endeavour in this chapter to discover what these accidental influences are.

Erections that give the alarm-signal, are a function of the external occlusory muscles, as we have explained in Chapter 20. They can also be occasioned or aggravated by pressure from an overfull bladder or rectum. Above all we must avoid all tension in these related functions. And on this account we have already dealt with the control of the other two functions in such a detailed fashion in Chapters 16 and 17. Although the subject may appear far from idealistic, if we can only thoroughly control the urinary and intestinal functions, we shall have fulfilled one of the most important conditions for a regular sexual life.

From our childhood even, before any sexual urge exists, we should be careful of the connection between urinary and intestinal tension and erections, and begin to practice self-control. And we should begin early to observe what other causes of erection there may be. Then as we reach puberty we shall not fall into the common error of regarding every erection as a call of Nature to the exercise of our sexual function. For we know from our own experience how greatly many different kinds of excitants may contribute to it and lead us to despair.

And all *mechanical* factors also, which accidentally increase the internal pressure in the abdomen from time to time, will at the same time increase the tension in the seminal vessels and the venous stasis. Over-filling of the bladder and rectum acts powerfully in this sense; and if both cavities are over-full at the same time, the seminal vesicles are compressed between the two distended organs. This must be regarded as of the greatest practical importance.

Similarly the pressure in the seminal vesicles is mechanically increased by too hearty eating or drinking, especially at bedtime. And if we remain seated too long at a time, the abdomen is doubled up, especially if we bend forward; fatal symptoms of congestion and venous stasis may even occur.

I may also mention the wearing of tight clothes which is still the barbarous custom among females; the corset has been largely responsible for prolapsis uteri and excessive menstruation[1].

On the other hand, congestion of the pelvic organs may be very effectively relieved by physical exercises and muscular exertion, especially if these be performed in the open air.

On the other hand, monotonous mental strain may only too easily occasion congestion of the brain, especially of these centres which govern our sexual functions.

Besides these mechanical stimuli which cause increased pressure in the seminal vesicles and blood-vessels there are also *chemical* substances which, taken as spices, medicaments or poisons, excite spasmodic contractions in the seminal vesicles and ducts because through their chemical effect they stimulate or even inflame the mucous membranes involved[2].

These substances are all known to the laity as aphrodisiacs. Everyone who has ever suffered from catarrh of the bladder (see chapter 19) knows what it is to irritate the epithelial surfaces; in this condition the presence of even a few drops of urine in the bladder causes spasmodic pain, just as if the bladder were full to bursting. So, too, in conjunctivitis, the smallest moisture causes smarting and burning as if there were a grain of sand in the eye. In the same way the sexual mucous membranes will be extremely irritated by such chemical irritants, and the organs in question stimulated to the most intense contractions, even if they are almost empty.

Important in this connection are those substances, which we have named in Chapter 16 as exciting the production of urine, and in Chapter 19 as exciting its excretion, and which we have also considered as possible stimulants of sperm-cells, or at least of the production of the other components of the seminal fluid. There is ample evidence of these drugs being able to excite us sexually, for they irritate the mucous membranes, increase antagonism and cause congestion. Meanwhile we may mention that the effect of these substances may vary greatly according to the dose, the combinations, the accessory circumstances and particularly the mental associations; there may also exist individual idiosyncrasies owing to which certain persons are peculiarly sensitive to one or another substance.

1. I remember the case of an elderly lady patient of mine, who frequently came to me to have her prolapse-pessary cleaned, until one fine day she happened to leave her corset off, with the result that the trouble suddenly disappeared. And how many women and girls there are who complain of menorrhagia and yet will not discontinue wearing corsets.

2. See once more Chapter 5 where a parallel is drawn between the onset of puberty and an inflammation.

In order to discover these chemical influences and to judge them individually there is nothing better than the degree of erection produced. This blood pressure manometer is extremely sensitive. Every adult can thus ascertain[3] for himself what drugs or spices, foods or drinks stimulate his sexual feelings, and then he can accordingly employ or avoid them as he desires.

The effect of alcohol and of all alcoholic dishes, sweets and perfumes on the sexual feelings is most complicated The elevating effect of small quantities always produces the impression of raising a man's spirits; but even at this stage a diminution of inhibition and coordination is evident, which is very dangerous.

And it is specially the finer ethical motives of self-control which are swamped by even small doses of alcohol. Let us imagine a polite gathering of relatives or friends. Everybody, of course, would be careful to avoid all sexual improprieties, especially if unmarried persons were present, for whom sexual abstinence is already sufficiently troublesome.

But as soon as they all get a little elevated from the effects of a little alcohol, and one of them makes a rather daring joke, they all follow suit, because each individual criticism is paralysed by the alcohol. The best proof is the following: if in such a party there is only one abstainer, who will not join in even "par complaisance", the one aim and object of all the others is to drag him into it, so that he shall not continue to be a "spoil sport". Later, if they have drunk a great deal more alcohol they will present a much less tempting picture, and finally throw off all reserve.

And yet alcoholic beverages are almost always served on occasions when a maximum power of resistance is vital. Most young people who have gone to ruin for sexual reasons, have failed through this combination of sexual excitement with the loss of their powers of resistance through indulgence in alcohol.

We must now devote a few words to the use of meat as food, as the flesh of animals may in various ways act as a sexual stimulant. Firstly, the extractive matter of the meat acts as a stimulant to the nervous system, and in particular stimulates the heart causing a quickened pulse and increased blood-pressure. For that reason we drink a cup of beef-tea before a meal, or a strong meat soup at dinner. This effect agrees exactly with what we mentioned in Chapter 4 about the organochemical substances; and we know quite well how greatly the sexual life may be stimulated by the latter. Secondly, this extractive matter keeps us awake, like tea, coffee

3. In the female organism we find the same erectibility in the spongy tissue of the clitoris, with its congestive phenomena, but here the whole apparatus is on a smaller and finer scale (like a lady's watch).

or chocolate, which only heightens the misery of loneliness at night. Thirdly, it has been empirically established that meat and soups and dishes prepared from it, have a constipating effect, and we have already seen in what way this affects continence[4]. Fourthly, the intimate psychic connection between carnivorous cruelty and sexual recklessness can be fatal to higher ethics; and as the saying goes: animal food makes beasts of us.

In the question of meat diet we not only have to take into consideration the extractives of muscle fibres; but in adult animals the organochemical metabolic products of the thyroid glands, testes, ovaries, etc., are carried into the circulation; a most important category of secretions which exerts an extremely powerful effect on our whole sexual system[5].

If later it is found that these metabolic products are allied to toxins, the parallel drawn in Chapter 5 will be still more illuminating. It would be of interest to enquire whether the effect of the meat differs if it comes from a male or from a female animal. In this connection there may be a deeper reason than we suspected for doctors ordering veal for certain patients rather than beef.

The current belief that the eating of eggs specifically increases sexuality, seems to me to be only symbolical. Their great nutritious value would of course have some effect; but as far as I am aware, there have been no scientific researches to support this opinion.

One thing is certain, and that is that the ordinary diet of many unmarried people and of travellers is the least calculated to encourage sexual purity. Wine or beer at table, together with meat and hot condiments; after the meal stimulating coffee and a good cigar or cigarette perhaps containing opium... Can we be surprised if after a stimulating evening's enjoyment, the brothel seems to be the only remedy indicated?

The principal point in every scheme of diet is moderation, and at the same time a certain regularity, by means of which in the course of time at least, a certain amount of immunity may be acquired against such damaging influences as cannot be entirely avoided. And if one has accidentally absorbed a too highly spiced or irritating dish, the evil effect can always be diminished by drink-

4. We can readily convince ourselves by experiment that even if we compensate the constipating effect by laxatives the stimulating effect on the nervous system remains. So the latter is not entirely dependent on the constipating effect.

5. In regard to these products, hormones, endocrine substances, etc., see Dr. A. Weil's recent book, "Die Innere Sekretion", Julius Springer, Berlin.

ing a lot of water after it, or by taking a weak solution of Epsom salts[6], which cools the blood, and acts as a slight laxative.

Do we possess in contrast to the aphrodisiacs, drugs or food substances which have a calming or depressing action on the sexual system? We certainly do (see chapter 34), such as some salicylic and quinine preparations, bromide of potassium which is very lowering, etc. Chronic nicotine poisoning from excessive smoking may also end in impotence; but all these remedies not only depress the sexual system, but the entire vital energy suffers from their use, so that the remedy is worse than that disease. And it is still questionable if extract of the pineal gland, which has been prescribed in cases of satyriasis and nymphomania, does not produce undesirable effects in other directions.

But the occasional use of volatile substances such as camphor and validol seems to be free from objection.

Besides the mechanical increase in pressure and the stimulating drugs, there is an important category of exciting causes whereby sexual congestion to an unlimited extent may be voluntarily called forth, viz: all local skin-stimuli. Thermal and mechanical skin-stimuli are most powerful in producing congestive symptoms; their effect is prompt and sure. Nowhere is the causal nexus so clear. Through warmth and an alternation of pressure and non-pressure a congestion can be created at any part of the skin-surface; but most easily of course in the sexual organs which are so easily congestible, and are so little accustomed to change of temperature and mechanical stimulation.

What powerful congestion of the skin is produced by a hot bath, or by the reaction after a cold one, and locally through rubbing and scratching! For this reason it is always advisable to practice cold water treatment and rubbings in the morning, and never in the evening just before going to bed. Warm clothing, overheated rooms and too hot bed-clothes of a night greatly increase the sexual irritability, and for this reason rich people and town-dwellers are often more excited sexually than country folks who suffer much privation and exposure to the weather.

How very effective mechanical stimulation of the skin may be in this respect, is best illustrated by the birching of naughty boys at school in the old days, which nearly always caused strong erec-

6. The following makes a very mild aperient water: Epsom salts 1 oz., Glauber salts ½ oz., water one pint. A little may be taken several times a day, or at bedtime only; but only just enough to act as a gentle aperient. As it has a marked action in the secretion of saliva, it quenches thirst and cleanses the mouth. As it also causes an increased proportion of water in the bowel-content, any exciting substance unwisely taken would also be diluted.

tion. In certain so-called massage establishments similar treatment is extended to elderly impotent men for the same purpose.

In general the frequency and intensity of our erections depend more on accidental skin irritation than on an actual overfilling of the seminal vesicles. The most trifling causes may often produce the most powerful erections, even when the seminal vesicles have only been emptied a few moments before. This sensitiveness to thermal and mechanical stimuli rivals the sensitiveness of our finest physical instruments.

But all this is far surpassed by the sensitiveness of our nervous system. Let us consider how the sexual system reacts to nerve-excitment. We have explained at length in Chapter 20 how intimately the sexual muscle contractions and sexual congestion are functionally associated with the central nervous system and also the brain.

These mutual influences are, however, so extremely sensitive that in the majority of cases we really do not notice the connection between cause and effect, and so we are not conscious of its existence. So anyone thinking of erection would surely suppose that the seminal vesicles were terribly full, whereas perhaps only a remote association of ideas has occurred. And vice versa, anyone thinking exclusively of the psychic emotions would imagine that the sexual impulse was only a psychic one. The latter go so far that they regard the bodily sexual function as a desecration of coarse materialisation of love. If however, we attempt thus to separate the love-life from its material basis, a just judgment of the causes and effects becomes simply impossible; and thereby all rational self-control disappears.

It is a well known natural law that the mental image of a physiological function may produce to some extent the same effect as the function itself, only in a lesser degree, e.g., if a dog sees a piece of meat, his mouth begins to water just as if he already had the bit of meat in his jaws.

So the most powerful erections may be caused by the sight of any sexual act, or even by merely thinking of such. The Roman Catholic clergy, rendered hyper-sensitive through sexual abstinence, believe it is not possible to see any part of the body naked without thereby being sexually excited.

There appears to be a wide field for self-control in the psychological sphere, if we notice particularly which associations and suggestions are specially fraught with fateful consequences for each of us. Loneliness and darkness are specially dangerous for one person, while another is excited most by brilliant light, heat and a crowd of people.

Exciting causes which we cannot abolish may sometimes be diverted into other directions. Just as thermal and mechanical stimuli of the genital organs may be diverted by similar counter stimuli of distant parts of the body, so psychic sexual stimuli may be diverted by giving one's psychic interest to other subjects. Music and agreeable conversation with people of strict morals, but sociable and kind, are among the best remedies for keepng us from excessive sexuality. Also memories of our childhood, when we were not yet sexual, and the encouragement of higher ideals, are very helpful as counter-excitants. Useful work and efforts carried out amongst sympathetic people, especially if these aim at the well being of others, have a still more powerful effect.

In concluding this chapter I would like to mention a stimulant with which I really ought to have begun, because it is a prototype of what is physiologically called a stimulant, and that is the sting of an insect, as this gives rise to intense local itching.

From the flowers it is now generally known what an important part insects play in fertilisation. But the parasites of the human skin play an equally important part. With our asexual or antisexual training, what would become of our sexuality if we did not learn from our earliest youth, especially through occasional insect-bites, to relieve local irritation by rubbing, and if we did not notice as we grow older that certain portions of the body are particularly sensitive to this sort of massage, and that the genitalia are especially differentiated for this purpose? The proper development of these specially appropriate organs depends on this practice. For I have often found, that persons specially sensitive to insect stings or bites, are sexually most sensitive, and vice versa.

There is, however, a greater danger attached to this practice. Massage is a useful corrective in all ordinary, slight and uncomplicated irritations of the skin, as by every involuntary movement we bring this massage to bear all day long with instant good effect; but if after an insect sting, the sting itself or a trace of formic acid is left in our skin, then in a case thus complicated every movement only increases the irritation and renders it unbearable. So the first timid movements of a child may prove a useful schooling for self-consciousness; but so soon as the sexual urge becomes too powerful in us and remains unsatisfied, even in childhood, these irritating movements become a passionate habit, and it is then true that with every voluntary movement the state of things becomes less bearable.

Chapter 33

INCREASING OUR SEX POWERS
OF RESISTANCE

WE HAVE just discussed in the last chapter what influences we should avoid, in order that our sexuality should not be needlessly excited. But it is not always possible to avoid every source of excitement; the normal sexual life itself still remains as the fundamental exciting cause that cannot be avoided.

No evasions are any good here, we must seek our strength in ourselves. When the time comes we must be inflexible, not to yield. We must arm ourselves with an increased power of resistance. Just as we must be able to defy heat and cold, we must be able to resist the sexual excitement by our own strength.

And we can accomplish much in this respect by a strict and natural mode of life, by roughing it and training, by energetic occupation, sport and cold water, by plenty of muscular exercise (best of all in the open air), long country tramps or cycle rides, preferably with companions of both sexes. Our life should be well filled, full of change and interest, as energetic as possible, then this one kind of excitant would not master us entirely, for there would be a good counterpoise for it. The higher we fix our life's aims, the more inflexible we shall be.

Still, even when we are armed to the teeth, it always remains a hard struggle. As this excellent mode of life improves our health enormously, it ensures at the same time a normal, i.e., a strong sexual urge. And then if one tries, as in cases I have seen, to avoid this last danger by diminishing one's food, by self-denial and asceticism until one is thin and pale and wasted away, unfortunately one finds that this does not attain the desired result. The sexual impulse may be kept within certain bounds for a while, but it is the last of all impulses to die within us. And before one has been brought so low, all one's higher powers of resistance will long have been exhausted. It is of the greatest importance that we should be aware of the extent of our power in this respect, so that we may

159

save ourselves from endless disappointments, tortures of conscience, and despair.

Even if we seek only a moderate degree of success in this struggle, our power of resistance must be encouraged and exercised from our earliest years. The system in vogue in many families "to give way to children as far as posible" leads in maturer years to the principle "we should yield as much as possible to sexuality". This is a reaction against the principle which was formerly too frequently acted on, "give way to children and to sexuality as little as possible". Both extremes are highly fatal.

We must learn from the beginning to control our reflexes by simple and regular rules of living. First of all our secretory reflexes. That is the second, the educational reason for my having gone at such length into the question of the control of the two other secretory functions. This is indeed the most rational and natural method, to teach the child from the beginning regularity, diligence and forethought in all his behaviour, as though it were second nature.

Little children often find it hard to properly govern their urinary secretion; later one can never finish learning the control of one's intestinal function; then finally one moves up into a higher class, in which the same system of self-control must be extended to the sexual province; always noticing attentively the connection between cause and effect in order to become master of the situation in this respect also.

The more we can govern this sexual world as we grow up, the more do broader perspectives open out before us, and quite other ideals than only the control of a physiological function. For only then do we fully realise how greatly all our life's happiness depends upon it. It is no longer sufficient for us to increase our power of resistance so that we shall not fall in the fight, for this after all is only the negative aspect of the problem, but it is indispensable to direct our sexual life into the proper paths, so that it may become more beautiful. Every increase of blood-pressure should spur us on to better endeavours.

We have seen in Chapter 21 that erection is an impulse to procreation and in Chapter 29 why we should not seek solitary satisfaction. It is the manly erection that wakes us from our childish slumber, so that we may seek a full sexual life. Henceforth all our energies must be strained to this end, and not only to the avoidance of evil. We want to fight for a good position in the world, so that one day we may found a family in a warm little nest of our own. And we hope, long before that, to fall in love and become engaged, charmed by the prospect of this great happiness.

And now all the spectres of the psychic and vaso-motor exciting causes which have so long tortured us and robbed us of our sleep, fade away of themselves. Now we feel these exciting causes as a foretaste of the subsequent fulfillment of our ideals. All these influences which we have so greatly feared are now metamorphosed into useful motives, as stimulants to our energy, to help us to reach our great aim. Empty wit and stupid jokes, everything which ridicules what now is sexually sacred to us, we find simply unbearable. They wound our ideals. Questionable books and plays and pictures all disgust us, bore us, for we have something better in mind. We no longer avoid friendly relations with the oppo-

160

site sex, but prefer it, and always as respectable as possible, because that harmonises with our beautiful ideal. To approach our new ideal is our highest aim; no effort is too great for us to make, and we have now no time for sexual dreaming; the sexual reality is beckoning us forward. And if unfortunately our lot is not such a happy one and there is no prospect before us of the fulfillment of our ideal, that should not hinder us; on the contrary, every sexual impulse and every sexual congestion should be a warning to us not to rest until all the many obstacles in our modern society against a pure and happy sexual life have been cleared away. Why should so many persons be condemned to wither all their lives, without ever having blossomed? We should all strive for a better organisation, and especially for a better sexual organisation.

In conclusion I would like to resume what I have said. Just as in fighting infectious diseases, safety in the sexual province has been sought hygienically and educationally in isolation. That was in the middle ages with its morbid and exaggerated asceticism. In our new era, however, we prefer to try immunisation. Spiritually we shall best succeed in this if we not only fight against our lower instincts, but above all strive for our high ideals.

Chapter 34

CONSCIOUS CONTROL OF OUR SEXUAL LIFE

SO we have enquired into the practical means of controlling our sexual passions. Now if we only carry out that good advice ... yes, *if* we behave accordingly, but here we are confronted by a great difficulty. Just in those very moments when a sexual stimulus occurs, we *want* to be thus excited, and at the very instant when we ought to avoid this excitation we do not wish to avoid it.

Nowhere is our unwillingness so great as in sexual self-control. Here we are only too glad to allow ourselves to drift. And if we have once given way, and especially if we have often given way, then it soon becomes so habitual that we no longer wish to do otherwise, and we no longer think of what we are doing. That which we did at first more or less consciously, in the course of time we do unconsciously, more and more automatically.

Thus it is with married people in marital intercourse, with youths in masturbation and with old bachelors in prostitution. If we once become the slave of passion, what can be done? And especially in a sphere that is already so full of animal impulse. Of course St. Anthony might as well have preached to the fishes, for they, at any rate, are cold-blooded.

To make my meaning clearer I will quote as a concrete example an every day occurrence, not taken from the sexual life, but from one just as impulsive, alcoholic intoxication. In the police court news appears the following: "During a quarrel in a restaurant X... fractured his friend's skull with the leg of a chair... Homicide, with extenuating circumstances... two years' hard labour."

On that fatal Saturday night, when the guilty man was overcome with drink, he was no longer responsible; but the previous afternoon his will was perfectly free and open to reason. He was a most respectable man, all his companions liked him whether they met in the tavern or out in the country. He said to himself: I have worked too hard all the week, (first mistake) it was really too bad; but now I have done good business and want to have a bit of fun, (second mistake). Now the weather is so fine I might take a brisk walk out in the country with some of my friends, that would be the best recreation." No sooner said than done. But as he was going along the street his friend and tavern companion, the one whom he struck down later, met him. He was quite sober and jolly and called to him from a distance: "God's truth, old chap, is that you? You look so tired out, come along and let's drink a pint together. All the other

162

fellows are coming tonight, too, we shall have a fine time, that's the best way to pull yourself together." In reality the good man was a *little* annoyed at the unexpected meeting, which upset his plans for a quiet day in the country and would much rather have said "No," because it was such a fine day for a walk. Before he had pulled himself together, (third mistake), and because being so tired he did not feel in a mood to resist, he said: "Oh, all right, I can go for a walk any time," and went along with his friend.—The first thought that in order to enjoy himself he must do something foolish was more powerful than the hygienic idea of going for a walk, and so it won the day.

Principiis obsta! Be careful at the beginning. Many things which are recommended in this book may represent for the author and for the reader the little stimulus which exerts a deciding influence at the right moment, when one is first tempted to fall from pure speech and thoughts to the less pure; but has no effect when one has become too fascinated.

The question now arises, what will lead us to choose wisely at the critical moment? What motives ultimately influence our will in deciding? When we have once found that out, then we can begin to employ these valuable motives for our future actions.

In order empirically to discover the prime motive that governs all living creatures, we must go back to the history of evolution.

It is one of the most remarkable facts in the organic world, that all living creatures aim at self-preservation; they shun injury and seek what does them good. We find this principle in the lowest order of all unicellular organisms, as far as they are capable of changing their position; that is to say even in such creatures as have neither nerve-system nor consciousness, but in which the entire cell consists of a drop of semi-fluid albumen. We know that albumen contracts under detrimental influences such as heat, frost, metallic poisons, alcohol, electricity, desiccation, concentrated fluids, etc., and if such a living cell of albumen contracts on one side, the danger side, and remains fluid on the side remote from the danger, then it changes its position, moving away from the noxious influence and towards the favourable one.

On a somewhat higher stage in the scale of evolution the same object is better attained by the vibrating movements of the cilia or other similar microscopic processes of the albumen, specially differentiated for the purpose, and which act like the oars of a boat. Because these contract much more actively on the side nearest to the unfavourable influence the tiny organism, just like a rowing boat, will turn its stern to the danger, and if it has stored up energy from the food stuffs absorbed, will rapidly flee from danger. The smooth muscle-fibres in insects and the striped muscle-fibres in the higher animals are still more finely differentiated; these fibres are indeed particles of albumen even more highly differentiated into organs of locomotion. We are endowed with an organisation which allows us still more accurately to avoid everything injurious and to seek everything favourable. The sense-organs are like so many outposts and are in telephonic communication with the muscles, through the medium of the nerve-fibres. The central nervous system acts as the switch-board.

The sensitiveness of our nerve-cells, especially those which lie in protected clusters in the central nervous system, is so great, that they not only react to a danger which threatens life, but to the finer shades of pleasure and pain; they are even so sensitive that not only the pleasure or pain of the moment, but even the memory of previously experienced pleasure or pain influences our every decision, so that in the latter case, we can avoid it in future.

If then, we enquire what are the motives that generally decide our choice, we see that in general the instinct of self-preservation stands first. This is the

163

life-sustaining principle of all cell-life, and our most powerful weapon in the struggle for existence.

And with this also must be associated the instinct of the protection of those persons who are the most nearly related to us, who so to speak form part of our existence; which is often, though inappropriately, called the instinct for the preservation of the race. We wish to live happily in common with them.

We generally find this instinct of self-preservation united with this altruistic feeling of solidarity, more highly developed, the higher we ascend in the series of animal species. The highest development of all we find in mankind, inasmuch as we have accustomed ourselves to trace out consciously the chain of causes and effects. Only thus are we able to judge after full consideration what is good or evil for us and ours in any particular case, whereby conscious self-control will be the soonest assured.

Yet it would be difficult for us to make the thousand and one daily decisions which are necessary, if we had to stop to think each time of everything we must weigh in the balance. So we only do this in the most serious decisions. Generally we decide very quickly, and choose more intuitively, or, if you prefer it, instinctively, that which appears the more favourable. It is evident that one can deliberately acquire the habit of never deciding too rashly. And all our higher education should have as its object the broadening of our views and our sense of the higher pleasures and aims of life, so that we may make the right decision in any particular case, without too lengthy a consideration or hesitation.

However, there is another category of influences of the highest importance, based on the very essence of our mental organisation and all the harder to control because they are outside our consciousness. When we find ourselves in a dilemma, the question is not merely which solution is the better for us and ours, but also which is the easier one. The decision which comes easiest to us, always possesses, without our being aware of it, a great advantage.

The more often in our psychic life a certain course of action has been followed by a good result, the more rapidly and comfortably will the same path be followed in the future; the following of this path then becomes a habit, a routine, something in the same way as a foot-path when worn smooth is more readily followed. The resistance in our brain seems to diminish. So in the course of time we can acquire a certain virtuosity in making swift decisions, and the making of a wise choice becomes second nature with us, just as though it were an ordinary reflex. One need only think of the rapid fingering of an expert pianist, and of learning by heart, both of which are only attained by endless repetition.

If we once thoroughly study this unconscious influence, we can also turn it to our own use. For we know what a powerful factor the force of habit is with us, and how enormously important it is to accustom ourselves from childhood to good habits and correct principles. This more than anything else, gives us a future assurance of proper decisions, even if we find ourselves confronted by a difficult dilemma.

Closely related to this preference for that which we have already often done, is the preference for that which we have preserved in our memory, not indeed as an accomplished act, but as a mental image. We have already seen that a mental image is only a degree inferior in its effect to the reality. Hence the great importance of good plans and intentions. The making of these good plans has in and for itself perhaps no great value, but it may be the first step towards realisation. Good intentions will be especially effective, if they do not simply affect details, but the whole of one's mode of life. That is the strength of the ideal. Then an entirely new perspective of heightened joy is opened to us, which makes us feel happy in anticipation.

164

Similarly related to this preference which we feel for what we have already done, is the preference for what we see or hear others do around us; for in this case also we have only to work on an image that we have before us, which is always easier for us than creating an entirely new one. This is the force of suggestion through our environment, and in the case of our co-religionists or fellow members in a party, we call it mass suggestion. Even the thought of a faithful friend, of our mother, our betrothed, or our children may restrain us from many an act, at the last moment.

Here however, we must make a certain reservation. Of course, when persons who are sympathetic to us are concerned, we willingly decide in agreement with them; but if on the other hand, the people are unsympathetic to us, then we are predisposed from the first to do exactly the opposite to that which we observe in them. These sympathies and antipathies play a most important part in the sexual life. We are always anxious to attach a particularly sympathetic person to ourselves; we are always happy to do whatever will please him, especially if it should bring us both future happiness.

And now we come to partial sleep, that hypnosis which is connected with suggestion in this case auto-hypnosis together with auto-suggestion.

Reader, have you ever stopped to think why it is that a quarter of an hour in a street car may seem far more tiresome to you than a whole night in an express train? It depends on what we have already discussed. As soon as one gets into a night express, one settles if possible in a corner, and a sort of hypnosis occurs at once. One pays no atttention to time and place, and often starts up astonished from dreaming, when one has almost reached one's destination.

Another example: a half-hour's walk through the town is too far, one takes a car. But if one is on a holiday tour abroad, six hours' walking per day is not too much. Why is this? As soon as one sets out on a long excursion one adopts a regular rhythmic step; one picks no flowers and collects no stones from the wayside. Good walkers keep silence. They look straight ahead and think only of their goal. Perhaps they hum a melody which is constantly repeated[1] and in a short time they have fallen into a hypnotic condition; indeed on forced military marches it often happens that some of the men fall asleep while continuing to march. The few muscle-groups which are indispensable for the march continue to work automatically, all the other groups of muscles rest; our brain is at rest, we feel no hunger, thirst, cold or fatigue. And with what a fright we awaken from our lethargy if a friend cries: "Hallo! are you there?" We should not be more frightened if we suddenly ran into a wall.

Professor von Nippold, the learned author of the *"History of the Foundation of the Church"*, in the course of his walk, came one day to the parade ground, which he began to cross without noticing that there was a parade on. He did not hear the threatening cries of the sentinels until he was in the midst of the troops. From respect for the old man they parted their ranks and let him through.

In like manner, and oblivious to all, with only one idea in his mind, many a soldier braves the hottest fire, and a rescuer heeds no danger in fire or shipwreck. So died the heretics at the stake, singing psalms.

And so also in the face of sexual temptation. Affective mental images are crowded out by more affective ones, motives of prudence smothered by sophisms. But whoever can then steel himself against the temptation by excluding every other idea and concentrating all his energy on the thought "I will not", can perform miracles, he cannot be moved.

"He who conquers himself is greater than he who taketh a city."

1. The last note of each verse and the first note of the next are almost always the same; hence the easy repetition of the melody.

Chapter 36

CONTROL OF SEXUAL DREAMS

IT IS a pity that all these measures of self-control should be entirely ineffectual at night, in the realm of dreams, where the sexual obtrudes itself more than at other times. And yet our sleep occupies about a third of our whole existence.

Oh, how these dreams can excite us and torment us! They leave us no rest, and lead us during sleep to the most riotous phantasies, to extremes of exaggeration. In our dreams we are already gay and experienced Don Juans, before we have ever really slipped from the path of virtue, and we do the most stupid things in the sexual province before we have really performed even the most reasonable acts; phantasies that are felt so deeply and vividly that when we awake we are still quite under their influence, curious, crazy ideas; in short, a school of the devil.

But it is nothing of the sort! First of all it is not the dreams which excite us sexually of a night, but on the contrary our sexuality which finds its expression in our dreams. Dreams are therefore a school for self-knowledge, Through them alone can we trace the violent congestive phenomena which stirs us inwardly during the night.

These congestive phenomena have a certain periodicity. Every morning when we begin our work the blood pressure rises in the organs involved, whether it be muscles or the brain. At dinner-time the venous congestion is localised a little lower down in the body, that is to say, in the stomach and intestines for digestion. And during the night still a little lower, in the lower portion of the spinal column and in our sexual organs; and these latter may also suffer from a local stimulus such as a too warm bed, a flea, or a desire to urinate, etc.

Thus our dreams are dependent on fixed laws and subject to the chain of cause and effect. The more we study these laws, the more the whole magic play of the dream-life is revealed to us as an unveiled mystery, most instructive as a mighty adjuvant to self-control.

But we must now go a little more deeply into the subject, for

Chapter 37

MODERN METHODS OF SEX EDUCATION

FOR THE majority of parents and teachers the sexual life is a terrifying apparition: for sexual maturity makes young people not only energetic and independent, but often obstinate as well; and what is to be done then?

Even in adolescence it is difficult to direct the awakening sexual life; and how easily later on may a quite unexpected caprice of love suddenly spoil everything that has been so laboriously attained by a careful education! Most parents try to keep their children ignorant and naive in this respect as long as possible; they would be glad if children would always remain children.

But children soon become aware of this negative standpoint and then lose all confidence in their parents; they feel instinctively that the parents have not really got the good of their children in view, but are rather obeying a traditional dogma which is hated by the children and drives them to resistance. They now begin to seek explanations elsewhere, and are most likely to get them from impure sources. But they keep all this a secret from their parents, and when the latter notice evil tendencies in their children, the proper time for their protection is already past.

Has not the time arrived when parents should be reasonable, and instead of honouring the rule to "hide whatever you can", should at last do the contrary, and develop, ennoble and further the sexual life and direct it into the proper paths! Young people would then be able to trust their parents and prize their advice in all things; and if they perhaps made one false step, they would be honest about it to their parents, and would never be so depressed as is now so often the case.

With boys an asexual training almost always fails; with girls, owing to the more hidden situation of their organs, it often succeeds only too well. Thus unnatural, weak-minded girls are brought up, who remain children even when grown up; and having been purposely kept in such ignorant simplicity, as soon as they are exposed to the temptations of ordinary life, they fall only too easy victims to the seducer. I have often seen such cases in rescue work among unmarried mothers.

172

And then when these ignorant girls marry they may be very un-happy; this does not only occur in novels. Medical men often see cases like the following, especially in strict Catholic circles.

A young lady was brought up from childhood to regard everything sexual with horror, and soon after leaving a strictly kept boarding school, she married. The moment she was married, she was frightened by her husband's sexuality, he was rough, brutal and vulgar, as she had learnt to fear. The first night was a night of tears; the bride felt deeply wounded and insulted; for years she bore the unbearable with the resignation of a martyr... until at last a distant relative appeared, who understood her better, comforted her, fell in love with her, and gradually awakened a reciprocal passion in her.

These are the fruits of such a carefully guarded training! And it must not be thought that this is an exceptional case, or that I have painted it too black. Extraordinary and almost incredible, is another incident which actually happened a few years ago in the village of H...

In this case a little girl was perhaps three years old when her mother had a little baby boy. The girl was already no doubt imbued with the idea that a certain organ was something very improper and shameful. Imagine, however, the mother's horror, when she came into the room one day, to find during her absence the little girl had cut off her baby brother's member with the scissors! In the child's mind it was quite logical to remove what was hateful and wrong! A neighbor was called, from whom I learnt the whole story later, but the poor little infant bled to death in a few minutes. What a warning against such teaching!

Poor parents who in entire ignorance of the beauty and sa-credness of the sexual life, are so naive as to choose a foundation on which to build the honour and chastity of their sons, a horror of everything that is naked or strange, or that excites a feeling of immodesty! They forget that as soon as their sons have learnt to understand this association of repulsion and pleasure, the repulsion will more easily turn to pleasure than the pleasure to repulsion. Indeed, then it will be: the more repulsive and dirty the more pleasurable. Thus it happens when the parents try to be more clever than Nature. And if the normal sexual act is constantly represented to them as something so repulsive, they will be led to prefer masturbation and homosexual practices.

Sexual education is only a part, though a very important part, of our whole education. We should master our reflexes; first in ourselves and then in little children.

In the very first days of its life the doctor often notices quite well that the tiny baby is spoilt and tended immoderately, that it is nursed and fed the moment it cries, even when it cries because it has been given too much! How can people expect that the little one will be able to control its reflexes later on?

The usual rules of bodily cleanliness prepare us for sexual purity.

With regard to his childish erections, the little boy may be taught later from what accidental causes these may arise, although

173

at this age no sexual need exists; he will then later on not fall into the general error of which we spoke in Chapter 20.

He should learn to control himself in the years of puberty; he who cannot force himself to continence in his youth, feels miserable later when he is married. And the younger one acquires this virtue the better; for the more one is accustomed to indulgence the harder will he find the task.

To what extent one should demand absolute, and to what extent rational standards when the sons are grown to manhood, is one of the most difficult questions the parents must decide for themselves. Views on this question and our ideals differ too greatly for any general rule to be laid down.

Control is the first educational step towards inculcating good habits in children; we have already shown in Chapter 34 how their own free will can be directed into the right paths. That this task is so difficult and always only partly successful, is due to the intricacy of the problem. So we must be satisfied even with partial success. And in regard to many points, each generation must go a step further than its fathers and forefathers went. This often appears to us to indicate a failure, but it really gives the best proof that our training was right.

In this work we have dealt with most sexual details in their proper order. The most effective method for all sexual education is the co-education of both sexes from the very beginning. We often think this to be a modern ideal, but in reality it is only what we nearly all had, when we grew up in a family as boys and girls together, to the great advantage of both. Only now this same principle is to be carried a little farther; education as a whole has become more of a public institution.

The artificial separation of the sexes during childhood is one of the greatest mistakes of the dualistic view of life, recalling the medieval monastic ideals.

Practically it is a very convenient way of simplifying supervision. But it artificially excites curiosity, and provokes an exaggerated sexual consciousness. And precisely on account of the diminished necessity for supervision, other evils often flourish unhindered.

Fortunately this artificial separation is less practiced in recent times. This is more necessary because the number of children in families is on the average less than formerly, and so it becomes less common for many brothers and sisters to be brought up together at home. So much the better, for to grow up with other children gives much broader education, and a better preparation for all the social virtues, than the former narrow-minded family egotism, when "we" and other children were sharply contrasted.

Especially during adolescence, in the grammar-school or the college, and later at the university, during the last century co-education has brought about a fundamental change in the mutual relationships of the sexes. In the good old times people spoke either of "friendship" or of "being in love", and the hero of many a novel worries himself with the question: "Is it love or friendship that I feel!"

174

Now, however, every school-boy has 100 girl-friends, and every girl 100 man-friends, with all the intermediate stages from 1% of being in love and 99% of friendship, to 1% of friendship and 99% of being in love. And then there are scores of degrees of dislike as well! And if finally one of them gets engaged it is generally with someone else altogether, or with one of whom he had always said: "I'm sure I can't bear her!"

Yet there are still people who are terribly afraid of co-education, and they talk about the most dreadful things that have happened as a consequnece; yes, even of most shocking cases. As if terrible and shocking cases had never happened before the institution of co-education! Even between members of the same family one sometimes sees the most ridiculous things.

Once when I was attending a dying infant, and the mother was standing by the cradle with me, I saw in a bed behind her a boy of about 8 and a girl of 5 (they were born in the East Indies) making the movements of coitus, quite naively, like lambkins playing in a meadow.

The same thing happens in older children.

I remember a well-to-do but somewhat dissipated family, where the daughter had to be locked in her room every night because her brother would not let her alone. In another careless family the son was lying in bed with a broken leg in plaster bandages, and his grown-up sister was nursing him. One day when I called in unexpectedly, I found the big sister shamefacedly hiding under the bedclothes instead of being on her chair at the bedside.

Of course, as long as children are children, they should be looked after, with or without co-education.

People who are entirely against co-education should not have more than one child in the family, but that would indeed be going too far, for nothing spoils a child's character more than loneliness and boredom. This is a far greater danger than co-education. Indeed, the proverb "loneliness is worse than vulgarity" is right. A babbling brook will often carry slime and dirt along with it, but a stagnant pond becomes ever more foul.

The opponents of co-education insist that children should only associate with their own sex, but then they would only get their first sexual impressions from members of their own sex, and we know how decisive first impressions are for the whole after-life. Thus the separation of the sexes is the surest method of confirming homosexual tendencies in young people, if they have any predisposition of that sort.

The difference in sex is specially shown in children by the difference in dress; but one should always display tact in this matter, not to draw attention to the difference too early or in too striking a manner. Only when the distinction is very discreetly made, is it a means of paving the way for the later essential distinction.

175

Most parents, however, are rather easily tempted to exaggerate the difference in sex somewhat too early.

Mamma finds it so delightful for little Louise to behave like a little coquette, or for tiny Karl in his first pair of breeches to stalk proudly up and down and imitate his father. Many parents go a step further and add to the unnecessarily exaggerated difference in dress, a difference in rights and duties, in the freedom of movement of the two children and even in the amount of pocket-money. So they purposely cause envy and disappointment on the one side and a brutally domineering spirit on the other. And all this because the parents thought it at first so funny.

It is still worse if the parents carry their nonsense with their children's clothes so far as to dress up a boy like a girl and curl his hair; they then run the danger of developing the failings of both sexes in him, and of making him a pert and arrogant creature. And if the girls are dressed like boys there is the same risk, but in this case there is at least the advantage that the girls get rid of a lot of prejudices, and are freed from many conventional and unhygienic restrictions.

Furthermore this formal duplicity may really disturb the sexual differentiation, which should never be artificially disturbed, especially if there is a possible homosexual tendency present. From Dr. Magnus Hirschfeld's celebrated book, "Die Tranvestiten" we see what a preponderent role dress plays in homosexuality. It is true, as we have seen in Chapter 4, that the sexual urge is a predisposition caused by particular organochemical substances, but this urge is not always so absolutely differentiated in the one or the other sense, that it may not be modified by youthful impressions, example, habit, training and self-training, and either diminished or reversed.

While we are on the subject of clothing I wish to mention that tightly fitting clothes should always be avoided for reasons of hygiene; there should be no tight bodices for girls nor tight trousers for boys.

Nor should the circulation in the pelvic organs be interfered with by too long sitting, as is often the case in schools. This not only occasions artificial irritation of the genitals, but also interferes with the metabolism in these organs, preventing them from properly developing, which is of such great importance for girls, because it may make child-bearing such a martyrdom in later life. For organs can only develop in proportion to their metabolism.

In this chapter we have spoken all the time of the parents, but this does not mean that they have the success of the education in their power. In the sexual sphere in particular, there are other influences of far-reaching effect which one cannot always anticipate. The older children grow, the less do they remain under their par-

176

ents' influence, while economic and social influences make themselves continually more felt.

The children's permanent character is only finally formed when they have to go out into the work-a-day world and struggle for existence. The parents have only been able to lay down the general lines. Pain and difficulties can never be avoided, and even a broken engagement may leave behind it a precious treasure of experience of life.

Chapter 38

PRACTICAL OBJECT LESSONS IN SEX
INSTRUCTION FOR DIFFERENT AGES

THE FIRST introduction of the child into the mysterious world of the sexual life, which is such an acute question in these days, was once upon a time no question at all, for originally the sexual life was no mystery whatever.

As the morbid outgrowth of a dualistic view of life, in the course of time sexual ignorance and sexual secrecy has become the ideal and the privilege of the "better" classes, who may permit themselves this luxury.

Yet, everywhere in the country, and in our great cities where people are still living in a more primitive and natural manner, everything is much less concealed. In some exceptional cases this leads to great evils, but as a general rule I have found more real modesty and chastity in these simple and natural people than in the rich. It is only a pity that the spirit of imitation which leads to a preference for the errors of the rich has not been ineffective, and even amongst the most reasonable people the bad example of hypocrisy filled with unchaste thoughts is ever more honoured, while at the present time the more educated families are at last beginning to abandon this stupidity as far as they themselves are concerned.

The more everything is artificially concealed at first, the greater is the necessity afterwards for judicious enlightenment. It is, however, very hard to correct what has once been spoilt. For here we are dealing with the souls of children, who are already in a state of more or less sexual exaltation through the old regime of hypocrisy. Here we must individualise very tactfully, for it is a biological law that morbid cases display much greater differences than normal physiological cases. And thus the characters of our children, falsely developed through concealment of the truth, diverge enormously, just as the educational tact of the parents differs enormously.

In family circles opportunity is readily found to broach the sexual question, perhaps through an event in plant-life or animal-life, or a pregnancy, or a chance remark of one of the children. These opportunities are generally neglected, for people think "there is plenty of time". And then comes the time, almost before one expects it, when the children are no longer so innocent, and evil influences have already begun to make themselves felt.

I was quite astonished at the brutal way a mother answered her 8-year-old son when he asked, "Mummie, where do babies come from?" She replied: "Who's told you about it?" "I don't know, mummie." "You know very well; who has been talking to you about it?" "Dietrich who lives next door" (a much older boy). "And what did Dietrich say?" The boy repeated a little stupid nonsense. The mother then said: "Dietrich knows nothing at all about it; when daddy comes home he will teach you better." But I never heard whether when daddy came home he taught the boy a little of the truth, or gave him a box on the ears. Perhaps the mother had forgotten the whole incident before the father came home; and the boy would be all the more pleased.

In the school it is not easy to find a good opportunity; but lessons on plant- and animal-life, or the story-telling hour afford sufficient opportunity even in the primary schools to give the scholars an elementary idea. Furthermore, it is absolutely impossible to instruct them correctly in the life-history of plants and animals without touching lightly on the subject, unless it is purposely intended to keep them in ignorance.

An Object Lesson in Sex Instruction

A little curly head may unexpectedly pop up and cry: "Please, teacher, where is my little brother coming from?" The teacher: "What do you mean?" The scholar: "Yes, mother said I was going to have a little brother and I asked her where he was coming from, and then she said she coudn't tell me now, but I should know when I was bigger." Teacher: "Fritz, what a silly question for you to ask: where do the little brothers and sisters come from? Where does everything in Nature come from? Why everything grows. You all know very well that little children grow too, don't you? First of all they are so small that they cannot be seen and then they keep on growing until they are grown up. You are half grown up already. Then again, when things grow it is not like building a house, where we bring wood and stone together and lay the pieces one on top of the other; growth comes from the inside, like the pips inside an apple, which some day may grow into new apples. Just in this way also the first tiny beginning of a human being grows inside the body of a grown person, and bye and bye becomes a child and grows up too. Otherwise it would not be possible."

"Does the father also have children?" asks one of the scholars. "No, the father does not have any children; he has his work outside to attend to, but the mother looks after the children, doesn't she? And that is why your mother loves you so much, at least, when you are good. And that is why you should always be good and never disobedient. Your mothers take a lot of trouble with you, especially when another little brother or sister is growing; you must understand that it is rather hard for her. The little baby grows rather big, and then it seems as if everything in her must either bend or break. But when it is all over, we are all happy, and then you can play with your little brother bye and bye."

Of course, the older the scholars are the further one may go with the explanations. Sooner or later we come to the definite question: what part the father takes in it. This seems to be an almost insuperable difficulty with children.

A mother of delicate feeling once showed me a good way out.

I was attending a confinement in a simple but honest family and all at once a cock began vigorously treading a hen. The little girl, a pretty child of about

7 years of age, asked her mother: "Mummy, what is the cock doing, biting the hen?" "No," replied the mother, "that has to do with the laying of eggs. You like nice fresh eggs, don't you, Annie?" "Does the cock lay eggs then, mother?" "No, you know very well only hens lay eggs." "But, mummy, what is the cock doing that for?" Violent labour pains interrupted the conversation; when all was quiet again, the child asked once more: "But what does the cock really do, mother?" "You should ask the doctor; he can explain much better than I can." "No, no," said I, "you are telling her so nicely about it." And then she told the whole story.

"If there is no cock, there are no eggs, and if there are no hens there are no eggs either. Each of them can only make one-half of the egg: the cock has half-eggs, so small that they cannot be seen, and the hens have tiny half-eggs just the same. The cock lays one of these half-eggs in the hen's warm body. That's what he was doing just now. And then when the two half-eggs have become one egg, and this has had a few weeks to grow big, the hen lays the big egg in the warm nest in the fowl-house. If it is left there and the hen sits on it and keeps it warm all the time, then a little chicken grows out of it; or if you eat it instead, then you grow and become a big girl."'

The child wanted to hear more, but her mother's pains increased, so she was sent to a neighbour's.

On some such plan quite a good explanation may be constructed. It can certainly not seem strange to any child that the little egg should remain for a time in the body and then pass out, while with the more advanced children one may speak of how it lies midway between the urinary canal and the intestine. How far one may go in this direction depends, of course, upon whether sufficient anatomical instruction regarding the human body has been given or not.

In the secondary schools we can briefly trace the course of the development of the individual from the ovum to man, and finally the sexual evolution, as we will attempt to do in Chapter 40. Perhaps here and there it will also be possible to give the pupils a correct insight into cell-life by means of the microscope or cinema.

If by chance the child has already acquired some impure impressions of sexual things, he must be energetically reminded of the seriousness and sacredness of this subject, and the banal will then disappear from his mind. Much depends here on the teacher's tact.

It is easy to repress untimely mirth if one of the scholars as "enfant terrible" says anything disconcerting, by promising reward or punishment according as the scholars know on the morrow what has been taught today; a few words of foreign origin that they must learn with it, work wonders. Thus an impression of impure feeling will be changed into one of proper modesty.

But after all there is one difficulty that the schoolmaster cannot overcome. He is master of the situation in the school; if he were not sure of himself there, he would not have broached the subject. But in the scholars' homes! Although he may have carefully explained the importance and sacredness of the subject, it is not his fault if the child chatters stupidly about it at home, in and out of season. Then the storm breaks:

"Child, you ought to be ashamed of yourself! Where did you learn such things? Good gracious, do we send our children to school to learn these things? Let the fellow hold his tongue!" and so on.

Although that does not matter to the teacher, it is not very agreeable. At any rate the storm does not last very long, and the child will be thankful for the truth on this problem about which his parents had always deceived him. And the next time the child will be more careful.

But the child's words may call forth jeers and cause jokes when he is talking, not with his parents, but with narrow-minded people. Poor child, to be trusted to such people! Yet in this case it is doubly good that the teacher has done his duty; otherwise the narrow-minded people would have had the first word, and the good impressions would have come too late. Now the teacher has immunised the child beforehand, and he will feel an aversion to anybody shameless enough to profane such a holy subject. The teacher has saved the child in time. And if by any chance he is blamed, and told that such things are no part of school instruction, he may reflect that such reproaches are always heaped on those who tru' 'try to do their ` y; and always by persons who neglect to do theirs.

Of course, every teacher will have sense enough to make a very cautious beginning, if he does not know the state of public opinion in his district, so that he can first feel his way, and at first he will give only some little explanation appropriate to the occasion. He will then always find that this is very thankfully received.

Part IV.

EVOLUTIONARY DEVELOPMENT OF ALL FORMS AND MODES OF LOVE INTO THE COMPLEX SEXUAL RELATIONS IN MODERN IDEAL MARRIAGE

Chapter 39

Introductory:

PRACTICAL IMPORTANCE OF A STUDY OF SEXUAL EVOLUTION

IT IS of the greatest importance to study Evolution because through it we gain a more objective foundation for our judgment; for we may see to what extent our theories correspond with the line of progress of Evolution, and this is the best criterion as to how far we are right, and to what extent we may expect the fulfillment of our ideals in the future.

Such an objective standard is especially needful in the sexual sphere, because here opinions are so divergent. To one man the sexual life is the chief motive of his existence, to another it is, with equal exaggeration, only a temptation of the senses, except when it aims at reproduction, for which it is indispensable.

We have already decided that the extraordinary intense feeling of pleasure is the result of the great internal and external obstacles which are always attached to the sexual function and which must always be overcome. And it is just through the victory over these obstacles that our energy is so greatly sublimated, and that ethically speaking, happiness depends so much upon our sexual life.

We will now consider the sexual life in its general biological significance for the whole organic world and in its development. We shall also briefly review the pre-historic and historical details of the love-life in both man and animals, and we shall see how the sexual impulse was originally only an impulse to detumescence directed to the secretion of the reproductive cells for the relief of a local internal tension, and that it was only much later that it broadened into the impulse to contractation — to a desire to hold another in the love-embrace. This broadening of the Material to the Spiritual is nowhere seen so beautifully as in the history of sexual evolution.

Chapter 40

HOW HUMAN SEXUAL LIFE DEVELOPED

a) The Asexual Period of Evolution

IN THIS chapter we shall touch on a question to which, so far, too little attention has been paid by the scientific world and which nevertheless is certainly one of the most important fundamental problems of the whole of Biology—the origin of the sexual life.

In embryology at first one only knows vegetative growth and the vegetative method of reproduction. We must now try to find out what was the first cause for the sexual method of reproduction to develop side by side with the vegetative method.

On acount of its superiority in the Darwinian sense, the sexual method later entirely superseded all vegetative methods of reproduction in the higher species of animals.

A brief review of its evolution will best demonstrate this. In recent times sexual processes in lower organisms have been carefully studied, but the asexual stage, the most primitive of all, has up to the present been greatly neglected. We shall now endeavour to repair this omission as far as possible, even if only hypothetically at first; proofs will then be further adduced from present day experimentation.

The first, most primitive forms of animal and vegetable life, which lived in water or moisture, were, as is now generally admitted, unicellular organisms; just as nowadays the most primitive form of life, such as bacteria, yeast-cells, many algae, amoebae, etc., still exist as unicellular organisms in countless quantities.

They grow by the absorption of nutritive substances, and when such a cell at last becomes too big and powerful to remain organised as one single cell, it reorganises itself and splits into two new individuals: an increase in number which is quite in accordance with the ordinary vegetative growth, and which, if the process is repeated at short intervals, may become very considerable, although quite asexual.

Indeed through their immense energy of growth, their countless numbers, their simple and frugal mode of life, and their almost limitless powers of resistance, these unicellular organisms have always in competition with the higher forms of animal and vegetable life shown themselves to be the most indestructible. And all our later complicated organisms, no matter how superior they may be by virtue of their higher differentiation, are, mankind included, often defenceless against these tiny intruders, to whom we ourselves must finally fall victim; and only cremation itself destroys both the intruders and the victims.

All our modern hygiene does not serve to bring us a free pardon, but only a postponement of our execution. But when the organic world had already long been in existence and had collected here and there large quantities of organic waste matter, it must often have happened that somewhere or other fruitful soil was produced, a fertilisation by means of which the plant world (and as a secondary consequence, the animal world also) was enabled to develop more luxuriantly than before.

This modification of growth, the formation of multicellular organisms, signified at that time a new era in the organic world with possibilities of evolution hitherto unsuspected. From the unicellular green algae strands were evolved which under favourable conditions grow continually longer and may even branch. By their side parasitic colourless fibres of mould formed, as if they were descended directly from the colourless bacteria. The multicellular animal organisms, too, then found an excess of vegetable substance available as nutriment, and so were able to assume greater dimensions.

It is very remarkable, and I will state at once that with sexual phenomena it is always the same story.

Firstly, some hypertrophic growth as an external expression of greatly increased reserve energy, and then a separation into single cells, as an adequate expression of the impossibility of a further growth. Thus we nearly always have in the first place a tumour-like formation, and indeed in the higher plants the formation of flower-buds, in the higher animals the formation of testes and ovaries, by means of which in due course the reproductive cells will be expelled just like the spores in the case of the inferior organisms.

The majority of these innumerable spores are hopelessly lost; so their vast numbers are not of much use. Furthermore, spore-formation, like everything sexual, is only localised in a circumscribed spot, while at the beginning the vegetative reproduction represents a general function of the whole body. Thus in the phenomenon of sex the increase in numbers does not seem to be the most important thing; the phenomenon of sex is rather an adaptation to the economic conditions; it is indeed no rejuvenescence, but an emigration on a large scale!

b) *The Sexual Period of Evolution*

Up to the present we have considered only the asexual period of evolution, at most including spore-formation as the first attempt of nature to come to the rescue when ruin threatened. Thus we sketched out a scheme of vegetative evolution. But now we come to the period in which the phenomenon of sex becomes ever more prominent[1]. Because we have the good fortune to live in this latter

1. In chapter 41 we shall show that in the course of this period of sexual evolution, vegetative growth has also developed further and has, in the higher animal forms, been compelled to yield entirely to the phenomenon of sex.

period, the history of evolution from now on will be much less hypothetical.

The fusion of two ordinary cells occurs as a transition stage to the actual sexual phenomenon even in fairly low forms of life.

We call these organs the "sexual organs" and describe as female those which produce the fewer but larger cells with abundant store of nutriment, and as male those which cast off numerous small cells without reserve nutriment. The difference between the cells makes chemotactic attraction of the one for the other particularly striking. In higher plants a pollen-cell eagerly combines with an egg-cell, and the higher animals a sperm-cell with an egg-cell.

The different characters of the two conjugating cells and their origin in two different organs, cause a far greater differentiation in the descendants than the copulation of two similar cells. But at first there was still a certain amount of uniformity because the two combining cells had been produced by one common individual, or else by two individuals who were both bisexual and consequently almost identical.

In the history of evolution this is the hermaphroditic period of transition.

In the further course of the history of evolution hermaphrodism has also had to yield to the separation of the sexes. This is the usual process of differentiation, according to the principle of the division of labour. The transition is evident. When by chance in one of the hermaphrodite individuals one sex, and in another individual the other sex, temporarily or permanently fails, then the surviving function can develop all the more strongly in such individuals. Such functionally specialised individuals (for we humans are all specialised in one or the other sex) must eventually survive in the struggle for existence.

The first appearance of such one-sided development may at first, apart from accidental or individual peculiarities, quite easily have been occasioned by great variations in the nutritive conditions of the various individuals. We have already seen that luxuriant growth favours the formation of females and vice versa. I shall now also refer to Prantl's experiments, which show distinctly how immensely important a part is played by nutritive conditions in the history of sexual evolution.

Prantl found when he sowed the spores of the fern "Osmunda Ceratopteris" in soil very rich in nitrogen, that he did not get the ordinary hermaphroditic prothallia, but only prothallia with exclusively female organs. In soil extremely poor in nitrogen he only obtained prothallia with male organs. So he could at will, simply by

188

modifying the conditions of the plant nutrition, convert the old hemaphrodite stage into one of separate sexuality, and even deliberately choose the sex.

In the animal world especially the separation of the two sexes has gained the victory. This has enabled the difference of the sexes to appear with its rivalry and its special lures, by means of which a higher civilisation and greater perfection were produced. And this is undoubtedly the reason why the division of the sexes has had such an unqualified success in the animal world, but not in the plant world where there can be no question of a conscious sexual selection. In the plant world most flowers have remained bisexual. But even here self-fertilisation is avoided as far as possible by the most varied arrangements; only in the case of necessity it was a useful resource.

The existence of two distinct sexes, this fusion of two cells of different character, if they are both fit representatives of the same species, is the summit of the sexual life. We ourselves are living in this stage, and we owe it all to our advantages.

Only increase in numbers is rather retarded as a result of the sexual system. For reproduction has become dependent on the combined action of two individuals—a considerable complication in itself. And while in the unicellular organisms each cell-division causes a doubling of their numbers, the sexual fusion of two cells means a halving of the numbers each time. Especially in view of the vast number of reproductive cells, frequently as numerous as the sands on the sea-shore, we must come to the conclusion that in comparison with this number, the practical success of procreation may almost be considered as an exception; it is only a few that can be saved. For we see from actual experience that since in the history of evolution, the sexual life has assumed the task of procreation, the prolificacy of these higher species has constantly diminished. However, the biological and economical advantages of the sexual method are enormous and constant[2].

If, however, two dissimilar cells fuse, then besides the above-mentioned advantages, there will also be an enormous increase in the variability, because among the resulting offspring some will display more of the father's peculiarities, and some more of the mother's.

And even this variability betokens an immense progress in the struggle for existence; for no matter what further events or catas-

2. So we see how much nature has improved her methods of evolution; at first especially among the unicellular organisms, we see the vegetative principle of mass-production with mass-rejection of the unfit, whilst under the influence of the phenomenon of sex, we observe the principle of improvement through constantly decreasing prolificacy.

titudes and the most complicated efforts[3]. Also that this function may find expression in such a fundamentally different variety of way: alone, during sleep, together with another individual of the same or opposite sex, even by the employment of almost every conceivable object with or without life.

The strength of the resistance that must be overcome shows us clearly why it is that the sexual impulse is so invigourating for the adult; just as a mother finds herself so invigourated after a confinement. In this way the sexual life acts both physically and psychically as a powerful uplifter, imbuing us with the highest degree of life-energy.

Just as in plants the sexual life represents the closing scene of a leaf-bud formation, in many of the lower animals it only appears at the close of their existence; the male often dies soon after the act of copulation and the female as soon as she has laid her eggs. In the higher animal world and in mankind something similar is to be observed. For though the casting off of the reproductive cells is not delayed until the end of life, yet it does not appear until the close of the youthful period of growth.

The whole situation is entirely different in the animal body only because the latter is quite differently constructed. The body of a plant always exhibits, just as before the beginning of all sexual life, an organisation of parts of equal value; in the higher plants there is a series of stem-segments or internodes, constantly forming new segments until finally the formation of flowers appears. But since in animals the sexual method of reproduction has become the only one possible, the number of segments has become limited, and they have all grown together in one single concentrated and enclosed organisation, by means of which a far higher division of labour is rendered possible.

On account of this central organisation, the animal body reacts to harmful influences much more energetically than a plant. At the slightest local infection by dangerous substances (for instance, bacterial poisons), a number of unicellular organisms (the pus corpuscles), form in the body, and then find their way out through ducts or by some destruction of tissue.

And so we see that just as in plants, so too in the animal body, the sexual crisis is called forth as a means of salvation by a certain condition of exhaustion.

3. Klotz in his remarkable book, "Das Welträtzel Mensch", Dresden Verlag R. A. Giesecke, 1921, is right when he draws attention to the advantages of the traditional posture assumed by animals in copulation, compared with the position usually adopted by human beings, but it must not be overlooked that many animals, especially of the marine variety, also perform the act in the same posture as we do.

This argument is splendidly confirmed by the counter-proof. If, exceptionally, the vegetative growth is not hindered, the sexual growth-modification does not occur.

The more luxuriantly the vegetative life develops, the trees in superfluous masses of leaves, and mankind in superfluous fat, the less may great fecundity be expected. And breeders dread obesity in animals wanted for reproductive purposes, or in hens for laying.

But when the vegetative growth of a luxuriantly growing tree is injured in some way or other, for instance if a few roots or branches are lopped off roughly, so that it begins to droop somewhat, it then starts to bear fruit.

The control-test is differently manifested in man. As soon as a woman has passed the period of fertility, it almost invariably happens, as with castrated men, that she begins to put on fat.

Practically, this principle has long been known as a sort of rivalry between two diverging functions; the sexual and the vegetative growth. Gardeners have taken advantage of this principle from time immemorial. In order to produce flowers instead of leaves, they place their plants in the smallest pots, with an abundance of light and sunshine. The control-test as a proof of this is easy to perform. I once planted, in a flower-bed that lay partly in the shade, some pelargoniums in pots, carefully putting a flat stone under the hole in the bottom of the pot, and raising the rim of the pot a little above the ground, so that the roots could not grow beyond the pot. They all bore plenty of flowers, except two which stood in the shade, and these had too many leaves and no flowers at all. When winter came, and I took up the pots, I found that these two had managed to push through and had strong roots in the soil beneath. Only here the symptoms of exhaustion and with them the flower-formation were absent.

Countless examples of this diverging effect might be drawn from horticultural practice; sharp bends made in the stems of branches of fruit trees trained on walls and trellis work; carrots pulled up by the roots at the end of the first year and transplanted in a sunny spot with plenty of manure, so that they should produce few leaves but plenty of seed; and all transplanting of seedlings with the same object.

When grape-vines and fruit trees are pruned, if it is properly done, a rich crop of fruit is obtained at the expense of the leaf-formation.

The Japanese gardeners follow the same principle in the production of their dwarf trees; they sow the smallest seeds in the smallest possible pots, the roots are kept very short from the first, the soil as poor and small in quantity as possible, with a minimum of moisture. They thus succeed in growing fruit in a nutshell.

We need not, however, go so far as Japan for examples! Who has not noticed, when clearing his garden-path of weeds, how between the hard gravel the tiniest plants often grow; real dwarfs, deprived of moisture and nutriment, yet still blooming in the hot sunshine with more flowers than leaves!

Thus we obtain a thorough insight into the contrast between the vegetative and the sexual growth. The different value of these two complementary phases of evolution lies in the difference of their needs and products. That which is good for one often injures the other, and vice versa; and on that account the functions are divergent.

Now that we are able to trace the causal nexus of the sexual growth modification, we can go on to enquire which factors favour and which hinder the vegetative or the sexual growth.

This knowledge is of the highest practical importance in the breeding of all animals and the cultivation of all plants. By its means we may possibly succeed in time in human education also in postponing the sexual crisis, that turning point in our lives, for a while, so that first the vegetative, and then the sexual life may flourish and come to perfection.

Of course, the majority of living conditions can affect both phases of evolution in a similar way. Therefore, the popular idea is not so erroneous that, in general, favourable living conditions will produce both luxuriant growth and a good yield of flowers. This holds good only for moderate influences which are beneficial in every respect; but not for excessive influences which border on the pathological. These may have a one-sided effect.

In mankind we can study this question thoroughly in all cases of early puberty and of retarded sexual maturity, of which ethnography affords us so many samples. The natives of tropical countries are precocious, although their health is so prejudicially affected by the climate and by social evils, because the stimulus from light and sunshine is maximal; but not those of polar regions, where all influences are unfavourable. Thus a comparatively early awakening of sexuality often occurs amongst the children of the working classes in our big towns, where the living conditions are just as faulty, but where an excess of sexual stimuli is felt.

This conception of the case is confirmed by the general educational experience of all ages, that a reasonably restricted but good nutrition, together with plenty of muscular exercise in the open air, with careful avoidance of artificial sexual stimuli, exerts the most happy influence in the prevention of precocious sexual maturity. In the simple life of rural districts, it has been noted from experience that a retarded sexuality occurs as frequently as precocity in the towns. Now we can understand the great importance of chastity in childhood, on which such great value has always rightly been set.

That in time we shall meet with practical success in this direction seems to me all the more hopeful because I believe that our higher civilisation compared with that of the primitive races, can already show some success in the course of the history of evolution.

Sexual Method of Reproduction
Governed by the Surface of the Earth

In concluding, we shall endeavour to review the whole history of the evolution of the species, but specially now in its dependence on the history of the evolution of the surface of our earth, which after all governs everything that happens to us. It will then be seen that the gradual and complete conversion of the vegetative into the sexual method of reproduction, is ultimately an adaptation to the catastrophes of the earth's surface, which have always governed those influences which we have recognised as decisive.

In the beginning, when the surface of the globe was covered everywhere with a layer of water, there was nothing but water-organisms which only increased their numbers vegetatively, without sexual stimuli or sexual life.

Then later on, when the earth's surface became uneven, with local heaps of organic débris, the mosses which require moisture above everything, developed; at that stage vegetative reproduction was still the principal thing, while sexual reproduction remained the exception.

Still later, as here and there large tracts of dry land appeared, still covered, but now with marshes and bogs, the vascular cryptogams evolved, and sexual reproduction began to take a step forward with these. On dry hills and mountains, however, the coniferae grew, which high in the sun and air almost exclusively relied on sexual reproduction.

The majority of our monocotyledons also still prefer a marshy soil, and increase as well by bulbs and rootstalks, as they do sexually by seeds. In the tropics, however, the maize, rice and palms increase in the heat of the sun, just as corn in well manured land does with us, almost exclusively in the sexual way.

Like the latter, most of the dicotyledonous species prefer a loose soil and plenty of sun; they then reproduce mostly, and many of them exclusively, through seeds. Especially in the mountainous regions they revel in an abundance of sunshine, through which the most beautiful and abundant flora develop and delight us.

In the animal world, the vegetative form of reproduction was forced to give way much earlier and more completely to the sexual form, because animals possessing the power of locomotion can seek the sunshine for themselves, and their bodies are in various ways exposed to all kinds of local stimuli; whereas the plants, so thoroughly vegetative, are always doomed to lie quietly half buried in the darkness and moisture of the earth. Yet since the earliest times there have existed many varieties of worms and such-like which spend all their lives in darkness and water or moisture; and in many of their species the vegetative method of reproduction still rules rather than the sexual.

Fish and amphibia live in the water, but spawn in the sunshine.

of our evolution; and who knows what may not be accomplished in the future by the ennobling of this function! In the struggle for existence we have won through mostly by the antagonistic and alternating effects of the development of the brain and the development of sex, and we hope that this will continue to play an increasingly important part.

In the succeeding generations of the species the functions of the brain and of the sexual organs have not only developed in their numerous aspects, but they have always supported and stimulated each other more and more thoroughly. The two functions reach the apex of their development in every individual at the same age. The more beautifully the one forms, the finer will be the development of the other. We have all been struck more than once with the simultaneous occurrence of unimportance in the one with unimportance in the other respect; and the association of inspiration in the one respect with inspiration in the other. Numbers of celebrated men and women might be mentioned in this connection. So with regard to Saint Augustine it cannot be denied that the ardour of his religious belief and his African sexual temperament represent the two opposite sides of his character[2] and cannot be considered apart!

We cannot but be amazed at the extraordinary sensitiveness of our brain cells, which are so specialised for sensibility; but we must be equally astonished at the extraordinary plasticity of the reproductive cells, which can give rise to an entirely new individual. On the one side cells of a creative genius, and on the other, cells that can really give rise to another generation.

Still better shall we be able to weigh the values of the two great powers of our existence, if we first see what evolution has to teach us in this respect, so that we get some insight into the manner in which the two poles of our body have so widely differentiated, with mutual division of labour.

In the foregoing chapter we studied the history of *sexual* evolution of *vegetative* growth, how it has gradually modified its type under the influence of the sexual.

Only the sexual life remains unchanged in its essential principles. Pollination and fertilisation are almost identical; each of them merely a transfer of single cells, characteristic of the sexual life from the first. The vegetative growth, however, has undergone a complete metamorphosis under this sexual influence; it has been forced to adapt itself to the sexual.

2. It was just on this account that he was able to combine the belief in a personal God that he had inherited from his mother, with the abstract and therefore absolute idealism of Plato; as he himself confesses, the study of Plato was the first step towards his conversion.

And so the whole history of evolution has gradually come to symbolically represent an apotheosis of the god Cupid. The little rascal who at first only gave his aid exceptionally, has wormed his way in more and more, and was not content until he had modelled vegetative growth after his symbol the egg, and had led us humans all to join the band of his avowed admirers. And he likes to play the mischief with us all individually even now.

In the vertebrate animals, the nervous system, the organs of respiration and especially the circulation of the blood are entirely centralised. Yet man still possesses two fully formed segments which carry extremities, i.e., the pelvic ring with two legs, and the shoulder ring with two arms. The remainder of our vertebrae carry two ribs or at least two lateral processes, but they no longer have extremities.

Let us, therefore, consider as the end-point of development our own skeleton, and firstly the hindermost portion of it. Here as an expression of the telescoping with a forward curve (in harmony with the oval form), it strikes us at once that several vertebrae, which could be distinctly recognised during embryonic life as separate spinal joints, have grown together and shortened in the adult, and form the massive sacrum, while for the rest of the vertebrae nothing remains except a rather useless coccyx, which resembles a rudimentary tail.[3]

Here in the concavity of the embryo as it lay rolled up in the mother-egg, the two reproductive organs developed, and here the newly-formed urogenital system acquired its present form. Afterwards when the pelvis has grown up as a bony framework the mature ovum can safely lie sheltered in the maternal body until it reaches full development.

In contrast to the head, which represents a cavity surrounded by bone, and to the thorax with its bony grating, the frontal wall of the abdomen, as the last wall of the body to be closed, has remained free from ossification. So this is the most suitable spot for adaptation to the bowel contents and for changes of blood pressure, which latter reaches its highest point in the sexual congestion of the blood-vessels. And just because the impulsive variations in blood pressure are the expression of our varied moods, this free play of our blood pressure is of particular importance. In former times when one was of a melancholy and morose disposition, this state was termed hypochondria, because not without reason it was thought that this painful condition was localised beneath the cartilages of the ribs.

On the other hand, the amount of nerve substance in this portion of the body is inferior to that at the upper pole, for in the abdomen there are only a few small scattered collections of nerve centres.

Fortunately we still have nerve centres which are not enclosed. Together these form the sympathetic nervous system, which transmits only vague, but so much the more intimate sensations without further localisation, and further intervention of the consciousness. So here the sexual life develops as an indefinable but powerful sensory excitement, that can only be disturbed by the interference

3. When the tail was no longer required as the ship's rudder, this organ comprised of so many vertebrae, developed differently in the different groups of animals: the beaver employs it in his building operations, the horse and ox to drive off the flies with it; there are species of rats which use it to carry their young, in the kangaroo it serves for jumping, and in birds it is the aviator's rudder.

of the intellect, an antagonism which is thoroughly characteristic of the sexual passion.

Fortunately the process of the telescoping and bending forward did not go any farther at this lower pole, or the act of parturition would have been rendered impossible; but still it is often so difficult, that some of the finest developed children cannot be brought into the world alive, and many a young mother is sent to an early grave. Thus here the limit of possibility has been reached.

Let us now turn to the other pole of our body.

What an immense contrast we have here to the other pole of the body! Here everything crammed with nerve-substance, and there room for the free play of the circulation.

And this vaulting over of the brain in the vertebrate animals[4] is more striking the higher they mount in the scale; in man, for instance, it is strongly developed that the brain actually protrudes over the features of the face. As a result, man and the anthropoid apes were robbed of their last means of escape: they could no longer save themselves from an imminent danger by swimming, because with their heavy heads their breathing organs sank too deeply beneath the surface. So they began to scramble with all four extremities up trees whenever flight was necessary; and this led to a complete change of attitude and form of body.

With this development of the brain, the limit of possibility of existence is almost reached at this pole also, for what a great number of individuals are drowned every year! And yet with the increase of civilisation and mental effort the high vaulting of the skull has constantly increased, as we shall observe if we compare ourselves with the prognathous type seen in primitive races. Yes indeed, our skull is filled with nerve substance to such an extent that here, in contrast to the other pole, is scarcely any room for the circulation of the blood, so that mental strain soon leads to headache. The difficulty of circulation in this organ causes endless suffering, and the slightest effusion of blood in the brain may lead to an apoplexy from which so many people, especially educated ones, perish.

So we see that at both poles of our body, the evolution described above has almost overstepped the limits of possibility of life, and it is not surprising that we men stand at the terminal point of evolution. Our further evolution lies, therefore, far more in a

4. In most of the other animal species we also find an ovoid rounding of both poles of the body. It is very pronounced, for instance, in the crabs and shrimps, but these in contrast to ourselves have the greater bend at tne anal extremity and so this group of animals has not made much progress in the world; we know the wood-louse and the Balanus to be stunted descendants of the crab, which was always so well armed for offence and defence.

certain refinement, for which much moderation and self-control are needful. Civilisation, an artificial degree of domestication, now holds the mastery over the crude forces of nature. And instead of developing constantly more highly differentiated organs in our bodies, we are always inventing more highly differentiated tools, machines and implements.

Now that we have reached this high stage of civilisation, it is more than ever necessary that the two guiding motives in our lives should keep each other in equilibrium.

Too great attention to one pole is just as dangerous as too great attention to the other. The hygienic and ethical dangers of sexual excess are generally recognised; but a one-sided mental development causes in addition to the hygienic dangers a predominating ethical danger, the danger of a one-sided intellectualism[5], and to this the more highly developed individuals are the most subject.

Our brain certainly makes us reasonable and cautious, but we only feel happy when an increased circulation powerfully stimulates the whole metabolism and especially our oxidation, which goes on so actively under the stimulation of the sexual life. The functions of our brain teach us how we can even in the most complicated cases avoid danger and seek favourable conditions; but the sexual life fills us indeed with happiness and delight. And how much more inspiring and successful would many an intellectual work, many a sermon or lecture, many a legal judgment be, if not less cold reason, but warmer feeling were put into it.

5. At first, before man became so preponderantly intellectual, the seat of life was not thought to be the brain, but rather in the breath (Genesis II) or in the blood (Genesis IX:4).

Chapter 42

HOW THE SEXUAL PASSION DEVELOPED

THERE probably exists no substance which chemically and physically is so sensitive as living albumen which, biologically considered, is by far the most important constituent of the living cell. In Chapter 34 we have already seen how even in the lowest organisms, the contractibility of albumen and the consequent mobility indicate an almost incredible sensitiveness of the albumen to external influences. But in the higher organisms far keener sensitiveness is displayed by those groups of cells in the interior of the body which as nerve centres are exclusively differentiated for sensation.

The common sensibility of the skin retains its primary importance as long as we live; as we perceive easily in the magic effect of water-, air- and sun-baths, massage, etc., (see chapter 55), by means of which we feel our youth renewed. We only enter into relation with the outer world around us through this sensibility of the skin, but it is through the local elaborations of our so-called sensory organs, that the number of our impressions is infinitely increased, while our mental development keeps pace with them and enhances its value.

So we like all these impressions from the outer world very much; especially if they are endowed with movement, and above all the stimulating touch of our fellow beings, in so far as we find them sympathetic. Thus there arises in us the longing for companionship, friendship and love.

In the evolution of the species, mutual approach and mutual contact first assumed importance in the warm-blooded animals, on account of both the range of variability of temperature and the variety of the massage motives. The mutual approach is henceforward felt to be a permanent delight, and thus the sexual impulse of these species has developed into the love-life.

In the higher species this love-life assumes a form that is constantly more comprehensive and manifold, with the constant addition of more spiritual motives full of joy and charm, until finally in man love becomes something so spiritual that the material impulse not infrequently recedes entirely into the background. Also if we carefully observe our individual development from childhood to manhood, we can trace the same process of evolution, and can still distinctly perceive how greatly the sexual feeling is really only a special development of the sensibility of the skin.

The passionate feelings which we adults commonly experience almost exclusively in the sexual sensations, express themselves in children just as intensely, long before puberty, as a general sensibility of the skin.

The smallest child likes being tickled and caressed, on any part of the body, and soon forms sympathies or antipathies in consequence. Young children play as heedlessly together as kittens or puppies; they roll over each other and tease each other; sometimes they will put up with anything from each other and sometimes the contrary. Bigger children wrestle and fight fiercely as though their lives depended upon it. Thus manhood approaches.

Gradually through force of habit all parts of the skin have become insensitive or less sensitive to this local contact, but some of the more intimate parts of the skin still remain sensitive, because they are more concealed, and so far have been more protected on account of the proprieties, so that they preserved the whole of their original sensibility. We now come to a critical point in our lives; the awakening of our sexual impulse. Prototypes of these very sensitive parts of our bodies, are all those portions of the skin which are constantly sheltered from all rough handling by clothing, such as the neck, the armpits and the soles of the feet, but especially the regions where our urinary and sexual canals terminate.

These portions of skin were predestined to be the foci of all contractation impulses as soon as the sexual impulse should be awakened.

So here too, we are dealing primarily with a skin-sensibility. For, to be exact, it is not the erectile tissue that is so sensitive, but those portions of the skin that are alternately congested and depleted through the ebb and flow of the blood in the erectile tissue. From the period of puberty onwards this sensibility is appreciably increased through the stimulating effect of the sexual organochemical substances to which we have frequently alluded.

Thus one might well say that we have a sixth sensory organ, for here also we have an increased local sensibility of the skin combined with a complicated special apparatus. Only with this difference: in other sensory organs the normal stimulus comes from without, and only the abnormal from within; while in the sexual apparatus the normal stimulus comes from within and the artificial

Chapter 43

FROM COLD-BLOODED TO WARM-BLOODED

A S WE have seen in Chapter 40, there was once a time when all living organisms were asexual. Those self-satisfied people, wrapped in smug ignorance, who pose as apostles of morality, must secretly rejoice to think of this stage when this was the only mode of reproduction guaranteed free from all sexual desire! When there was nothing but cell-division.

In these primeval times the lower algae and fungi represented the highest forms of vegetable life[1], but even then these aquatic and moisture-loving flora must have shown quite graceful lines; for although the flora in that far-off age was not yet crowned with flowers, the lower forms were richly varied, and water-plants, because their weight is supported by the water, could at least attain a higher degree of elegance than land-plants, which are constantly exposed to the wind. But since all sexuality was absent, a certain coldness must have reigned, something like simulated death, or perhaps one might better say, like the Sleeping Beauty waiting for Prince Charming.

The later fusion of two similar cells, as in the conjugatae, looks already a little more promising. For here there was already a fusion. such as is the ideal of all lovers; and it was still without any inequality of rights or any other inequality, for both parties to the fusion were then equal in character and form. But this sort of equality was a little monotonous.

The appearance of hermaphridism is far more seductive: a difference of sex, but each of the partners can function as either husband or wife, or sometimes both at once! And still no pride of sex or sexual rivalry; for all individuals are still double-sexed, not simply temporarily as we men are in our embryonic stage, but perfectly formed, in a double ecstasy.

That our earth-worms and garden-snails are not insensible to love, we can perceive from their untiring patience in mating, and their loving behaviour before copulation; snails seem never tired of kissing each other! But then their kissing had another significance besides the symbolical one, for in these species, the genital organs lie near their heads! And they can make love to each other half the

1. A primeval epoch such as is revealed in the recent discoveries of the old red sandstone deposits of Rhynie (Aberdeen), which date back long, long before the formation of the coal-fields.

day without making a sound, revelling the whole time in double ecstasy. For them there is no question as to which is the more blessed, to give or to receive, for they both do both at once!

And yet it is far more romantic, if less Arcadian, when the division of the sexes compels each partner to seek a mate of the opposite sex. And how much more has variety in the love-life occurred since that time! In the plants it is still unconscious, in the lower animals only half-conscious, and the higher we mount in the scale of animal evolution the more conscious it becomes.

But a very long time elapsed before the slightest trace of tenderness was perceptible in the sexual relations.

At first copulation signified only the voluntary expulsion of the reproductive cells with the mutual help of the other partner, an evacuation, when the tension had become too great; nothing but a purely excretory function. A little while after fertilisation, the female laid the fertilised eggs in a quiet, sunny, safe place, where she would not be disturbed during this lonely excretory function, and did not trouble any further about them[2]. And these eggs hatched out in due time by the sun in a spot as sheltered and as safe, as if the place had been chosen with motherly foresight for the well-being of the new brood.

It is scarcely possible to observe parents caring for their offspring earlier in the evolutionary scale than the vertebrates. Even in some fishes there is already evidence of paternal care in the building and guarding of nests. Some reptiles cover their eggs with moss and leaves; some of the snakes coil themselves up over their heap of eggs as if to protect them; mother-crocodiles sometimes carry their young about with them.

Nor is there in the lower species any trace of enduring friendship or lasting love between the two parents; they separate after copulation and trouble about each other no further. Frogs and most fishes do not even have any internal mode of copulation, but both sexes simply shed their sexual product into water. But they perform their excretory function in communistic voluptuousness; the fishes by swimming close together in shoals, the frogs very pedantically by assuming the traditional attitude of a pairing couple, but really like the fish with external massage only.

Thus the reproductive cells are simply shed into water by both sexes, generally in a sheltered and sunny spot, where the reproductive process may proceed undisturbed and unlimited.

A few of the water-toads stay together from the time of copula-

2. The watchful care bestowed on the larvae and nymphae amongst the bees and ants does not come from the mothers, but from the sexually unfit female relatives, that is to say, mostly from the maiden aunts. And in many varieties of ants, it is the female slaves stolen from the nests of other varieties who are charged with this duty.

tion until the laying of the eggs; and the male of the Surinam toad (pipa Americana), assists the female to lay her eggs.

But it is only in warm-blooded animals[3] that we find really affectionate care bestowed on the young, of sitting on the eggs or warming the young that have been born alive; parents often living together and affording each other mutual help, especially in the birds. The tender affection that a pair of birds will show for each other, and the care that they take first of the eggs and then of their young might put many a human couple to shame. In mammals it is mostly the mother which does everything for her young ones, and must even sometimes shield them from the brutality of their father, but sometimes it is the father that protects the whole family.

Thus we see here two new important factors coming into operation at the same time in the history of evolution: a higher development of the sexual life and the occurrence of warm-bloodedness. We may now enquire whether there is any connection between these two factors. I am of opinion that an interchange of cause and effect cannot be denied.

In the course of evolution so long as the excretion of reproductive cells, mating and laying eggs were comparatively simple matters, the parents needed but little mutual help: and because this most powerful and intimate stimulus of life-energy was lacking, the increased oxidation it would have caused was also lacking and the animals remained cold-blooded.

Warm-bloodedness must vice versa stimulate sexuality. We have already seen (chapter 32) that increase of temperature is a most effective sexual stimulant, and in Chapter 29 that in the procreative act the mutual warmth of the parents plays an essential part. But mutual warmth is found agreeable in other circumstances also, not only as a protection against chill, but also as a reminiscence of former mating and a foretaste of the next, and so altruistic. And the protective warmth of the parents' bodies is indeed indispensable for the young brood.

Let us first try thoroughly to realise what is the position of a warm-blooded organism. Warm-blooded means that the organism has a temperature considerably higher than its surroundings and so is always in danger of losing its body-heat. Against this a warm skin-covering or nest can only provide a relative protection, i.e., a postponement of the cooling. In the life of wild animals, and also that of men up to the time of the discovery of fire, the mutual warmth of bodies in contact was the only regular and permanent source of heat, whenever the animal could not maintain the usual and necessary heat through its own resour-

3. All living cells produce heat by chemical processes; but in plants and cold-blooded animals the sum of this heat is so small. that the temperature of the organism is hardly distinguishable from that of the surrounding medium.

ces; the ingestion of food and the oxidation in the lungs, e.g., during the night and in the winter-time.

So then the companionship of the parents among warm-blooded creatures grew to be a lasting delight, which indeed attained its height in the procreative act, but was still at all times an emotional delight. The procreative act is now the climax of emotion. Thus the sexual impulse has been directed into emotional paths.

Chapter 44

FROM HUMAN RUTTING PERIODS TO
PERMANENT SEXUAL LIFE

WHEN in the course of evolution the sexual form of reproduction appeared as the latest novelty, it was certainly
at first quite an exceptional phenomenon, such as very
primitive organisms even now only occasionally display.
And even later, amongst the more highly organised creatures, the
sexual life does not function in a continuous manner.

The majority of phanerogamous plants bloom only once in their lives, others
only once a year, and many animal species mate only once in their life; most
of them only once or twice a year. That is the period of their greatest development of energy; many species of insects only get their wings at that time, many
birds then display their brightest colours, it is then that we hear in their music
their song of joy in the intoxication of passion.

Even the highest species of animals are then so dazzled by this passion and
tire themselves out so thoroughly that in a very short time they are quite exhausted. Many males die off as soon as the reproductive duty of their lives has
been accomplished; and in any case after this extreme exhaustion a considerable
time elapses before the males have regained their usual strength, and before the
females have recovered from egg-laying or bearing and suckling their young. So
it is easily comprehensible why in the case of most animal species such long rest-
periods are necessary, and sexual excitement and activity manifest themselves in
a new rutting period only after a considerable interval. Then the sexual life
emerges with overwhelming force, but does not last long, and the whole species
sinks into sexual apathy once more.

In domesticated animals, i.e., those living in a tame condition, whose impulsive reflexes have been inhibited for ages, we observe a quite different picture.
Here there is no such violent sexual crisis nor such exhaustion, but the act occurs
much more frequently. When the females of our domestic animals are in heat
and a single coitus does not bring about the desired result, phenomena analogous
to menstruation may be observed periodically every 3 or 4 weeks, until, as a
consequence of repeated copulation, pregnancy occurs. We observe the same
menstrual phenomena regularly in the anthropoid apes, the gorilla, chimpanzee
and orang-utang, in the zoological gardens.

So it is not surprising that in human beings with our milder
manner of living and regular customs, and a certain amount of
self-control, our women-folk show the same menstrual type[1]. And

1. In the course of my practice I have occasionally found a married woman express great surprise when I enquired about her periods; she looked at me, and
replied: "No, not since I was married!" She had been perpetually either pregnant or suckling a child.

their capacity for pregnancy and their sexual desire are normally constantly present, even if less evident in the middle of the inter-menstrual period.

As a reminiscence of the oestrus or heat period, many women even now only feel desire during their menstruation; which was of old their time for intercourse and increased fertility.

The same story of evolution, this shortening of the interval, is al-most more manifest in man than in woman; and it is the more strik-ing because amongst animals the male is the more aggressive and impulsive in his wooing. While they live in the wild state this is only true of them at the rutting period; otherwise they are im-potent and sexually apathetic. Our domesticated animals, however, such as the stallion and the house dog, "always libidinous and ready to cover." So in human beings the frequency of the sexual act may be very high at all times, sexual excitability is almost con-stantly present. Yet only man has learnt that he can control him-self without outside compulsion, and when required can either live in abstinence or be sexually active.

Man appears, however, to have reached this highest stage of sexual evolution only relatively late, so that we are still able to observe in historic times a reminiscence of the more primitive period. Amongst the most primitive savage races, and also amongst ourselves in some isolated districts many reminiscences may still be found of the folk-festivals of earlier times in which, amongst the members of certain groups or tribes a sort of promiscuity (freedom of sexual intercourse between all the parties) was the custom, as though it were a fixed law of nature, intimately con-nected with the original social organisation of group-life. Be-cause these public festivals took place from time immemorial at cer-tain seasons of the year, they also indicate a sort of official rutting period for human sexual intercourse in the primitive epochs, at certain seasons. In some parts of the world the nature-festival was held in spring or early summer, when the whole of nature awakens to renewed life; in other places, however, in autumn with its abundance of food and drink. Frequently these fairs were met with in both seasons.

Thus we see the rutting period in primitive human society oc-curring twice in the year; we see a reminiscence of this to-day in registry office records, at least in Rotterdam, where the birth statistics point to two periods of the year in which the number of conceptions falls to a minimum, viz: the depth of winter and the height of summer.

But in the course of time man became less animal, the group-organisation gradually changed into a geographical communal or-

211

ganisation; conscious behaviour took the place of instinctive acts to a greater extent, and this sexual resemblance to animals naturally tended to disappear. Culturally man became more domesticated. With his higher reasoning powers he has learnt to control his desires and thus to increase and multiply his pleasure. No longer a solitary bestial intoxication as in these annual festivals, followed by a year of dull depression, but always cheerful and sexually excitable.

This controlling of the sexual impulse, one might almost say, this normalisation of the sexual passion, is one of the greatest victories of the human over the animal. The energy and excitation of animals is a fierce flame of but very short duration, but a normal man is always excited, industrious, full of energy and sympathy. Man's whole appearance points to this. His upright carriage, an attitude that dates from the tree-climbing period and was later perfected by the use of weapons of offence and defence, an attitude which is only assumed by our domestic animals at the moment of the procreative act, is frequently to be observed among the higher species of apes, but the upright posture first became habitual in mankind[2], always energetic, ready for the fight or for procreation. So this attitude is always a symbol of our lofty dignity. Only the child, being asexual, still crawls on four legs, as his ancestors once did.

This transition, from the savage rutting period to a conscious and permanent sexual life cannot be over-estimated; it is the transition from animal to human. The triumph of the mind has also become the triumph of sexuality, and vice versa. Man stands at the top of the evolutionary series, not only on account of his higher reason, but also because of his higher sexual life.

2. In his original work, "Das Welträtzel Mensch" (pub. Giesecke, Dresden, 1921.) Ernst Klotz advocates the horizontal posture on all fours for men as for the animals. He is right in so far as every change from our usual posture represents a thoroughly useful massage.

Chapter 45

FROM GROUP RELATIONS TO
PRIVATE AFFAIRS

I HAVE already observed that the sexual life was formerly intimately associated with the social organisation of the system.

But we have now become, especially under the influence of Roman Law, such confirmed individualists that we can scarcely imagine at the present time what that means. And even if we read about it, it seems still more obscure, for from a sense of decency we always speak of "group-marriage" and this term seems to us to be something contradictory. For we scarcely know of any other marriage than the various forms which have developed from the custom of stealing the bride, and they are all intended to be wholly individual.

The group-relation, however, originated in far earlier times, and even existed among animals. The reader will doubtless remember that allusion in Chapter 43 to the shoal of fish in the sunny sheltered corner of the pool, swimming so close together that they rub each other's sides for a long time, and all mutually provide each other with sexual satisfaction. This is indeed sexual communism in its purest form[1], because the fish know no individual intercourse; but it is just because of its simplicity that this example is so illustrative of the principle.

And man also, defenceless as he is when isolated, must first have lived in groups in whch the members either sprang from *one* mother or from *one* grandmother, i.e., in groups really composed of blood-relations; groups which constantly split up into new groups, as soon as the original group after a few generations became too numerous to be able to find food for all the members in *one* single place of residence.

At first, of course, there was no generally valid law to regulate sexual intercourse, and originally, like everything else, it differed in different tribes, according to their particular requirements and their traditional habits and customs. But sexual intercourse appears to have usually restricted to persons of similar age; so that sexual intercourse between parents and their children was excluded from the first. Of such relations nothing remains at the present time but a few scattered mythological legends as reminiscences.

1. In regard to the oldest system of organisation in mankind, as described by Morgan in his work *Ancient Society*, reference may be made to my article: "Experimental Enquiry into the Oldest Family System with Which We Are Acquainted", which appeared in "Geschlecht und Gesellschaft", March 1922; the origin of people's names, which at first appears so obscure, then suddenly becomes perfectly clear.

Of the intercourse between brothers and sisters there only remain isolated traces in a few primitive savage tribes in the denomination of family relatives, and here it was usually a case, not of sexual intercourse between brothers and sisters of a blood, but rather between cousins, because these grow up together in the group as companions of similar age. In such groups cousins of both sexes naturally predominate. In historic times it is only in the ancient Egyptian reigning dynasties that marriages between brothers and sisters or cousins were quite usual.

Historically and ethnographically, however, we now know only periods and tribes in which sexual intercourse between members of the same group was stigmatised as incestuous. Thus it appears as if, even in those days, too many children in one's own group were no longer desired; and in this connection there were also other interests to be considered. If members of friendly groups hoped to have sexual intercourse with another group, they would bring gifts. There was never any question of gifts within one's own group, for there everything was common property. So a love affair in which the wooers brought gifts was naturally far more distinguished and respectable, and also more advantageous for the group, because the gifts were not presented to individuals, but to the tribe as a whole. So it is easy to understand why unions between members of the same group were early discouraged, and soon expressly forbidden. Once this became a custom, the natural selection of the breed favoured this exogamous tendency, for it produced a much more energetic and vigourous race than if interbreeding took place within the group without any kind of effort.

But men did not change their habitation on account of love affairs; each one spent the whole of his life in the same house and farmhouse in which he was born. If he moved away he was obliged to leave behind all that he possessed. If the day's hunting had been successful, and it was a fine night and the moon was shining, he would slip over to one of the friendly groups with a portion of the booty. Here the gift of game would be the best introduction to ensure a hearty welcome, not only from the male members of the group, but also from their sisters; he would have no particular preference beforehand as to which of the sisters he would choose. So this was a group relation, not only for the girl, but for the young man also. For if one man was recognised as a regular visitor, then all his brethren were also welcomed as wooers. The gift was not an individual one either, but from one whole group to another.

This unsophisticated and natural method of procedure gradually evolved to a well organised social system which as such

214

is termed "the tribal or group system", and as a sexual system, "the matriarchate[2]. The children live with their mothers and mothers' brothers, or with the grandmothers and *their* brothers, i.e., the family descends through the female line. The man seeks sexual intercourse outside the family group; as is often the case in the country even now, where the young man spends only the night in his sweetheart's house. On that account I have hesitated to speak of marriage in this case, because it is really only what we call a regular liaison.

But the more the man showed in the course of time a personal attachment for a woman and her children, in preference to his sisters' children at home, the more the relation became individualised, so that as long as it satisfied both parties, it resembled our marriage to some extent. So they came, first as an exception and then as the custom, to live together for short periods, but the husband always as his wife's guest and within her group.

Gradually, however, through frequent changes of locality, and from the exercise of various trades, which led to a division of interests, the feeling of solidarity in the group of blood-relations became more and more undermined; and finally the common family name was often the only remaining sign of the blood-relationship.

Thus the whole group system gradually disappeared. In the course of time it has been forced to give way to a more individual organisation, in which the community no longer depends on blood-relationship, but includes all the families who live in the same spot. Nor is the family composed as formerly of blood-relatives living together, but of an individually chosen sex-companionship.

How this fundamental change occurred, we shall now discuss.

2. Reference may be made to my brochure on the development, rise and fall of the matriarchate: "History of the Development of the Communal Life of Man, with Special Reference to Maternal Rights and Marriage" (*in German*) "Kultur and Fortschritt", 379-80. Published by F. Dietrich, Gautzsch, near Leipzig, 1911.

Chapter 46

SEXUAL FREEING OF WOMAN

AS WE have already remarked, in many species of mammals the brutality of the male was greatly feared. And it has unfortunately also gained the upper hand in mankind. In some places sooner, in others later, the friendly relationship of the sexes, such as existed is the matriarchate, has thereby been entirely destroyed.

How did man come to be such a kill-joy?

All the previous social relations were now overturned. Formerly through food-shortage prisoners of war could not be kept alive, but now the boys and girls were driven to work as slaves. Thus man acquired private property, and the first sort of property was female slaves. The conqueror had unlimited power over them; they must live with him and bear his name; and any children they had were his private property and bore his name also. And thus originated marriage with paternal authority that still exists in almost every country in the world.

In this way the original feeling of solidarity in the group system of blood-relations was quite ended; every man sought to conquer new territory by force. And what could the woman do against such deeds of violence? At first she tried, mounted on horse-back and armed like a man, to maintain her individuality — hence all the legends of the Amazons, but as Herodotus tells us, she was nowhere successful; and without man, woman would have died out anyway.

The male priesthood which now began to take the upper hand, was not favourably inclined towards woman; because formerly, in the time of ancestor-worship, woman was the honoured priestess with special attributes of sorcery and prophecy! These happy days were gone forever.

Whilst the fertility of Nature was symbolised in the old pagan temples of India by statues of a many-breasted goddess, among the Greeks and Romans the same idea was represented by the masculine symbol, the naked phallus of metal or of stone.

After the favourable period of the old Vedas, the Brahmins of India went the farthest in the subjugation and despisal of woman.

There were, for instance, the custom of marrying tiny maidens of school age, the veil that woman must wear, and the cramped court-yard with its open-air kitchen where she must spend all the days of her life even if she belonged to one of the higher castes; and above all the widow's suttee, which indeed has only been repressed very recently.

Thus there were four effective, but very cruel means of pro-tecting public morality as the priests understood it; so at least it was ensured that there was not one single female who was not in some man's power.

Amongst ourselves in Europe the canonical (ecclesiastical) law was even harder for woman than the Roman law; and harder still was the priesthood with their countless burnings of witches, the moment they suspected that one of them had entered into com-munication with occult powers. And economically, in the Middle Ages and unfortunately even much later, woman who from time immemorial had always done the hardest work, was scornfully called "the weaker sex". A halo was placed around her weary head only as the *"mater dolorosa"!* Woman as the slave of man! How greatly this must at first have destroyed all the tender feel-ings of love. *Yet Nature is mightier than the power of the priest-hood or of any weapons, and the sexual life is so strong that in spite of everything, woman has won the victory through her ten-derness and devotion.*

Her condition has improved almost everywhere, and even if mar-riage was a hard lot for her, outside the married state there always remained a trace of individual freedom, which, it is true, might degenerate into licence, but which was often redeemed by heroic devotion and mutual idealism.

Although Greek history according to Herodotus may have opened with some typical cases of marriage by capture, and the history of Rome begins with the rape of the Sabines, still the classic literature of the Greeks and Romans gave us wingéd Eros and the roguish Cupid. And this god of love reappears in the Ren-aissance. Minstrels and troubadours glorified love; not, indeed, legalised unions, but only those in which the gallant knight carried off the fair maiden in secret.

Just as in our adolescence the awakening of our sexual spring-time is not publicly announced, but comes to us in quiet dreams, so also in the world-history the love of kindred souls appears as the supreme height of passion, proceeding not from science or from the law, but awakened as a lofty ideal in loving hearts by the charm of poetry and of art. Only much later did this ideal penetrate into formal marriage and lend it a higher meaning.

Legally woman is still unfairly treated, theoretically she is highly honoured — still, the practical result is that she no longer feels herself to be the slave of her husband, but is becoming more and more his life companion.

217

Chapter 47

THE SCIENCE OF SEX ATTRACTION AND THE ART OF COURTSHIP

THE power of sexual attraction is so great that Darwin made a separate study of sexual selection, and considered it as a special variety of natural selection.

In the wild state the male goes to all kinds of trouble to attract the female and win her for himself. The lower animals do not possess such perfect means of subjugation as man, and the female can always refuse either by running away or by some abnormal position, and so the male must try to win her over with affection. Thus in the animal world it is the male who displays the lures: gay colours, song, dramatic courtship, and above all, strength and energy which will give him the victory over all the other suitors.

It must have been thus in the dawn of human life too. It was the man who appeared regularly with gifts to ensure himself a good reception in a friendly group. But when marriage by capture had become the custom, these steps were no longer necessary; all that was necessary was to fight to the death and carry off the prize.

But in the course of time he found it wiser to escape all these evil chances and all the feuds arising therefrom — we may remember the ten-years' Trojan war for the sake of the ravished Helen — by the preliminary payment of an equivalent tribute, first as compensation, later as purchase-price; perhaps a pair of good horses or a few oxen.

It is remarkable that in the course of the centuries the purchase price of a wife has constantly diminished! And now it has been reduced to a free gift, as though to increase the ceremonial festivity, or even simply gifts for the affianced bride which she brings back when married.

Indeed it has now gone so far that the parents think themselves lucky if they find somebody who will look after their daughter so that they willingly give a trousseau or a dowry with her. And this dowry must not be small either. And then the young husband is perhaps so obliging as to put up with the prospect of a legacy, so that he may settle down on his wife's parents' property. But at

218

the present time all this is insufficient, and even prior to the great war one half of the marriageable women remained single.

In contrast with former times, it is now the woman who must employ all kinds of lures to attract a suitor, and she practices the same lures as those used by the males in the animal world[1]: gay clothes, a little music, graceful manners, and last but not least that key to all doors: money!

Whence comes this depreciation?

Apart from her sexual charm, the principal value of woman originally lay in her capacity for work, and secondly her fruitfulness as a mother. In this chapter we will only refer to her working capacity.

It is well known that in uncivilised countries the hardest and most tiresome work devolves on woman; it is equally well known that in the course of time, as milder manners came to prevail, woman, partly because of her slighter build, has gradually been spared the heavier work, and her efforts have been directed to less difficult and lighter tasks, the importance of which was not really so great. Besides there were always plenty of women to be had for this sort of work, so why should they be valued or well paid?

The prettier girls were especially relieved of all heavy work, and finally became courtesans, and so gradually idleness and self-adornment became the typical ideal of many women.

Indeed many women who work terribly hard in their own homes, dress up when they go out so as to appear as if they do nothing at all. Many ladies who go shopping have even the smallest parcels sent home. And many a one, instead of being pleased when the baker and the milkman deliver the bread and milk at her door so early in the morning—necessities that woman once had to get for herself, milking the cow at dawn and heating the oven overnight—is now only cross because both the worthy tradesmen ring and wake her up so early in the morning. Happy indeed is the husband whose wife does not squander everything through her vanity and neglect. Can we then wonder, if depreciation has occurred?

Fortunately nowadays the tide is turning again, and woman showed her value during the war. Woman is awakening and shaking her golden chains; she is no longer willing to be a petted slave or a bird in a golden cage. She wants to have a mind of her own, and to be free to marry the man of her choice. Even the young girl seeks to earn her own living! She wants to be able to feel independent under all circumstances and not to let her brothers

1. It seems an ironical lack of taste on the part of our ladies that they often use the same feathers and furs that the male animal has already used for the same purpose of allurement; sometimes even the same odours, such as his genital musk, etc.

keep her after her parents' death; which prehaps they are not at all anxious to do either. And if she marries and one day her husband falls ill, she will be able to provide for the household and take care of him and the children.

And when the time comes for her to marry, she will be able to do so from inclination and affection, not merely in order to have a roof over her head. She brings her education and her training as her dowry, and consequently she can teach her children better when they are well, and nurse them better when they are sick. She is her husband's companion; but there is a division of labour, and each one of the partners has his own individuality. This is far better than it used to be, when all the women of the village dressed alike, thought alike and talked alike — if they ever really thought when they talked.

There is now a new era in courtship for both sexes. The animal lures are no longer required; neither man nor woman needs to use them now. They must both be polite, chivalrous and considerate to each other. So at last sexual intercourse is no longer a surprise or an outrage, but a mutual surrender of two loving souls to each other.

Chapter 48

THE COMING OF BIRTH CONTROL AND
VOLUNTARY MOTHERHOOD

THE other reason why a woman was so valuable was that she could bear children. The male slave could do very heavy work as well, but only the female could produce children: sons, many sons, so that there would be plenty of warriors for future wars; daughters, many daughters, so that they could be sold in marriage.

Unfortunately, in historical times nothing has depreciated so regularly and systematically as the value of human life and this has been proportionate to the increase of population. And in this connection we can readily understand the decrease in value of the woman as a producer of children. It is the counterpart of another equally constant phenomenon; that is, the rise in the price of land with increase in the population. These are two sides of the same problem.

We, therefore, observe, in all classes of society, a general disinclination to excessively large families, in spite of the rulers and their satellites, who would like to urge everybody to produce as many children as possible.

"With pain and sorrow shalt thou conceive and bring forth children!" was the curse laid on woman at the fall. On the other hand, the prohibition of sexual intercourse within the group itself acted as a considerable check; so too did the prohibition of intercourse during the menstrual period, which is almost as ancient and sacred; then came the organisation of marriage, with which was associated a contempt for extra-marital intercourse; and finally even the idea that sexual abstinence was itself something superior, praiseworthy and pleasing to the gods. It all had the same tendency.

But whenever it became evident that all these various factors in prevention were not sufficiently successful, men were driven to adopt the most terrible repressive measures: cannibalism, the systematic slaughter of children, girls especially; the killing off of all aged people, the exposure of newly born infants, and abor-

221

tion. When all these were found too cruel, then sorcery, herbs and decoctions of all kinds were tried[1] to prevent conception. The same aim, prevention of conception, may be perceived, always and everywhere.

Is it then surprising that woman should be so little valued as the possible mother of children, and must even bring a dowry in order to get a roof over her head?

But a way out has now been found. At last we have succeeded in finding what has been so eagerly sought after for centuries, a practical and valuable, though perhaps not absolutely infallible method of birth-control[2].

With the coming of birth-control ends the depreciation of human life and of woman as the bearer of children. The efforts of Dr. Mensinga, who was a really pious Christian and a very human gynecologist, and of many others, have at last freed woman from the curse laid cn her in Paradise. Married couples can now be happy together, and still not produce more children than is expedient.

Just as involuntary motherhood lowered the status of woman, so birth-control and deliberate motherhood will bring her once again into honour, and her creative power will again become a blessing.

1. See the remarkable work by Baron Dr. Felix von Oefele, *Contraceptive Drugs*, published in "Die Heilkunde", a practitioners' monthly, pub. Vienna, 1898. Edited by Dr. Julius Weiss.

2. It is not within the scope of this work to dilate on the subject of birth-control, but those who wish to be well informed on all the arguments *pro* and *con,* would do well to read my book, *Rassenverbesserung* (Racial Improvement), an authorised translation of which by Clifford Coudray has been published by Richard A. Giesecke, Dresden, 1923, under the title of "Eugenics and Birth-Control". (208pp. 4to, with 6 tables.)

Chapter 49

THE TWO DISTINCT FUNCTIONS
OF MARRIED LOVE

THIS one great sexual function with its love and its pain, with its supreme delight and its birth-pains, has now become differentiated into two distinct voluntarily separated functions: the charm of love if love alone is wanted, and the production of children if children are wanted.

This highest of all stages in evolution has only tardily been reached, but it has been reached at last. It is not really surprising that it took so long. It is only since the discovery of the microscope enabled the reproductive cells to be recognised, that the study of the whole process of fertilisation has been possible, as we mentioned at the end of Chapter 15. Up to that time we had only been able to form fanciful notions of the origin of individual life, somewhat like the uncertainty in which we stand about the origin of cell-life on the earth.

Indeed the question has long been discussed whether man originally suspected the causal nexus between the procreative act and the occurrence of pregnancy; so much time elapses before the latter is noticeable!

And how could he light on this conclusion at a time when every normally constituted female had regular sexual intercourse. Experience at that time, on the contrary, went to prove that very often sexual intercourse had no further consequences.

The counter-test, that when there was no intercourse there could be no pregnancy, was only made later, when animals were kept in captivity, or men and women in separate prisons.

Explorers such as Rothe, Strehlow and Spencer Gillens have recently established the fact that even at the present time there are tribes in Australia who have absolutely no idea of the connection between the two functions. But almost everywhere, among the primitive races, the people are convinced that sexual intercourse exerts a favourable influence on fecundity; and it is interesting to note that Professor Wilken has observed in Java that the native farmers, when their fruit trees produce too little fruit, imitate the movements of coitus against the trunks of the trees.

In this latter case we see expression given to the notion that the sexual act between the married couple may under some circumstances even exert an unfavourable influence on their fertility. It is perfectly clear to us that a crude empiricism may often have given rise to this idea, for we all know that nothing excites the sexual impulse so powerfully as enforced abstinence.

In a higher stage of civilisation it is thought that though it is indeed the man's physical movements that produce the physical effect, the soul first enters the new creature at the third month, as a divine gift.

So it is not surprising that the causal nexus remained so long unknown, and that even now so many people look upon it as a profanation of a sacred mystery, and fight against it as if it were mortal sin, when science reveals this causal nexus and wishes to make the knowledge available for the public.

It was only in 1850 (the year in which I was born) that DuBarry for the first time observed the penetration of a sperm-cell into the ovum of a rabbit, rendering the connection of cause and effect in this secret process as clear as it is in all other human processes for which we feel personally responsible.

After this observation we had only to notice how nature goes to work to make the procreative act at one time fruitful and at another sterile, and man can also do that now voluntarily.

It is indeed a fixed law in the whole of evolution that the higher we mount in the scale the fewer will be the offspring. For then it becomes ever more indispensable for all the conditions of life to be harmonious before a new living creature can be produced.

In this evolutionary tendency, the highest stage of development is reached by the human brain, which is the highest of all the products of nature. Nowhere else can it be so clearly seen, how Nature attains her object. and for this we must thank her.

To a certain extent she attains it through the introduction of all the sexual obstacles and difficulties which, as we have seen in Part II, bulk so largely in the higher species. And now we can thoroughly understand what many a reader must already have thought out for himself when all these obstacles were mentioned; he must have wondered how it is possible that Nature herself has not overcome them all long ago through natural selection in breeding. But no, these very obstacles were so many aids to the higher evolution of the species, because on the one hand they stimulate desire and on the other they limit prolificacy. But the higher reason of man, which seeks to bring both objects into harmony according to his conscious intentions forms the crown of this endeavour.

The great importance of this differentiation is, just as in all differentiations, that each of these functions can now perfect itself. At first, of course, all such innovations meet with a certain amount of opposition, as though they were an attack on customs which on account of their ancient traditions have become sacred to us. The same is true of every newly occuring point in evolution. We may be quite sure that the first pre-historic man who made weapons for himself—such as hammer, axe, spear or club, by fixing a flint to a stick—had to bear

224

the reproaches of his companions, that he was a coward who could not conquer by his own strength alone! Meanwhile personally, he surely would feel very proud that he was so much more successful in hunting than his comrades.

Only now can sexual love in and for itself be honoured and guarded in its lofty significance, while formerly all these higher feelings were sacrificed to the question of fertilisation, because this is of such primordial interest. A book like this, in which the sexual impulse is at last honoured in its primary significance, would formerly have been treated with disdain as a useless and insidious work. Now, however, the charm of love may be honoured on its own account; not only as a means to an end, but as an aim in itself.

Ethically also, this is a great advance. The sexual life now includes two different objects, two separate chapters: the ethics of the sexual feelings and the ethics of procreation. Each can now be considered separately and its principles better studied.

From the ethical point of view this separation has had good results. Formerly, when the fear of pregnancy was the leading motive of chastity, it only concerned the woman; the dual morality, i.e., *one* law for the woman, *another* for the man, could not be avoided. Now, however, self-control and chastity for both sexes are actuated by higher ethical considerations than the crude fear of punishment. This signifies a far higher standpoint, a new conception of ethics, which makes itself felt in all moral teachings.

Chapter 50

PERFECTING THE SEXUAL LIFE

AMONG the lower classes of animals the female, as bearer of countless numbers of eggs, is frequently bigger and stronger than the male with his microscopic reproductive cells. It is only when we reach the vertebrates that we find the male decidedly the stronger. In him the sexual impulse and the obstacles to mating are increased to such an extent that the procreative act almost takes on the character of a rape. Furthermore, in the human race this process was continued first through hunting and then by warlike exercises.

In modern times the more our mental and ethical development proceeds on a higher scale, the more this difference in the sexes tends to disappear, while differences between individuals come to the fore.

Indeed, recent experience shows ever more clearly that with similar antecedents, training and exercise, the individuals of both sexes can prove of equal value. So the time will soon come in which presumptuous behaviour of the male partner will be considered as an anti-selective factor.

Until now, on account of his social position the initiative of a proposal of marriage lies with the man, and on account of his more aggressive sexuality the initiative in the procreative act also; but it must not be forgotten that just at the decisive moment of fertilisation, it is the egg-cell, so richly charged with nutrient contents, which takes the initiative towards the sperm-cells; just as it is primarily the woman's charm which draws the man to her.

Besides, Mendel's experiments (see chapter 4) teach us that in general the big egg-cells and the tiny sperm-cells are equally good carriers of hereditary traits[1]. It really makes no difference either in the numbers or the characteristic of the descendants, whether for instance a cross-breed of sheep is started with a black ram and a white ewe, or vice versa, with a white ram and a black ewe, the result is the same.

This is indeed a most decisive proof of the fundamental equality of the two sexes.

1. In some cases the sperm-cell, and in rarer cases the egg-cell, has one chromosome more.

We have still to speak of the secondary sexual characters.

The typical organochemical substances which are elaborated by the testes and ovaries act as powerful stimuli to all the epithelial tissues (see chapter 4) especially to the growth of hair[2]. Secondly, through their influence in the above-mentioned organs, the descendants of the suppressed embryonic epithelial cells are re-awakened and stimulated to fresh prolificacy. And then the sebaceous follicles are also irritated[3] sometimes so greatly as to cause formation of pus, which often causes acne and comedones in young adolescent men, while in young girls the mammary glands increase in size. So this principle obtains in both sexes. Thus too we see that the young people of both sexes are not all unjustified in their sexual selection in attaching great importance to thick glossy hair, smooth skin and fresh complexion. In many species of animals, too, the care bestowed on the fur during the wooing of the mate is remarkable.

But still there is one difference, and it is just these details which cause man's sexual pride, and which really seem to brand woman with inferiority. The woman remains as beardless as a child, has a high childish voice, and a slender bodily structure like a child. In several passages in his *Descent of Man,* Darwin states that where there are differences in the animal world, it is the female type that mostly resembles the infantile type.

But is that a disadvantage? Once the woman is old enough, she too grows a beard, although not such a flowing one, because the energy of growth of her entire body has declined; she also acquires a less graceful exterior, and a rougher, deeper voice. But man displays these phenomena of age much earlier than woman, but is that any reason for pride of sex?

Thus *a priori* considerations are a poor weapon in the battle of sex; this must be waged empirically. And the best solution of this problem will appear more clearly, the more it is rendered possible for all individuals of both sexes to fully develop their individual talents and to use them to advantage. And the sexual life will also come sooner to perfection.

This may be the evolution of the sexual life in the near future.

2. The hair is a very prominent epithelial structure and hairs begin at the age of puberty to grow freely in the axillae and on the pubes in both sexes.

3. The gland-cells of the sebaceous follicles are really only epithelial cells turned upwards; and the milk glands may be considered as a sort of immensely enlarged and branched sebaceous follicle.

Chapter 51

Introductory:
STUDY OF ALL VITAL FIELDS OF SEX SCIENCE IS ESSENTIAL

I FEEL sure that many of my readers, every time we have to talk about glands and tumours, blood-vessels and organochemical substances, have felt inclined to say impatiently: "But what has all this to do with the refined and tender feeling that we call love?" The time has now come for me to answer this question.

It is quite a simple matter. The materialistic processes which we have dealt with anatomically in Part I, and functionally in Part II, force us to seek a partner, and it is the stimulation of the affections, the emotions, that are thus called forth, it is this nameless longing that we call love. In this section we will take these emotions as the subject of our study. Just as one must first know all there is to learn about the mouth and tongue before one can understand the sense of taste, so it was necessary to study the genital organs before it was possible to understand, to evaluate and to control love.

Even the most rigid of materialists will not wish to restrict his knowledge to the raw material, he will only begin at the beginning so that he may better gradually reach the heights of knowledge. And thus it was necessary for us to discuss the crude details of the lower spheres of our bodies, although possibly it may have annoyed some of our readers. It is something like the shudder that goes through us when we see a skeleton for the first time in our lives, for we forget that such a skeleton is living inside us, forming the frameworks of our physical and mental structure; and yet, it is useful to know it, for otherwise we can never understand the processes of our daily lives.

There is something painful to our feelings in this: the facts themselves so simple and so cold, and the rapture so transcendent. Quite right! And everything that we read here about the love life will surely be hopelessly far behind what we shall really feel, as soon as we actually experience it for ourselves. That will be smoothed down when we begin to speak about it, and even more when it it read; paper is so cold, and so is printers' ink. But the author should not be expected to set all his lady and gentleman readers

230

in a sexual ecstasy; that would indeed be asking too much! This realisation remains for each one as his own life-drama. And everything that I mention here, my dear readers, as feeling myself, can only possess a meaning for you in so far as it finds an echo in your own feelings.

But it will have a scientific value for you only if you read it in connection with all that we have already written in this book. Only then will you see cause and effect clearly, and also be able to control this life-impulse for the future.

This incongruency between the physical foundation and the spiritual feelings is not only met with in the sexual sphere; it lies fundamentally in the mysterious combination of the material with the psychic. What likeness is there, for instance, between the water-white fluid which we chemically term alcohol, and the intoxication of an evening spent not too wisely, but too well? Or if we wish a physiological example instead of a pathologic one: what is warmth? Warmth is a quickened movement of the atoms composing our bodies; but we feel our bodily warmth as an agreeable sensation, that affords us much pleasure. And what is a bed? A collection of materials which are poor conductors of heat in which a tired half-nude person hides himself; yet we feel it to be a warm nest in which we can lie in comfort.

So also sexual occurrences stimulate our circulation, respiration and psychic life, so greatly that we feel ourselves imbued with redoubled energy. And in this sphere it is one of the finest duties of science to study the connection of cause and effect.

This has unfortunately been too long postponed. Embryology, obstetrics and venereal diseases have been studied, but the relation of the inner love-life with the material processes has only too often been omitted from the course of study. In the sexual sphere we have up to the present clung far too much to dualism, and that has done us a fearful amount of harm and caused untold misery. Parents do not understand their children, once they are grown up.

Then the maiden revels in dreams of yearning and longing:

"Oh! ask the stars whether I love you."

which at first looks so very poetical, till the time comes when she pines and fades like a rose watered only by tears; while the youth only too often drags down into vulgarity what should remain sacred. Both of them feel very miserable. Ah, how many young people I have seen go under most pitiably in this way!

together, nothing wicked, just a little cuddling and kissing, nothing more, perhaps only a little unintentional touching and fondling... then the world cannot find enough stones to hurl at the "old reprobate"! Of course it is sometimes justified. "Woe unto him who offends one of these little ones; it were better for him to hang a millstone round his neck and to cast himself into the sea!" But to be just, one must really admit that a child can often be a consummate coquette; not really bad, only in play; but it is a pity when a child begins to play with fire.

Then there is the judicial enquiry in such cases. The child tells such dreadful things about the old gentleman that they cannot be repeated in public. And how could a child know such things if they had not happened! But a child is a miniature man, and can already be corrupt and cunning. The teacher or the judge who thinks that the only truth comes from the mouths of children, proves that he is not fit for his office. The child may not be wicked, but possessed of a boundless imagination. I have known cases in which the most dramatic stories naively told by children have led to the most terrible accusations, and which were really lies from beginning to end. It has been proved after all that it was nothing but a tissue of falsehoods imagined by the child. One may read of many such cases in medical jurisprudence. The child often does this merely for the sake of causing a sensation. She soon notices that she attracts great attention with such a story, and that all eyes are then fixed upon her.

These are, however, exceptions. I only mention them as an instance of the fact that in the child there exists sufficient inflammable material potentially, if not actually, and that little flames dart here and there long before the ripening sexual feelings set all ablaze.

And it is not only a little sexual idealism that is to be observed in the child: the crudest realism is not always lacking; this we may see among the lambkins in the meadow or a litter of puppies. And there is the uproarious laughter of children in their games, which follows the teasing and tickling of no matter what part of the body.

Long before this childish general sensibility has dwindled with succeeding years and become limited to the sexual organs in particular, the little rascals have noticed for themselves that these places are especially sensitive, and this is the first temptation to precocious excitation of these organs. This sometimes begins with birth itself (see chapters 11 and 12) and becomes a confirmed habit at puberty. It is always a threatening danger, which requires much tact and patience on the part of parents and teachers, but which may be overcome.

A fine healthy child, that is kept agreeably employed and brought up strictly will not fall into bad ways, and sexual reveries will only bore him. A child is of itself inclined to both good and evil, not only to evil. It is much too active to think of this one point so much that it becomes a passion. Everything else seems much more important to him than sexual things. And even when it happens that the child has got into some little bad habit, it is easy to break him of it. He has his lessons and his play to take up his mind during the day, and at night he needs rest. He thinks of nothing else, that is, if he is a fresh healthy child properly trained and sufficiently looked after.

No matter how many evil influences may surround us, and no matter what gross faults we may sometimes discover in our own children, their characters have not yet acquired a set form, so that with loving but firm treatment all may be put right. And sexual errors are not so deep-rooted in children.

The best that we can wish a child, therefore, is that he should remain a child as long as possible, that the slumbering forces should not be awakened too early, for once aroused, they cannot so easily be quieted.

that there were any other people in the world. We only learnt of them long after our birth; at first these strange people worried us, and we often cried about it.

Bye and bye we gradually got used to them and then we found out that amongst these strange people, too, there were some who were kind to us; and so we admitted them to our circle of friends, with our mother. But never so close to our hearts. For no matter how far we might be separated from her in later life by circumstances, she always occupies the chief place in our hearts. Even if the whole world is against us, whether we are guilty or innocent, we can always be sure of one thing, that is that our mother will remain true to us.

And then these learned gentlemen naively enquire: but how does man become altruistic? ... And we were altruistic long before the struggle for existence made us egoistic.

But now let us return to our sexual theme, and enquire: how can these feelings of affection in the heart of a young child brought up as asexually as possible, be already so coloured with sexuality? How, for instance, can the picture of a childish infatuation familiar to all of us, if we have studied children, be not merely a simple imitation of what the child sees around him, but in spite of his tender years, be already felt in special connection with the genital sphere?

This question is of fundamental importance, for we are here concerned with the delicate inmost nature of the sexual life, as the most intimate combination of the material with the spiritual.

And the affection also, which attaches us to our mother, shows the same double-sided character. Our mother not only caresses us and comforts us with her spiritual love but cares for us materially as well.

She it was who nursed and fed us, and she it was also who kept us clean when we dirtied ourselves. She it was who cared for our genito-urinary organs with motherly gentleness.

This was a sacred duty for her; and thus her affection differs from every other.

But as we grew up, needed her help less, became more and more independent, and perhaps nearly or entirely separated from our mother in the struggle for existence, constantly attracted by new charms, — then the image of the mother's love gradually faded from our minds, as the moonlight fades at the rising of the sun. And often, when later on in our lives we felt lonely and disappointed, a longing for home and such love and tenderness came over us. Then we rediscovered the same intimate tenderness in other, more youthful persons of the opposite sex, and the light of the bright sexual day rose at last on our horizon, the more the childish twilight faded.

Sexual love is the reproduction of mother-love in a new form. Our mother caressed us and cared for us at both poles of our body, whenever she put us to the breast or cleansed us. So also the newly married clasp each other in love, both body and soul partaking, as they kiss, and finally copulate.

Whenever our mother had tended us, we fell peacefully asleep, conscious of her watchful presence. And indeed many a child cannot drop off to sleep if the mother has not kissed him "good night" or held his little hand for a while, as if to induce hypnosis, or if he does not hold some little toy that he is very fond of, clasped in his hand, as a substitute for his mother's tenderness. Is there a more beautiful picture of the married fidelity that he will know later?

It was our mother who taught us to regulate and control our excretory functions, and if by accident we had failed in our self-control, we went weeping to her for comfort. So, later on, if we fall into sexual errors, the mother may still give her son good advice, or save her daughter from some desperate act. So, too, married people who have been unfaithful, beg each other's forgiveness with hot tears of repentance.

It was our mother, too, who gradually weaned us from her breast whereby as we grew older, we were not so often in need of her; but the feeling of sympathy remained unchanged; just as married people as they grow old, and age estranges them physically, remain attached by the same bond of sympathy. Like mother-love, conjugal love can never be replaced by anything else.

Thus it is mother-love that blossoms forth ever anew in the younger generation, and continues in the reproduction of our race. Each young generation is a new link in the chain of continuity of this love[1] which joins all generations like a holy bond of union.

This picture of the evolution of the psychic sexual love may settle many a problem that up to the present has found no solution; problems that have become burning questions of the day. Steinach has surprised the world by discovering the material principles by means of which the direction of the sexual impulse may be controlled from the age of puberty. Here there is a psychic principle through which the direction of the impulse may be foreseen in the earliest years of childhood. Thus it also appears that in this sphere as well, the psychic and material influences are most closely connected with each other.

We can now realise how it is that a little boy often feels a childish infatuation for a grown-up girl or even for an elderly lady; it is simply because she to some extent represents his mother. So we also understand that though boys often feel a childish infatuation, little girls do so still more frequently, and the latter feel like little mothers. And that this infatuation is of such an unselfish character, and is much more a protecting and altruistic devotion

---

1. St. Augustine and his successors always shed tears over the continuity of evil; we have just as much right to rejoice and be glad over the continuity of everything good.

239

It is a revelation to the young man that such an ideal world can blossom forth from what was at first only a material sexual charm. For the young girl it is a revelation, when she finds at last the material solution to what she had so long felt spiritually.

Henceforward they feel themselves united in a new enthusiasm. They are happy only when they are together; and everything they are working for, all they do, only possesses a value in their eyes insofar as it may help them to meet each other again, and to prepare their future life as a united couple. So they pass imperceptibly from springtime to midsummer, when all will be in full bloom.

They toss to and fro in their beds at night, feeling more lonely and abandoned than before; all their thoughts are with the loved one. They control their sensuality, and keep themselves sacred for each other. All their efforts and energies are strained with one object; soon to be united, to that end no trouble is too great. The heart beats more quickly, the breast heaves higher, and how one can blush at times! But no longer from fright or timidity as in the calf-years, but now from anticipated pleasure.

I willingly leave the finer psychic analysis to the poet and novelist. Psychology and art begin with the ideal and finish with the material realisation; but as a physician I have rather chosen to proceed from the material to the spiritual, and so we both at last reach to the same result. To my mind poetry is often a little indefinite, I am perhaps a little too concrete for the artistically minded. At any rate it is necessary for the reader to try to reach the ideal from the concrete side; both methods have their special advantages and are complementary.

In love there is also a wide field for biological research. This is no profanation; for here also a higher self-consciousness is the first step to improvement. There are so many rocks and shoals that might have been avoided! And this world so rich in pleasures may be enjoyed still more and appreciated more consciously.

With all these sexual stimuli, we experience an increase of the energy of our heart-beat, of temperature and strength. These we thoroughly explained in Part II. Especially we feel increased massage-therapy. In Chapter 25 we discussed the question of the normal body-massage through all our movements being greatly increased by love's awakening; we will now go a step further and enquire how this intensified massage can also react and again increase the charm of love.

First of all, we must reflect that the proper satisfaction of all these finer stimulations demands much time; there should never be any undue haste. With machinery, if we wish to get tremendous rapidity we can do so, though the result is frequently some terrible accident. The intoxication of love, on the other hand, can no more be hurried than sleep can when we go to bed.

As I have said already, it is the gentlest and most delicate ca-

242

resses which, because they are so soft and ethereal, charm us the most. And this is a fundamental difference between the biological cell function on the one hand and mechanics on the other. In the latter case, the result is proportionate to the force expended, while the biological consequence of these caresses is not.

There is, however, one mysterious thing in this connection. Why is it that every touch of our doctor, or friend or lover brings us calm and peace, while there are other people whose touch would horrify us and be most disagreeable?

We must learn from massage, if we would solve this problem. We can indeed think of sexual love as the high school of massage; and vice versa a knowledge of the secrets of massage is the best method of perfecting our sexual relationships. Thus a well-informed man can always further refine and multiply his more delicate mental and physical feelings. The love of the heart will thankfully recognise this. And all that I am going to say now applies not only to the mutual caresses of engaged couples, but even to the sexual intercourse of the married which is the climax of courtship.

What does a celebrated masseur or accomplished masseuse do? They never show undue haste; on the contrary, they are always quiet and gentle. They pay attention to every detail, particularly the temperature and degree of moisture. In delicate cases the masseur will never begin without first bathing his hands in hot water. And during the massage, chill must be carefully avoided. And indeed a sudden cooling down of the massaged portion of the body, which might prove injurious, should always be prevented, for instance, by rubbing it with a warm dry towel.

The real secret of accomplished massage lies in a very gentle beginning and end of the operation; the movements should be more energetic in the middle, i.e., there is a gradual rising and falling curve. This applies to each individual movement, as well as for each treatment, and for the whole series of treatments prescribed. This is the secret of massage, just as it is the secret of Nature; Nature always works on this principle, always on the plan of this curve. And that is why the principle is always found so beneficial.

In psychic intercourse also, this principle is important; and not only in the psychic intercourse of lovers, engaged couples and the married. A medical man attending children, or even approaching animals, sees this very well. If he approaches them too suddenly he frightens them at once.

Further, the more extensive the surface massaged, the greater the success, a masseur will never limit his attention to the exact spot in which the pain is localised. Just as a little child who has been given some *bonne bouche* enjoys it the more, the greater the surface that can be brought into contact with his face

243

and hands, so can a couple feel much more pleasure when they have passionately embraced each other for some time, instead of abruptly performing the sexual act.

The younger a person is, the more sensitive are all parts of the body, even to the gentlest touch. We should, therefore, be very chary of rough handling of the very young, because their delicate sensibility would thereby be quickly dulled. And naturally those spots retain the greatest sensibility which are always only very gently touched: our mucous membranes, so soft and warm, and our genital organs. These latter should never be touched at first, so that later on the greatest excitement and the highest ecstasy may be felt from them; at the final moment the ecstasy may even amount to pain.

But at those portions of the body which feel no stimulus, sensibility cannot be developed; sensitiveness to touch is lacking, for instance, on the surface of the back, especially at those spots which we are unable to reach with our hands. So a person who was never caressed in childhood, must go through a regular schooling before he can be at all capable of feeling and enjoying caresses.

In concluding this chapter, I want to consider a turning point in our love-life, I mean the transition from purely ideal to conscious sexual love. One person arrives earlier and another later at this point in life, where the two streams, the material and the ideal, converge; or to speak more correctly: at the spot where we become aware that these two streams belong most intimately to each other.

This individual divergence, by means of which the one is conscious of it so much earlier than another, constitutes a certain danger between the two lovers. For the one who awakens first, thinks that the other one is fearfully cold, does not reciprocate, and feels himself cruelly deceived; for he feels so warmly himself! Whilst the other finds him sensual, animal, disgusting. Both feel wounded in their most sacred feelings, without knowing exactly why; nor can they explain the reason to each other. I have often seen a love affair that started out beautifully, wrecked in this way; and frequently the couple have separated in horror of each other!

Here again, the same undue haste may spoil everything in the love life. If, for instance, this ardent wooer lover had only devoted sufficient time to his female partner to help her to the same consciousness, she would soon have acquired it, and who knows how doubly happy they would have been together.

And no less for complete happiness later on in their married life, it is of the greatest importance for the wife rightly to appreciate the material side o. 'he question; she should not merely accept it more or less indifferently. Both partners should eagerly seek to know each other's value, both should endeavour mutually to increase and improve the charm of their love. The love and caresses, I might almost say the provocation, cannot always come from one side without danger. Many a true wife disdains to be thought a courtesan. Quite right! The word courtesan now has a double meaning and a harsh and bitter taste; but courtesy is and will always be a virtue and a grace. To neglect it, just because one is married and tied together by law, is a sin of omission, which is dearly paid for, for it renders so many marriages ice-cold and loveless.

Chapter 55

AWAKENING OF THE SEXUAL PASSIONS

IN ORDER the better to understand the connection between psychic love and its material foundation, as this is manifested especially in the male, we must now turn our attention specially to this material aspect.

We must let our thoughts carry us back to the transition period, when we were too big to continue to play with children, and yet the adults would not acknowledge us.

Then we feel nervous and depressed... until all at once there is a new impulse, and we feel that we are nearing manhood.

We have all been through that in our youth, not merely in imagination, but we have experienced it in our circulatory system, and felt it in our sensory nervous system. The external congestive phenomena, which are caused by the internal phenomena of congestion, further stimulated our heart and our whole circulation. Words fail to fully express our feelings at this time, but still we shall endeavour to analyse this new impulse.

We felt ourselves henceforward so courageous, so imbued with manly strength, and yet we felt a little shy even of ourselves. Whenever we blushed, we showed that we were betraying that which was burning within us, and feeling this, we only blushed the more. Oh, this troublesome blushing in the years of puberty, as the effect of that other congestion! We did not then realise how greatly other people envied us this flush of the dawn of our lives; it worried us so much, and we tried so hard to conquer the habit, all in vain. And the birds and the insects too, just like the flowers, show their brightest colours on reaching sexual maturity.

The beating pulse of our life is the blood pressure, just as in plants it is the osmotic pressure. Those of my readers who perhaps look upon our animal life with all these sexual changes of blood pressure as something improper, often prefer the vegetable kingdom all the more for that reason. But in this kingdom, erection plays the most striking part of all. Possibly not so impulsively as with us, yet to such an extent that rocks are split asunder by it, and paving-stones lifted right into the air.

But we warm-blooded creatures possess a circulatory system, with the heart as central point, and with microscopically fine ramifications in every organ, bringing nourishment, life and strength to every part, by means of which we are constantly renewed internally. As modern intellectuals, we believe that our psychic life centres in the brain, but that stimulation proceeds from deep breathing and increased blood pressure.

I have only gone into all these details in order to show quite clearly that we are dealing with a fundamental biological law; and it is only now that we can understand how the sexual urge, with its congestion of the blood vessels, represents the climax of our consciousness of happiness, and how, combined with it, love as its psychic phenomenon leads us to the acme of delight. But the most highly organised of all creatures with their higher differentiation, only have one specialised organ in which this phenomenon of the blood pressure reaches its climax every time, and that is the erectile tissue of the penis in man and the clitoris in woman. But these organs are specially organised to this end, and admirably fulfill their function.

Which of us does not remember the occasion in his youth, when in the bath or by some other accidental touch, he was overtaken for the first time in his life by the sign of manhood, by the surprising sensation of this increased blood pressure so intimate and imperious; and he felt rather shy about it. His childish fancy had often imagined it in some form or other; but this surpassed everything, and was so unexpected! Only yesterday a child, and now a man. It is the revelation of an impulsive power within us. Just as a caterpillar metamorphoses into a butterfly, and all these insects take wing, the sexually ripe young man will soon fly out on the wings of love, far from the parental roof.

Even the childish erection, this modest congestion, is felt from the earliest years to be something agreeable. I remember the case of a tiny boy still an infant, to whom I was called for inguinal hernia; the child was crying loudly, and this rendered my work most difficult; all at once there appeared a strong childish erection, at the same moment the child was quiet and happy, greatly to the relief of the neighbours who were standing round. He stopped crying and the hernia was reduced at once.

But the adult erection is something quite different: a voluptuous glow and pulsation that takes complete control and makes the breast swell with pride. In young girls, the breasts really do swell at this period of their life, and in their case the swelling remains, internally and externally. This congestive delight may best be compared with the astonishing sensation in a hot bath, or the stimulating reaction after a cold one. The pulsation is not only local; for all our pulses beat, all our nerves are stimulated from delight, the whole spinal marrow is in ecstasy.

We can best see what an important part this ebb and flow plays in our life, from the suffering that generally occurs, when erection disappears owing to advanced age. The well-known abdominal disorders then appear with venous stasis and a sluggish circulation, such as piles, hypertrophy of the prostate, hypochondria and constipation. The remedy furnishes the best proof. All these disturbances are best counteracted if we replace the failing erection in good time by stimulation of the circulation in other ways, such as: walks, home-gymnastics, massage, cold-water treatment, and stimulation of every sphere of our body. By using such substitutes we can keep young for a long while.

The sexual erection has also another quite special task to perform. In the lower species of animals with their limited brain capacity, this strong erection does not exist; it is only amongst the highest categories, on account of their immense brain power, that this counterpoise is necessary. Especially in man, because his triumph in the struggle for existence depends chiefly on his higher mental faculties. Thus the object of our whole life is the maintenance of this mental efficiency. All our beverages such as coffee, tea, cocoa, alcohol, etc., are only enjoyable because they specially stimulate these faculties. They cause a dilation of the blood-vessels of our brain, and the increased blood pressure renders us lively.

And what drug have we at our disposal, capable of diverting the blood from the brain if necessary? Not one! Even if we offered a fortune for it, it does not exist. Cold applied locally to the head, rest for the brain, energetic exercise of the muscles, all these may bring us a little relief in this respect; but above all we may be involuntarily *rescued by erection, especially at night, which diverts the greater part of the blood pressure to the opposite pole of the body.*

When this occurs, it is so beneficial that, quite apart from any associated thoughts of sexual things, it fills us with pleasure. *Erection is one of the most important phenomena of life; and the more so, the more highly the brain is developed.*

It is on that account that total impotence is so serious a disorder, and eunuchs are so greatly to be pitied. But even under normal conditions, as soon as this counterpoise fails owing to advanced age, we often see cases of the bursting of blood-vessels in the brain, which leads to apoplexy, or attacks of paralysis whenever one of the cerebral vessels, which has become brittle through arteriosclerosis, gives way. For *the circulation has lost its regulator*, and this loss becomes more and more painfully noticeable until finally the circulation ceases altogether.

We best realised how greatly this feeling of manly strength filled us with energy and pleasurable sensations in our adolescence, when for the first time one night, the reaction came as great a surprise to us as the joy of the ecstasy itself.

After the pleasant surprise of the first voluptuous sensation, and after these feelings had been experienced several times, we found to our great dismay, one morning on waking up, that half in sleep and half in a dream, the whole structure of our manly strength had collapsed like a house of cards, only leaving a sad memory as of tears behind. Our ecstasy had vanished into thin air, and we felt once again like a puling babe. And how glad we were, when after a little time our manly vigor blossomed forth again, as though nothing had happened!

I should here like to give a little good advice. If you want to remain young a long time, you must never purposely hasten this natural catastrophe. *Do not awaken the next period of life too soon through intentional increase of the sexual stimulus, the period of sexual activity, that we are next going to describe. Husband your strength, so that only in due time your entire physical and mental faculties may reach their full development, and your sexual life may attain its full power.* And even if at the present time the sexual urge is sometimes felt to be overwhelming, stand firm, and be glad of it; it is only now that the whole magic world of expansion will really reach its maximal point.

This period of our life is certainly the most difficult one of our whole existence. After the depression and apathy of the period just before puberty, which are sufficiently evident to every teacher, there succeeds a period of increased excitability, of exaltation, of enthusiasm, which often leads to remonstrance from the superiors. Especially in the case of young people who suffer from neurasthenia or a weak heart, these powerful impulses and sudden transitions are very hard to bear; and it is still worse if they are already in the habit of masturbation or addicted to alcohol or tobacco. Certain signs of fatigue, exhaustion and over-tension are often displayed, which may lead to a loss of all interest in life, so that at this critical period cases of suicide are frequent.

This ill-humour in adolescence may easily be confused with the depression consequent on prolonged abstinence at the adult period. It might be thought that the state of things would improve if sexual intercourse were allowed during the years of puberty. But

248

that is not the case. On the contrary, if sexual desire is found too fatiguing, sexual activity would only aggravate matters.

It is most necessary duly to recognise the painful situation of young people, and to show them all affection and sympathy. Everything that can make them happier and increase ther strength at this time of their lives, will comfort them. It is most important to calm the psychic nature, and to avoid mental strain and overwork. And it is a cruel wrong that just at this critical age, young people in schools and colleges especially, are almost always so crammed and wearied and fatigued, both by sitting too long and by over-study, while those of the poorer classes are often industrially exploited at the same age.

The real cause of all these unpleasant sensations lies far more often in our training than in the sexual life itself; but even if human society were so well organised and our training so healthful that the sexual urge and all sexual activity could occur at the same age, still, as we have explained in Chapter 40, the sudden change, from the vegetative to the sexual life-period must always be a crucial moment in our lives.

In the foregoing lines, we have only been speaking of the young man. The grown girl feels these increases of blood pressure more intimately, and often far more deeply than he. But what she feels, she does not understand, she dare not understand it, and no one dares to explain it to her.

Special care should be taken that the young girl is strong and provided with good powers of resistance at this critical age. For any neglect at this time cannot be repaired later on; even the preparations of iron that one would so gladly prescribe as a remedy for her anaemia, may increase the loss of blood at her monthly periods.

Chapter 56

IMPERIOUS APPROACH OF SEX MATURITY

THE nearer we approach maturity, the more powerfully does the sexual urge make itself felt, with constantly renewed intensity. For it is not in this case a question of an avoidable stimulation of one of the senses, but of an urge materially founded on a secretory function that cannot be evaded. No matter how much our attention may be diverted from it, or how much we may be taken up by our business, the urge always returns relentlessly, systematically, and with increased intensity, exciting us each time to an extreme degree.

At first it was sufficient for us to expend our energy on other objects. If we were able at that time to avoid all accidental causes of sexual stimulation, the sexual urge did not become too overwhelming; although it soon cropped up again. Although the urge might have been very impetuous for a moment, if we did not give way to it, we remained master of our passions, and soon felt quite calm in our minds again.

But the stronger the physical constitution becomes in adult life, the more the tension in the seminal vesicles increases, and the more the blood is stimulated by the presence of the hormones. This stimulation gives us no peace day or night; there are only short pauses, after which we feel doubly tortured and almost driven to despair.

After all it is surprising that such an excessive stasis of the circulation does not torture us still more!

So it finally happens, earlier with some people and later with others, that this same congestive tension, which so charmed and delighted us at first, becomes through its excessive increase so great, and so painful; feels so overwhelming and constantly more of a burden. At first the increasing tension caused feelings of pleasure, and the relief of tension was a disappointment; henceforward our only desire is to be freed from this troublesome impulse... it is this liberation that would now afford us the greatest pleasure.

Shall we yield to this urge? The reader will remember the picture of the child who struggled in vain against the impulse of Nature

250

(chapter 17). Unfortunately it is so in this case, for on the one hand the urge is so overpowering, and on the other the contra-indications which forbid us to yield may be so definite.

It is a conflict into which we shall always be drawn again and again, no matter how absorbing our other occupations may be. It often happens that we are so mastered by it in the midst of our work, that it is absolutely impossible for us to collect our thoughts and concentrate our attention on one point; and it is worst of all at night, just when we should rest. We have to fight the hardest battle in the solitude of the night, and without being able to expend our energy on any kind of work. This silent suffering undermines our physical strength.

Silent suffering — for if we tried to express it like animals — the cries of our domestic animals for instance — we should only make it worse. So we keep silence; and if we hear the cry of our domestic animals, it goes to our hearts; for as we are related to every living creature, we understand their language; but because we are afraid of betraying our feelings, we prefer to mock at the sufferings of these poor creatures. For no one troubles his head about us, if abstinence ruins us.

It is a hard fight. It disturbed our psychic life from the first, but now that the fire is burning so near us, it becomes really too bad, and we want to be freed from the torture. But how?

Masturbation is too childish, too messy, too silly and does not satisfy our minds or our longing for sympathy and affection. The idea of prostitution is repellent to us, that is still worse than masturbation; and we are too valuable to risk the loss of our honour and our health in a single night. But what shall we do then?

Now we come to regard nocturnal emissions in quite a different light from what we did formerly, when they were such a disagreeable surprise.

If everyone is so cruel to us now, and the remedy for which we long so intensely is kept from us, Nature is far kinder to us than even our dearest relatives. Right and duty are categorical, but under the veil of night, Nature gently lends us her aid, and affords us in pleasant dreams, even if only for a short time, the relief that we need so greatly. How desperate, however, must our condition become before this relief occurs!

Nor is that what we really require. We should like to run up the entire scale of passionate enjoyment with a chosen kindred spirit in full consciousness, in our waking hours, and not dimly in our sleep; we want to be able fully to express all that we feel so passionately.

It is no light task to find the ideal person and to get used to one

another. It is easy enou~ an example taken from the way we eat; for eating
what grave complic~~damental and impulsive need.
that sort of thi~~ce how a wild animal gulps down its booty, how an ape crams every-
to attain th~ ~ into its mouth, how voraciously a boar eats, although they all know that
much ~ ~s soon as the meal is over the taste disappears; it is an unlovely spectacle.—
b~ ~ But now let us see, how differently they do things in a decent family. The
careful housewife has taken no end of pains all the morning to get everything
ready punctually and in the best of order; the table is set as for a feast; everyone
has his own plate, so that he can take his food in small pieces, separately or
mixed, just as he fancies. The different dishes are tasted with care and attention,
as long as possible before swallowing the mouthfuls.

And now we come to the question of love. With the lower animals copulation is an attack, a sort of outrage. Think how in our
farmyard, the cock, generally so stately, suddenly forgets his dignity and pounces upon one of his hens, just like a bird of prey.
And amongst the most uncultured peoples the gentle art of making love is unknown; they have their intercourse, and that's an
end of it.

This is very annoying, especially for the wife. Because, as we
saw in Chapter 22, her function in the procreative act is entirely
different from that of the husband, she requires a much longer
time than a man for her congestive function to reach full capacity,
and it also takes much longer for her to reach the orgasm, the
turning point at which the convulsively increased stimulation abruptly changes to an agreeable release of tension. *The traditional
politeness, which permits ladies to go first, is only manifested in
public and as a meaningless conventionality, but not in this case,
where it really matters;* for this takes place privately, where no
formalities are required. And so many wives are deprived of this[1]
greatest of all delights.

But the wife may, in the most leisurely manner, gradually work
up to her full ecstasy with the method of coitus known as "Karezza"
or Zugassent's discovery, which we fully described in Chapter 22,
a method in which one can revel in pleasurable sensations as long
as one likes, because the final climax is indefinitely postponed.

This Karezza-method is also scientifically most interesting, because it is a proof that even when a woman does not experience
any abrupt climax to her ecstasy (see chapter 22), she still may
feel much enjoyment in coitus[2]. And many husbands find it most
convenient if their wives remain quite passive and leave the uncon-
ditional management entirely to them.

1. Later on, when he has grown old, she takes her revenge. When on account of
his advancing years, he is less easily stimulated, she will not take the trouble to
meet him half-way, and help him to the right mood for enjoyment.

2. So children at a party may laugh most heartily, or even immoderately, without
laughter turning to tears.

But it also happens occasionally that even when plenty of time is given to the wife, many women not only fail to reach the climax, but do not experience the slightest pleasure in the act of coitus.

That this frigidity should be so general in women, is certainly due to the fact that in the female organism the secretory function is much less prominent, and also depends on the many anti-selective influences of remote and ancient origin. Every girl who shows a passionate nature runs the great danger of being seduced and brought to misery, after which she feels a horror of men; or the risk of venereal disease, or despair or prostitution or even suicide excludes the majority of them from reproduction. Thus they are the victims of man's lack of conscience, and men then grumble at the frigidity of the other women.

This danger that threatens the passionate girl is doubly injurious in the sense that parents and guardians feel themselves called upon in the face of it, to repress her sexuality and to keep her as ignorant as possible of all sexual things; an anti-sexual education that is only too successful in the case of girls on account of the hidden situation of their genitalia. For if these organs are never subjected to local stimulation (see chapter 54) how can local sensation attain its full development?

But on the other hand this local sensitiveness can be greatly dulled through the brutal excitement of masturbation. Whenever women or young girls have come to consult me for loss of sensitiveness, I have asked them: "But when you were a little girl and touched yourself there, did you not feel anything?" and the answer was always that they had done so. In these cases the loss of sensation is not absolute, and improves in time.

For that which has been lost through perverted habits, can be regained through good ones. Meanwhile she must be content with a simply altruistic feeling of pleasure, i.e., with the satisfaction of giving her husband the joy of voluptuous sensations.

And the disappointment of the impotent man arises not so much from the fact that he feels no pleasure himself, for he does not miss it; but rather because he cannot afford his wife the satisfaction that she so greatly longs for, at least not by ordinary coitus. This "non possumus" does not exist for the frigid wife in her relations with her husband; for she demands nothing for herself, she is much more frequently ready to satisfy his desires, she does not even need to be excited and brought into the congestive mood. And this altruistic mutual aid may be most sympathetically felt by both, if the flame of psychic love burns high at the sacrifice.

Even in desperate cases this lack of feeling may later disappear.

255

I remember the case of a married woman, who told me that she had had absolutely no sensation for the first two years of her married life, and yet had had two children during that time. She became pregnant for the third time, but had a miscarriage, and during her convalescence suddenly became aware that she felt the sensation. Was it only because Nature had endowed her so tardily with those feelings that other young women often feel prematurely? Or was it awakened by the long rest in a warm bed, coupled with good nursing and kind treatment? Or was she so pleased with her recovery, now that she was free from the terrible fear of pregnancy, that haunting spectre which had paralysed her at coitus?

One thing is certain, henceforward she adopted preventive measures, and her subsequent conjugal life was very happy.

We should not be surprised that so many married women experience so little pleasure, because it is generally the husband who takes the initiative and always chooses the most favourable moment for himself. How humiliated he would feel if she were to take the initiative for once, and what a long time he would need to recover from his surprise. Even in the first love-proposals the man always thinks it is his privilege to take the initiative.

It is still more unfortunate that the wife is nearly always allotted the less advantageous position in the act of coitus, which renders freedom of movement almost impossible for her at the critical moment. But if just for once, this traditional position is reversed, and the husband lies underneath, so that the under-surface of his penis glides along in her vulva instead of the whole member entering the vagina, then she can be mistress of the situation, for once. She can now take as much time as she wishes, almost or quite independent of the question whether the husband is ready or not; she can now adjust the rate of movement to a nicety and reach the climax at the moment which suits her best. It is not difficult for the husband, lying in this position, to delay his orgasm, and as soon as it is his turn, to resume the position which is most convenient for him.

The secret of this inverted method of coitus lies in the fact that in ordinary coitus, on account of the inconvenient situation of the genital organs (see chapter 27) and still more if the wife is inclined to be fat, the clitoris is not rubbed or touched in the correct manner, and sometimes not at all[3].

3. That is why Ernst Klotz in his book, "Man the Enigma" (Das Welträtzel Mensch), pub. Giesecke, Dresden, 1921, says that vaginal coitus should always be effected with the woman on all fours, as was originally the case with all of the higher animals, so that the clitoris should not be crushed by the hard upper-surface of the penis, but gently rubbed by its under-surface, where the urethra projects like a soft ridge between two hard edges.

Now all remains as before (see chapter 27) inasmuch as the husband presses his legs together, while the wife spreads hers as wide as possible. This method can also be used as a supplementary one, if the husband has had his satisfaction too quickly. Indeed, if the husband is completely impotent, this method is always at least as satisfactory as the homosexual mutual coitus of two women.

The ideal, that the climax should be reached by both partners at the same instant. is a rare occurrence, and this makes no difference to the voluptuous sensation. Nor is coincidence an indispensable condition of conception, if conception is desired.

Generally speaking, it would be much better, if the husband had enough regard for his wife's feelings, only to approach her when he noticed that she was in the right mood, which he can easily ensure by kind words or by caressing her generally or locally. The charm of love should be conjured up afresh each time. And this is the more successful the more the couple get accustomed to each other day by day.

Every person has one or more erotically sensitve spots on the surface of his body, or there is some kind of handling or tickling that arouses his desire; and in the same way he finds that certain influences are destructive to these feelings and cause the ecstasy to disappear immediately. As erogenic spots I may specially mention the lips, the tongue, the nipples, the buttocks, the urethral orifice and the external genitals; and as erotic stimuli: stroking, pinching, scratching; or kissing, biting, licking, sucking, etc. These individual peculiarities do not simply originate from mere accidental experiences or from associations of thought or feeling, but go back to reminiscences of childhood, or even more remote periods of animal evolution, something like the mimicry to which Darwin has alluded.

Here there is room for a great deal of improvement before the actual state of the highest love will be so idealised that painter and sculptor, poet and composer can give worthy expression to this theme; just as they now depict a family festival or the loving attitudes of an engaged couple.

The magic charm that emanates from odours and perfumes may have a very direct and seductive effect. It is indeed a fixed law, that the shorter the distance from which our senses receive an impression, the more intimately will our consciousness perceive it. Our eyes and ears often receive impressions from a great distance; but we can only perceive odours when they are quite close. In animals the sense of smell is only surpassed by the sense of taste. But the climax is represented by the feeling of being touched intimately. Odours have a very different effect on various individuals. Strong and penetrating perfumes (see chapter 13) have the most exciting effect on people of a coarse nature; for more highly refined persons, however, the fresh smell of clean clothing has greater effect.

We come now to the great difficulty that generally stands in the way of harmonious satisfaction. Individual peculiarities differ far more in the psychic respect than in the material, and yet people long so greatly to afford each other the most wonderful ecstasy. One man needs jollity, gaiety, another seriousness or even a sickly sentimentality, in order to obtain the desired effect. Some people give vent at the last moment to coarse and immoral, or even indecent expressions; and there are men and women, too, who cannot feel satisfied until they have caused their partner or themselves a little pain. In most cases, however, gentle caresses are far more effective, just as a slight tickling on the soles of our feet drives us crazy, while a rough touch has no effect, or makes us cross.

All these individual differences are subject to the influence of temperament, habit, age and traditional associations; besides which they constantly change with the mood and circumstances of the moment. How greatly, for instance, alcoholic drinks can influence our moods and lead us astray. How difficult it is to come to a harmonious agreement in this condition, because we do not even understand ourselves properly, and our intellect deserts us. Words are useless, and the only expression of our feelings is an unconscious sigh, either of disappointment or of passion.

It is only when we reflect on all this that we can begin properly to understand the great mystery of individual love; why should it be he, and no other man? or why she, and no other woman? Why do these souls seem so adapted to each other? Yes indeed, we must even wonder that two congenial souls can find each other at all. In most cases people are led to love each other through a gradual getting used to each other that takes years, but sometimes through a sudden overwhelming rush of sympathy. The latter is indeed the more romantic, but the former is more likely to ensure lasting conjugal happiness. More cultured people insist on a long engagement before binding themselves by marriage for their whole life.

And in marriage, the longer the partners have shared joy and sorrow, the more harmoniously will they agree. Sexual intercourse then becomes more and more a harmonious satisfaction and as they get older is found more agreeable and beneficial than each new liaison, even if longed for eagerly, as a new charm. And who knows how harmful such temerity may prove to us, just on account of its unwonted charm?

Finally, with the advance of years, there comes a time when ordinary marital intercourse becomes too fatiguing and trying for us; and then we reach a period in which we still perceive the sexual urge and feel it to be highly agreeable, because it makes us feel so young and lively once again, — but if we yield to it we feel exhausted, enervated, disappointed, and doubly aged!

So we have gradually reached a similar transitory period, as once when we were young (see chapter 55), and we used to feel the urge as something so agreeable, and the satisfaction as a disappointment. The ideal of the full love-life must now yield to the ideal of asceticism, and henceforth we feel better if we restrict ourselves as much as possible.

At both of these transitory periods in our lives the procreative act appears to us to be a squandering of strength, an improper expression because after the act is accomplished we feel ourselves tired, exhausted and nervous, while at the same time when our manly strength is at its height, we feel calm and content after each normal connection, as though our strength were renewed.

To be able to judge in each particular case, which is the more indicated and beneficial to our psychic life, sexual abstinence or the manifestation of mutual affection, demands more tact and delicacy than most people possess. Formerly this was much worse, when the majority of married couples behaved far more thoughtlessly and inconsiderately towards each other than they do now. But in modern times, with our higher differentiation (see chapter 49), we pay more attention in married life to the ethical significance of our actions, and feel our responsibility to each other more strongly. It is greatly to the credit of those who preach abstinence that they draw attention to this sphere by their criticisms; it is only a pity that they often speak in such a dogmatic and stereotyped manner, and do not take the various ages and individual differences into consideration.

There will be no fundamental improvement until woman is more conscious than at present of her full value as an individual.

would say, quite unjustly: yes, he's only pretending, the hypocrite; last time he was not so pious.

One must not always show one's true nature, especially in the sexual sphere; this lack of frankness is often a duty of self-control. For instance, as soon as a girl shows openly how much she feels the need of sexual satisfaction, this frankness is only too quickly taken advantage of; even if only in words or in external behaviour towards her. And so in future she would be obliged to be doubly careful. I have often observed among young people, that it was just those who felt the sexual urge the most, who exercised the greatest self-control and appeared the coolest; while on the contrary, those who were asexual, tried to hide this defect by impudence.

If a man marries such a forward girl expecting to find a very passionate nature, he is terribly deceived.

If anyone incidentally seeks the sexual, it is not necessarily a sign of a deeply felt sexual need; the motives may easily be curiosity, coquetry, vanity, ambition, love of adventure or speculation about marriage: all motives of a mental order, that have nothing to do with the sexual urge. And this may lead us into serious error.

Also people with southern or oriental temperament, who have very lively and active habits, might easily give the impression that they are fearfully sexually inclined; while, although, we in our colder climate are less demonstrative, we perhaps feel passion more deeply and permanently.

These various examples show us how difficult it is for each of us to fix a standard of living for himself in this respect, and still more so to judge others. Especially in the sexual sphere, we should remember the warning: "Judge not!"

Chapter 59

THE VARIOUS HUMAN SEX TYPES
THAT NATURE PRODUCES

JUST as the majority of us feel ourselves sexually attracted to persons of the *opposite* sex (heterosexuality), so also there are men and women who feel attracted, with equally pure and lofty motives, to members of their own sex (homosexuality).

In this chapter we are not referring to those cases in which persons seek their sexual satisfaction with others of the same sex on purpose as an exceptional experiment, or because there is no member of the opposite sex available. We are now dealing exclusively with those persons in whom this individual peculiarity is deeply rooted in their mentality, either inborn, strictly speaking, or as such a direct consequence of influences to which they have been subjected in their early childhood, that it can hardly be distinguished from an inborn tendency. This preference for one's own sex may indeed be so marked as to be quite exclusive, with a pronounced dislike for the opposite sex. Here it is not a case of "are there such people?", but "such people certainly do exist".

It frequently happens that a hereditary tendency to this preference appears in a highly educated and honoured family; and even when it only occurs in individuals, generally the persons concerned are of a high intellectual order and idealists, such as literary men or very sensitive women. In the hey-day of ancient Greek civilisation it was the higher intellectuals in particular, who sang the praises of this homosexual ideal.

But just as in those days in ancient Greece, even nowadays the direction of the impulse is not always absolutely exclusive, and thus we can understand that even now some high-class, idealistic persons display this psychic peculiarity. For in people of a coarser and more realistic nature, raw materialism in their sexual intercourse manifests itself in an increasing measure as time goes on, and in this case, as we explained in Chapter 29, the ordinary, heterosexual connection is more indicated. But the more refined natures, in whom the heart speaks, and love is of more spiritual character, are not so eager for this mode of satisfaction. Ordinary coitus often seems to them to be too coarse, too material[1], and a

1. This is especially evident in the case of female homosexuals, because in the female sex the emotional is always felt much less than some local stimulation, and in their case the genital apparatus is not always by any means the preferred erogenous region. Many male homosexuals feel the same, and it cannot be denied that they may resemble the female type in that respect. (See chapter 53).

passionate embrace from an "affinity", a friend with a "sister soul", whom they feel very fond of, appeals to them as far more ideal. Persons with such lofty ideas are also called "Urnings", "Uranians" (from Uranos = heaven), because they feel just as much as we do that their love has something heavenly about it.

If there were no such powerful organochemical (see chapter 4), physiological (chapter 29) and psychological (see chapter 53) motives, by reason of which each new generation is formed again heterosexually, we should fully expect everybody to be homosexual. For a man would understand sooner than a woman what a man requires; and a woman too, would feel sooner than a man, what a woman feels. And not only all the material obstacles that we mentioned in Chapter 27, but also many of the psychic hindrances which we mentioned in Chapter 57 are non-existent in these cases.

In such a case heterosexual intercourse could only be maintained as an exception for the purpose of increasing the population.

In young children the propensity has not yet sufficiently differentiated, the specific organochemical substances especially, are not formed, and therefore cannot yet exercise their special stimulation. Even if our children were hereditarily or anatomically inclined to be homosexual (see appendices to chapters 3 and 4) we should not readily notice it at this early age. For if a child cherishes a special affection for a person of the other sex, we only think it to be friendship; how much more then would affection for a person of the child's own sex be regarded as purely friendship!

At the age of puberty both homo- and heterosexuals are traditionally and conventionally obliged to conceal and dissimulate their newly-born passions. Only when he has grown up and the heterosexuals are celebrating their engagement, the homosexual must persist in his hypocrisy, for the two paths now separate. And just on account of this secrecy, everyone thinks, ourselves included, that this propensity is extremely uncommon.

We should now expect that this peculiarity, which does no harm to anyone, would not be objected to; for although we do not share this feeling, we should at any rate respect it. But unfortunately, we are not living in a tolerant age; and it is just this intolerance which renders their unfortunate propensity an endless source of misery for these persons.

Formerly, e.g., in the hey-day of Greek civilisation, when people had not departed dogmatically from the simple feelings[2], this particular disposition was held in the highest esteeem amongst the upper classes. Intercourse with women, of whom only a very few (courtesans like Aspasia) had enjoyed the advantages of a higher education, they considered to be a mere gratification of an animal instinct; while friendly intercourse with celebrated men and youths distinguished by their beauty and talents, was thought by the aristocracy to be far more aesthetic and refined.

But times change. Rigid asceticism has spread over Europe from the East. I have often observed in my own practice, that the very men who have seduced many young girls are the first to throw

2. Homosexuality is very common among animals.

264

stones at the homosexuals, as if to excuse themselves—*they,* at least, they say, have been "natural".

Even at the present time the statutes of many countries display the same intolerance. While in Germany up to the present only male homosexuality has been punishable by law, both male and female homosexuality in Austria. In the French penal code homosexual practices in themselves are not prohibited; only all vice in general which takes place either publicly, even if under the eyes of one single person), or with violence, or is practiced on a minor under a certain age. Neither is homosexual intercourse in itself punishable in Holland, unless it takes place between a major and a minor.

This intolerance not only affects individuals who may be on occasion accused and condemned, but the disgrace is attached to all homosexual persons, because they are thus forced to concealment and hypocrisy. The consciousness of how severely they would be judged by public opinion if the matter were only known, demoralises them extremely. And all that only because they have not the same inclinations as other people.

Edward Carpenter affords us a deeper insight into the signficance of homosexuality in his essay on *Homogenic Love.* In our modern social organisation, says he, we cherish our tenderest feelings of sympathy almost exclusively for the opposite sex; we are too jealous and fearful of competition, with persons of our own sex. If we would only take a lesson from the homosexuals, and feel sympathetically towards those of our own sex, how greatly would our sense of solidarity be increased.

We often express pity for homosexual persons, if they were hampered in their choice of intimate attachments; but we totally forget that we heterosexuals are equally hampered. *It is just as if right-handed people should pity the left-handed ones;* but those people who are as clever with their left hand as with the right, i.e., who are *ambidextrous,* may claim to occupy a higher place.

Who knows if the time will not also come one day, when the highest class of people will be *ambisexual,* feeling affection for both sexes alike, according to the agreement and harmony of their characters, and not always considering the difference of sex as the cardinal point. When they will not be in love with the sex, but will feel attracted by personal human sympathy. Only then such highly gifted people would have the right to despise us ordinary heterosexual mortals as they would the homosexuals, on account of our limitations.

From a scientific standpoint the homosexual question is of great importance to us all. It is only through it that we can obtain a correct insight into the position that we ourselves occupy in the sexual world.

As we have seen in Part IV, one of the most primitive stages in the great scale of the evolution of the species is hermaphrodism, or bisexuality. We have also seen at the end of Chapter 3 that individually there was a stage in the beginning of our own embryonic formation when we were all to some extent bisexual. Our sexual organs have only differentiated later on in our foetal development in the uterus, so that finally, at the age of puberty, each person has become a separate individuality in one or the other of two sexes.

Still this differentiation is not absolute. For instance, every woman has a clitoris as though she were a man, and every man nipples on the breasts, as if he were a woman. And internally as well, some rudiments of the excretory system of the opposite sex persist in each of us. Indeed, in some exceptional cases (see chapters 3 and 4) testicular and ovarian tissues have been found mingled in the same individual.

So there exists a mingling of both sexes in us; just as everyone of us has originated from a mingling of the two sexes. The purely male type, and the exclusively female type, are only the two extreme ideals of an endless succession of intermediate stages.

From this point of view, the homosexuals are a most instructive and typical example of such a mixed form. They have the reproductive organs of one sex, and the sexual inclintions of the other; and at the same time they display in their choice of clothing the way they do their hair, and in their general behaviour, an intermediate type between the two sexes. So they should be regarded as one of the most important transition phenomena between the two extreme sex types which we are accustomed to consider normal, Indeed, in the ranks of the homosexuals, amongst both those men and women who are homosexually inclined, this same scale of degrees may be observed of masculine and feminine personality.

But now, when we study this freak of Nature, we begin to grasp that, as has long been observed in the mental sphere, almost every person possesses a double psychic nature. A child has in its early years, absolutely no preference for persons of its own or the opposite sex, nor has it any expressed characteristics of the male or female sex. These things only gradually differentiate. And then this differentiation is never quite complete, for we still remain human. In the personal character of every man we find traces of something that we should term rather feminine, and in every woman traces of the masculine.

But in most cases it must remain a matter of conjecture, whether it is one of innate mixed sexuality dependent on an anatomical cause (chapter 4), or of an adaptation to some particular environment or training (see chapter 37).

The more highly our stage of civilization is developed, the more clearly the individuality of each person may be distinguished. And that is why homosexual peculiarities are more distinctly expressed in the higher civilisation. It is just these minute differences which give such a variety of human types.

266

Chapter 60

THE DANGEROUS AGE IN MAN AND WOMAN AND IDEAL SEXUAL LIFE FOR MAXIMUM HEALTH

AGING would not be a necessary phenomenon, if in the life-history of the cell there was not always a slight disproportion between wear and regeneration.

Fertilisation and the beginning of a new individual only succeed if all the conditions are favourable. For this reason every individual begins his life with a good store of energy. In the first half of our life, the power of regeneration is more than equal to the wear and tear, so that in our youth each muscular effort leads to an increase of strength, and after a wound or a broken bone has healed, it is stronger than before the accident. But in the latter half of our life the un-favourable influences outweigh the others, and every great effort and all kinds of damage or injury leave a little deficit behind. This disproportion constantly increases, because our strength constantly decreases, until at last the decline can no longer be denied.

This decline is compensated or even more than compensated for a certain length of time, because the older we grow the more experience we possess; but there comes a time when the limit is reachd.

The first of our systems to betray a decline is the sensory one, because it is here that the most delicate workings of cell-life find their expression. The sensitive-ness of feelings no longer increases from day to day, as was the case when we were young; on the contrary, our impressions become more nebulous and indef-inite, something like the impressions obtained from a worn-out zinc block. On that account strong excitement should be avoided in our youth, so that we may long remain young. But when we become very old, all our nerve-cells are worn out.

We generally notice this dulling first of all in our memory; very often quite early, before anyone else suspects it. And it is very curious; it is not our earliest impressions that fade first; on the contrary, these gradually come to occupy our memory entirely; for in those early days we still enjoyed full sensitiveness. It is the later impressions of quite recent events that are so feebly felt, that they leave no trace in our memory. If one were only old enough, one would begin to forget everything, to lose everything, and to neglect everything.

And very soon it affects our finer sensory organs, which we have overworked every day of our lives; the clearness of our sight and sharpness of hearing often show signs of diminution quite early.

But even our sexual apparatus, which is the last to develop, does not escape the dawn of gradual decline in the course of time; sexually, one becomes less sensitive, and the secretory function

267

diminishes its activity. Whether we wish it or not, sexual inter-course, or if we are unmarried, nocturnal emissions, become less frequent, and at the same time our breathing and circulation less vigourous. Finally there are no more spontaneous emissions during sleep: a sign that the sexual urge has ceased to be as imperative as it was at the prime of life.

The diminution of the sexual urge may occur quite early. And just as the first appearance of sexual maturity was a mile-stone in our life, when our life-curve ascended (see chapter 61), the first failure of this function is also an important mile-stone, but this time on the downward grade. These two events may be com-pared to the opening of a flower-bud and the fading of the over-blown flower.

Who does not remember the first time in his married life, when he thought, after a tiring day or a lot of worry, that he would like to have connection, and then he found it difficult to get an erec-tion... but of course after a long absence or the usual period of rest it would be all right... and then he found for the first time that it was physiologically impossible for him to carry out his in-tention. After all, just for once it did not matter, and we were then young enough to quickly wipe out the slur, yet it was a first warning that we had to remember later on.

However, before we go more deeply into this new life-period, let us define a little more precisely the notion of sexual old-age. Once upon a time, when we looked on procreation as the main object in the sexual life (chapter 23), and only considered sexual enjoyment as something quite secondary, old age could only be defined thus: "He is old, who can no longer reproduce his kind".

This notion was specially derogatory to the wife, for she indeed loses her fecundity at a time of life when she is otherwise in full vigor, and sexually is still very excitable. But now we look upon this stage of her life as her second youth, free from the un-pleasantness of menstruation and the risk of pregnancy[1]. But we do not call a woman old until her sexuality is entirely extinguished, because we know how greatly this reacts on her entire physical and psychical constitution.

We shall now trace the history of the husband in his married life a little more in detail. At first, when he was newly married, the intercourse with his chosen bride was his greatest delight and charm. Then a little later, when they had become more used to each other, he still felt it much more beneficial, easier and more soothing than intercourse with strange women could ever be; and the older

1. Because her sexual enjoyment may be very keen, and indeed without these hindrances, this life-period has been termed "l'âge dangéreuse", but to my mind, sexually all ages are dangerous.

a couple grows the more they allow each other the repose that their age requires.

At last the time arrives when ordinary marital intercourse possesses too little charm to make it worth while to go to so much trouble, all the more as it may happen again, that our skill deserts us just at the critical moment; and we are not yet too old to feel ashamed for our failure, even if only in our own wife's presence. Abstinence is often very greatly encouraged by all sorts of accidental influences, such as coolness on the part of the wife, a cold bed, complicated contraceptive preparations for coitus[2]; and even sleeping apart in twin-beds is often a deterrent at this age.

Attempts at intercourse with other women, which at least have the charm of novelty, will be perhaps still less successful. And it will no longer be expected of him, that is, not by his former mistresses; they will poke fun at him now, and call him a played-out old man. And so gradually and imperceptibly we reach the years when we no longer need coitus, and of our own accord choose celibacy. One man reaches this stage very early in life, another much later; there are wide differences. Abstinence is not at first absolute, and it very often happens that from habit one ventures to indulge in sexual intercourse now and again, but only exceptionally.

Thus it can no longer be denied that such a person has arrived at the period of life which we mentioned at the end of Chapter 57: the sexual urge is still pleasant, and its disappearance is felt to be a disappointment.

One should not complain of this. It is nonsense to run to a doctor at this age on account of loss of sexual power to ask him to make one younger. Even if the power could be entirely restored, the fact that it has sunk so low, gives us in itself the physiological proof that such disturbing emotions are to be avoided for the future. This increase of blood-pressure and this powerful stimulation of the central nervous system, which are both so important to the adult man in the prime of life for the development of his full life-energy, are really in old age most dangerous and may perhaps cause premature strokes of paralysis and degeneration of the brain.

Henceforward one chooses gentler excitements and less exacting sexual sensations, as a feeble echo of the sexual urge that was once so overpowering.

And it is much worse if the sexual impulse does not decrease with age, while satisfaction is still felt as too great a tax on the nerves. This is not at all a rare occurrence, because many people

2. One can scarcely say which persons should be the more thankful for Dr. Mensinga's invention of the occlusive pessary: newly-married women or elderly men.

are only able to retire late in life. And just because one is old, one has such a desire for strong emotions — if one could only bear them. And then instead of husbanding his strength, many a man squanders it, either by a marriage with someone quite young, which he does not long survive, or in all kinds of dissipation, which ruins him completely. For it should not be forgotten that the sexuality of elderly men is almost more dangerous than that of young people. A young man, who still has to fight his way through life, will at least stop to think before committing a foolish act; but when a man is old, his self-control only too readily deserts him, and he finds himself unexpectedly in the midst of a conflagration that he thought already extinguished, because the watchman had gone home.

And for these reasons sexually excited elderly persons may be very dangerous for younger ones, because they are so blasé, that they require so many of the more violent stimulations which are not only distasteful and repellent to young people, but also really injurious on account of the danger of psychic contamination and exposure to seduction and debauchery.

Medical aid can be efficacious only if this stage of relative impotence happens early, when the doctor can prescribe regular habits and avoidance of excessive strain, and especially of mental strain, so that Nature may be able to gradually restore the disturbed equilibrium. The patient always thinks that the absence of the sexual urge is the primary cause of his psychical depression, whereas in reality it is almost always psychical strain or grave bodily exhaustion that is the cause of premature age. It would therefore be most unwise to prescribe aphrodisiacs; on the contrary, one should be content for the time being to avoid all sexual excitation as well as to practice self-control as explained in Part III. And on that account, especially at an advanced age, operative intervention which (even if only for a short time) restores the power of erection through the reintroduction of organochemical substance (see chapter 4) on Steinach's principle, should be avoided. And every waste of strength only makes matters worse. Only rest, and especially sexual rest, can bring relief.

If one has quite given up the regular practice of coitus due to advanced age, one may still feel the sexual urge from time to time, either during sleep or when half awake[3], not, of course, so imperiously as in former years, but rather as a welcome sensation.

3. Especially in the morning, just as we wake up, because the desire to urinate is one of the principal causes at this age (see chapter 20) besides which, the complete rest one gets only in sleep (see chapter 36) is necessary in order to produce sufficient congestibility.

One still experiences the blessings of voluptuous feelings with their periodical congestions of the circulation and their psychical stimulation; but only in a milder form, something like a rejuvenescence without fatigue. These are the lovely days of sweet September that are so restful after mid-summer heat.

Now we can more easily understand the correspondence between this life-period and our adolescence, to which we have referred above. For then, in that first transition-period, although we had no sexual connection, the sexual urge delighted us, and at that time, just as much as now, the avoidance, as far as possible, of all powerful sexual excitement was indicated. And how greatly we developed our energy during those years! Now this second transition-period may be regarded as a renewal of youth, by means of which our riper experience of life, and our more mature judgment can bear the finest fruit. In the early days we used our experience for our own further development, and now we use it for the public good in the widest sense.

At last, with the passage of years, we reach the final period of our life, when no congestion of the circulation occurs either day or night, either spontaneously or through any exciting cause; the disintegrating stage, in which the pangs of old age make themselves felt more and more.

271

Chapter 61

PRACTICAL ADVICE FOR AGED
MARRIED LOVERS

AND so we come to the last stage of human life, in which sexual stimuli find no response, while the vegetative functions continue for a time, although but feebly. This is the period of decrepitude, of senile decay.

In the male total impotence gradually becomes the normal state. If sperm-cells are occasionally produced, they are swept away unnoticed with the urinary secretion, if the power of erection has been lost as a symptom of paralysis consequent on diminished reflex excitability (see chapter 20). And yet many a grey-headed old man tries to awaken his slumbering passion with alcohol and debauchery, which can only hasten the end. The wise man thinks more of his honour and resigns himself to the inevitable. He will have to do so anyway, before he is laid under the cold ground or carried to the crematorium.

If one exercises self-denial, this period of life, too, may be crowned with blessings. Although childhood, without any sexuality whatever, is so very charming, there is something far nobler in the repose of old age. The needs and desires of the body give place more and more to spiritual ideals; one's love can now be free from material complications, with a free mind, free from all earthly considerations, an experience which is felt to be a foretaste of paradise, as though the soul were already detached from the body. Many an honourable old man, many a faithful mother, is in this way illumined by a glow of light from above; and indeed, long, long after they have left us, there survives in our grateful remembrance this halo of their holy lives.

The difference in sex is no longer prominent, and this encourages confidence in many cases where the sexual formerly represented an obstacle. And the person's disposition becomes calmer and more even, more forbearing and patient, and less immoderate in joy. One does not have to go far in search of happiness; one possesses a world of memories in oneself.

The advantages of this stage, in which one has risen superior to all the storms of life, are indeed so great that there are many people who are too proud of them, and would like to force their own asexuality on others, although these latter were in the middle stage of their lives and at the height of their sexual activity, and should therefore still be exercising these gifts. And sexual abstinence is held up as a virtue, even as the greatest of virtues; so that the preaching of this morbid principle spoils and desecrates pure conjugal happiness.

When we are young we should be very sparing in the use of strong stimulants, and especially with sexual ones, so that we may long remain youthful, but we should not think that we attain the same end, if we suppress the sexual function as far as possible when we are grown up. On the contrary, a regular, normal and approved exercise of the sexual function tends far more to ensure a lasting preservation of one's strength.

Indolence, too, only hastens old age, for one only becomes lazier; and the obesity that it occasions makes the approach of old age all the heavier to bear. One should do everything possible in order to get a little thinner as time goes on, so as to render the work of the muscles easier, and not to hamper the heart and lungs in their functions.

The female organism also is all the better for rest at an advanced age. With the approach of old age all the connective tissues lose their elasticity, so that not only do the charming curves of the female form disappear, but her sexual organ is no longer well adapted for intercourse: if children have been borne, it is too widely distended and flabby; and if there have been none, there is too rigid a narrowing of the orifice. All these are friendly warnings of Nature that the time for rest has come.

In Chapter 60 we have already spoken of the pangs of old age which make their appearance as soon as a stoppage of the sexual congestions of the circulation occurs. If we properly understand the meaning of this, the remedy is indicated at the same time. Then more or less as may be necessary, we should employ hygienic substitutes for the disappearing stimulation of the circulation; such as home-gymnastics[1], massage, lukewarm baths with a good rubbing down afterwards, etc. Especially should we take walks in the fresh air, or, if the weather should be bad, in the corridor.

All great fatigue, and especially continuous mental-strain should be avoided. The best book for an old man is the history of his own life. Cicero says in *"De Senectute"* that old people with their experience can be most useful to the younger generation. This is cer-

1. In the ordinary manuals of home gymnastics there should be a series of exercises for increasing circulation at the onset of the sexual period, and a series of very gentle ones for more advanced years.

tainly very useful to the younger generation, although its results often turn out quite different from what grandpa thought when he was vaunting his own young days.

In this connection, there is a special point to which far more attention must be paid than in earlier years. Because the circulation is no longer stimulated sexually, it is of the greatest importance not wilfully to hinder the circulation still more by neglect of the other two secretory functions which still remain active.

There is always great danger, because the urge is not so distinctly felt, that an old person will neglect these functions; vice versa, if he is aware of this latter danger, that he will continually worry himself over a possible forgetfulness, and it becomes almost an obsession with him. And he will also underestimate his own capabilities in this respect through diminished sensibility[2], and if his family is not aware of this, they put it down to incipient idiocy, which often proves very trying to the doctor's patience.

As our readers may see, the curve of our story has taken a downward course again, because we must again refer to those material details that we started with. But life is like that. When the old man becomes so helpless, he needs sympathy and help, just like a child, and it is very comforting to him, if his relatives quite understand his condition, and assist him kindly in his needs. Old people are like little children, they like to be spoilt a little. Little tit-bits and sweet things are also very welcome; for they can no longer eat much at a time.

And now we come to other typical troubles of old age; which in general originate from the internal decline, i.e., from the wearing out of the organs.

We referred in the last chapter to the lessened sensibility of the more delicate organs; finally, however, the general sensibility of the skin, i. e., the sense of touch, also becomes weaker and weaker. This may easily produce the impression on those around that the old man is indifferent, careless or dirty. But one should then remember how careful he once was!

And on that account he will no longer sufficiently notice harmful influences; or if he notices the danger himself, he will be all the more anxious. Fortunately, the sensibility to pain, and the psychic sensitiveness to suffering also become gradually lessened; and if compared with the sensitiveness in childhood, the difference is most remarkable.

Secondly, I must mention the diminished efficiency of the entire muscular system, especially diminished capacity for sustained effort If young men overtire themselves, their muscles will be painful; but this occurs very rapidly in old people, even if the muscles only have to maintain a certain position for a short time. And for that

2. When impotence is complained of, at the onset of old age, through the same lack of sensibility the erective capacity is frequently underestimated. There may also be an anatomical reason, in advanced age, why the amount of excreted defecation may be underestimated, i.e., when there is *prolapsus ani*. If the reverse is the case, and the voiding of urine is felt too greatly, it is often because the end of the prepuce is turned in through cold.

reason everything must be shortened now: short walks, with short stops for rest, and short conversations. Even sleep of a night can only last a short while[3], and thus a few little naps in the course of the day are found necessary to repair the loss of sleep; it makes them very happy when they can have "forty winks".

When they sleep in the day-time, they ought to lie down, instead of remaining seated, for they sit up too much as it is. If we take the trouble to consider all these things, we can reduce the troubles of old age to a minimum. At last there comes a time when all movements of the muscles are painful, slow and trembling, and all the joints then resume the flexed position they occupied when our lives began.

Thirdly, the power of resistance to harmful influences is reduced to a minimum, which is sometimes erroneously, or perhaps euphemistically called hyper-sensitiveness; and yet, as we have already seen, it is especially the sensibility which is diminished so terribly. While the strong man must brave a danger and learn to fight it, the aged man is obliged to avoid it like a little child. Happy is the man who glories in his strength, and especially his sexual strength, in the flower of his manhood, so that he can found a happy home and a family; for later on he can enjoy the rest and the attentions he needs in his old age. And then it will be seen who is the more fortunate, the young man who is able to work but obliged to work very hard and to earn his living by the sweat of his brow, and sometimes in care and trouble; or the old man who is in need of rest, who is able to enjoy his well-earned repose while he looks back happily on his former exploits.

But everything comes to an end, however faithful and loving the care may be. In this respect it is a great consolation that the end of our life generally comes more gently the older we are. For the curve of life has fallen to zero so long ago, that it is not so hard at last; often it is only a falling asleep.

3. Hence the paradox, that they are always complaining of sleeplessness, and yet they sit all day long nodding in their chairs, ready to drop off to sleep at any time. Even at the prime of life we often find the days and nights of our solar system far too long.

Chapter 62

THE SEX PERIODS OF OUR LIFE HISTORY

WE have studied the love-life at the different periods of our existence, and we have learnt that the sexual urge increases in strength and importance from year to year, until one reaches a certain maximum, after which it gradually diminishes, and our life-energy with it, as can be very clearly shown on a chart. This curve develops in a similar way to that which we called the massage curve (see chapter 60); like the ebb and flow of a tide, with the summit in the middle.

In this connection we have observed certain lines of demarcation between the sexual periods, which, like every kind of classification, are more or less relative, but which give a thoroughly practical insight into the question. These various sexual-periods are so decidedly influential in the fashioning of our lives, that they characterise the most important of our life periods.

We shall briefly review this division of our life into different sexual periods. The first three periods we shall not deal with here, because they all belong to the intra-uterine life. They are: firstly, the absolute sexlessness of the first few weeks of our embryonic life, secondly the development of the hermaphroditic or bisexual condition, and thirdly, the foetal differentiation of the future male and female sexual organs. These comprise the first three stages of evolution in the great evolution of species, as we explained in Chapter 40.

The really decisive alternative in sexual classification indeed lies in the question whether we are able to afford each other the mutual help in sexual intercourse necessary to ensure sexual satisfaction. This is typical of the adult age. So long, however, as this is not yet the case, we speak of childhood, and if finally this has ceased to be the case, we call it senility. And we say there is a transition period between childhood and the adult age, and between that and senility.

Sexual abstinence is found to be most beneficial at these two transitory periods. We feel ourselves mentally and psychically stronger; we are proud of it. But if we have yielded in spite of our best intentions, we feel enervated and annoyed; we are sorry that we were so weak, and are filled with remorse.

But, on the other hand, at the summit of our life, we feel a renewal of strength and are soothed when we have fulfilled our marital duty. And conversely we are sorry if we have failed in the least to reciprocate love. How greatly will many a man on his death-bed regret with tears in his eyes that he had not been kinder to his wife! And how cold and empty is the life of him who has never loved!

These personal feelings arise from physiological necessities. It is the same thing here as with all effort and exercise. We may say that at the prime of life the more exertion one makes, the more strongly will any function develop. If, however, too great efforts are made at a very early age, the function is weakened, and if we do this in old age, exhaustion results. These are the most essential points of the life-curve.

The different periods can sometimes change unnoticed into neighbouring periods: young girls, still children, who become pregnant; withered old men who attack a woman or even a child quite unexpectedly. And even apart from these abnormalities, how sudden may be the transition from child to man. And how easily it may have happened in the transition period of youth, when there was no thought of sexual intercourse, and one felt so sure of oneself, so perfectly happy with the most harmless caresses, and unexpectedly the impulse rose to blind frenzy, even if it meant death on the spot.

To shape our lives aright, we should follow the normal curve, and never confuse the different life-periods with each other. For instance, a little ignorance, naiveté and timidity is not out of place in a child, and on the contrary may lend it an added charm. At a later period of life, however, this uncertainty, this ignorance would be a fault, often dishonourable and almost criminal. And it disgusts us just as much if an old man tries to deny his age and to excite himself or his hearers sexually through vulgar "double entendres". He thinks that young people will find this funny, but it is only repulsive. And those young people especially who are freest in their behaviour when in each other's society only, now feel this behaviour of the old man to be a parody and are thoroughly offended.

Circumspection is still more imperative when acts are concerned. It is certainly criminal to excite a child sexually; this is universally admitted. But it is equally wrong to preach to married couples that they should live together like brother and sister, if there is no serious reason. Thus in many cases this separation into life-periods may become normal for us.

The painter, the poet, the writer have all kept these different sexual life-periods quite distinct in their masterpieces; it is indeed this which is so charming, so delicate, so refined, in their compositions. But judges have often sinned against it, when they have pronounced too severe a verdict. And moralists have done violence to Nature far more often, have praised the morbid, and extinguished life-energy.

And we as doctors must always take these sexual life-periods into consideration, not only when prescribing a régime, but when judging of pathological and especially psycho-pathological cases. In children and young people we should always watch for signs of masturbation, in the married we should not neglect to enquire if they find complete sexual satisfaction in their conjugal relations, and in the aged if they feel depressed through impotence.

This trio: masturbation, coitus, and impotence, together form a typical whole. They even form a complete history of life, from child-ish naiveté to senile exhaustion. It is a search, a finding of oneself, and a final state of exhaustion. Indeed these are the three normal phases in normal sexual intercourse: one always begins by caresses that are not copulation, yet are exciting; then comes coitus as the climax, and one ends in impotence. It is always the same curve of Nature with the apex in the middle. And as the mighty waves of the ocean are formed from tiny ripples, so also is our life-curve formed from the many little sexual curves.

Part VI.

HEALTHIER SEX RELATIONS
AND TECHNIQUES

**Avoiding Ever-present Sex Dangers and
Injurious Methods of Satisfaction**

Chapter 63

Introductory:

AIM OF THIS BOOK: TO HELP MAKE MODERN SEXUAL LIFE A SOURCE OF THE GREATEST HUMAN HAPPINESS AND DELIGHT

UP TO the present we have always shown the sexual life as the source of our life-energy, not merely showering life upon us in the future as the ultimate result of a rejuvenation but a renewal of our life-energy now, immediately. Just as with stocks and shares in the world of finance, the coupons are rows of little cheques that are only payable on certain dates at intervals of months, while the share itself, the original document, is the real property, of which we are proud. And this original share may be compared to the capital of love, which makes us richer and fills us with enthusiasm from the first.

Now comes the question: does the ideal which we have developed in this book really agree with our experience, as medical practitioners, of individual and social sexual life? Not in the least! This sexual life, which ought for almost everyone to be a source of the greatest joy and happiness, because it governs our feelings of happiness more intensely than anything else in the world, is really nowadays for the great majority of people a fruitful source of misery and even despair.

But this state of things is the best proof of my thesis. In reality we see on every side only glimpses of love and happiness. How beneficial and indispensable the sexual life is in its own way, is best evidenced by the misery felt by man wherever this ideal life is misunderstood, perverted or misused.

For many centuries now a "higher" form of love has been preached to us, in which every human heart should be filled with love,...and the elementary school of love, as mother Nature herself has shown us so clearly, has been systematically neglected, misunderstood and despised. So it is no wonder that this doctrine has met with so little success, because we have not yet been educated even in love's own preparatory school.

Let us, however, be quite fair in our judgment. Formerly, when man stood on a lower scale in his knowledge of the laws of nature and of morality, the spiritual and material seemed to be divided by an unbridgeable chasm, and our

280

leaders in their dualistic perplexity looked upon the senses as the source of all evil, and considered the sexual life—the most prominent of the manifestations of the senses—as a lust of Satan. The abnegation of all things sexual thus became the highest of all virtues, and those who practiced self-denial in this respect were classed as saints.

Especially in the East where unbridled sensuality appeared as a striking contrast, the oriental temperament only too readily ran to the other extreme in adopting this asceticism. I may mention Buddha as he is described to us, when he abandoned the voluptuous court life by which he had been surrounded; the first Christian martyrs in striking contrast to the depraved Roman society; St. Augustine, who became pious in his old age, and then deplored having spent his adolescence in immorality, and his manhood in sensuality.

The opinions and convictions of this last-named saint became the basis of Catholicism, especially as he represented the absolute supremacy of the church as the principle of all that was good, over the state as the principle of all that was evil. And to a still greater degree his doctrine became the foundation of Protestantism. And indeed Luther[1] was brought up as an Augustine monk, and Calvin's gloomy dogma did not originate in the gospel itself, but only dated back as far as the teachings of St. Augustine, the father of the church, who had declared sensuality to be the worst of all sins. And because it is through this self-same sensuality that the human race is propagated, he fancied he saw original sin in it. And the whole of the doctrine of salvation has as its *raison d'être* the saving of our souls from this original sin that began with Adam and Eve in the Garden of Paradise.

Thus in our higher civilisation, dominated by this austere dualism, the sexual life becomes continually more furtive, instead of flourishing in the light of day. As a matter of fact man is born sexual; theoretically, however, he is expected to have no sex: duplicity everywhere! A hypocritical morality is preached as the highest virtue; without it we cannot get on.

How many married people there are, who allow their sexual instincts to have their natural outlet in their conjugal relations and feel all the better for it, and who, like St. Augustine, and perhaps from their reminiscences of youthful days like his, yet cannot help thinking that really it must be something sinful, and who in consequence are tortured by this internal conflict.

And this uneasiness of mind is felt to a much greater degree when the sexual intercourse is extra-marital, even in those cases where this is not only permissible, but is actually indicated and ethically right.

So it is the preachers of a false morality who poison our ultimate happiness.

And economic difficulties have also upset our sexual life. The struggle for existence has taken possession of the marriage market; and so many a wife who has been successful, has had too much sexual activity forced upon her, whilst many of her unmarried sisters pine away from loneliness. Both categories of women feel unhappy. And in the market-place of unchastity, all that is holy is trodden under foot and smothered with filth.

We must therefore not be surprised that the sexual passion should be misunderstood and abused, and that up to the present it has never been sufficiently valued by Science. None of our functions

1. Although Luther did not approve of celibacy for priests, his attitude towards the female sex was not very edifying.

has been so little elevated to consciousness, so that we might make it subservient to our higher aims. To have done everything in our power to contribute to this result is the endeavour of this whole book.

In order to help to remove the prevailing errors and evils, we must now, in this last part of the book, carefully review these morbid manifestations. But this can be done only in a very perfunctory manner; for in every field the normal can be briefly stated, while the deviations from the normal are innumerable.

We do not intend to speak of sexual diseases in the narrow meaning of these words, i.e., of venereal diseases. They are only so named after Venus, the goddess of sexual desire, because in our climate they are usually propagated through sexual contact. Among the Esquimaux and such races, who all, whether young or old, embrace each other as much as possible on account of the severity of the cold, these diseases have absolutely no special connection with sexual intercourse. With the actual nature of the love-life itself, these diseases have no more to do than have theft and murder: which are not infrequent amongst unchaste individuals. We have already quoted the most important hygienic observations at the end of the first part of this work.

Chapter 64

HOW TO ATTAIN THE OPTIMUM
IN THE SEXUAL LIFE

Avoiding the Dangers of Sex Poverty
as Well as of Sex Excesses

MORALISTS are never tired of warning us against sexual excess, but I do not remember ever hearing one of them utter a warning against *too little* sexual intercourse. Even the Greek gods were always jealous of those mortals who enjoyed too much earthly happiness. I really believe, that if the act of procreation were something very terrible and disagreeable, these self-same moralists would prevail upon us just as continually not to avoid it but to perform this duty frequently!

From every pulpit thundering denunciations are continually launched upon our heads against unbridled passion, against steeping onself in sensuality and voluptuousness, as it is generally called,—and this, let it be remarked, in a world in which almost every person longs for a little more love, a little more affection, a little more joy in life! The stripling who has fallen into the bad habit of masturbation,—is that excess? That is sexual poverty!

To be engaged to some nice girl with the happy prospect of an early marriage would be his dearest wish, if that were possible; all those men who are obliged to live alone in furnished rooms and who sometimes from sheer loneliness and lack of affection around them give way to the temptations of drink and prostitution, is that excess?—It is absolute absence of the happiness of love.

Alas, how many persons with beautiful bodies and amiable characters there are in our modern society, who will never have their share of earthly happiness. And all the married people who perhaps practice marital intercourse with the greatest regularity, frightful regularity, to speak the truth about the matter, but who, however, are not at all suited to each other. They give each other no satisfaction, either physically or psychically. Their number is legion. They are hungry perhaps not on account of *too little* nourishment, but because the nourishment that is offered them is not suited to their digestion.

Of course there are persons who indulge their passions to excess; excess is harmful in this as in every other function, and for this reason it is advisable to speak of this excess now. But we must not generalise! As a medical man I can remember several cases of sexual excess both in and out of wedlock, but in far the greater number of cases there was a lack, a terrible shortage, and only very rarely a great wealth of enjoyment of love and life. I often witnessed a squandering of strength; but that is no excess, only a misguided use of power.

We have so often referred to this in this book! Especially to precocious excitation of the senses at an early age, and to a wilful artificial creation of a sexual urge; so all this need not now be repeated. Fortunately nature is our best teacher in this matter. Lusty, cheerful, energetic persons do not so readily fall into idle dreaming. And Nature herself sets a limit to profligate waste of energy through fatigue and exhaustion, just as in every other function[1].

If the moralists really want to do good work, they should help us to attain the optimum; they ought not, however, to be forever preaching the minimum to us. Poor humanity, if we are all doomed to suffer from the minimum!

But for the time being there is not much to be hoped for from our official preachers of morality. They are still living in the dark ages when people were absolutely helpless against excessive fertility and venereal diseases, when the preaching of sexual abstinence as the loftiest ideal was indeed a duty. Nowadays, however, all that has changed. But in order to uphold their old-fashioned views, they maintain a desperate opposition to all hygienic measures and practical advice, which are capable of improving the state of things in this field. Human happiness and the future of the human race must be relentlessly sacrificed to their out-of-date dogmas!

Yet there really are cases in which, through an earnest mode of life and finer gifts of observation, married folks themselves learn that greater moderation and reserve have more beneficial results than too frequent indulgence. Especially is this true of that time of life to which we have already referred in Part V as the approach of old age. And there are also many people for whom, for special

---

1. Masturbation, in particular, cannot be indulged in to excess with impunity. It is true that the cell-production in the testicles is almost as unlimited as that of pus-cells in inflammation (see chapter 5), and the production of mucus in the seminal vesicles still more so. The central nervous system, however, soon feels the strain and becomes debilitated.

284

reasons, the motto "the less the better" is found the best to follow: for instance, when fatigue and debility, or signs of a weak heart with fear of palpitation and giddiness are manifested. Life is then found to possess other charms, and only more moderate sexual excitement, which is still found very beautiful, will afford the fullest enjoyment in such cases. For as soon as excessive excitement is felt, and the stimulation too strong, especially at the approach of the orgasm, such persons feel too overwhelming an emotion, feel the sensation too much for their strength. They then always make up their minds, that they won't let it go so far next time. Such persons very often feel proud of their heroic resolution, and want to force their own continence on everyone who will listen to them. For them the most moderate indulgence then becomes an excess.

But the married life of fully developed, hale and hearty folk at the summit of their life-energy is quite different. They do not worry themselves or others; they go joyfully about their business or their household duties. Rest and recreation succeed work and activity without anxiety or nervousness. Now and again when their age, their affectionate nature and sexual temperament require it, they consecrate the intimacy of their conjugal bliss. When they reach its highest enjoyment, Nature beckons kindly to them, and they obey the call when it appeals to them. Every one of these occasions is a renewal of the sacred bond; and their sexual intercourse becomes a fulfilment of their conjugal vows to render each other happy.

They are not at all ashamed; they feel proud of it. They would feel ashamed if they were obliged to stifle their passion in loneliness; that would seem quite wrong and unnatural to them. And how cold and heartless! I once heard a young married lady, after listening to a long sermon in which abstinence had been held up as the ideal state for married people, proudly declare: "I think *that* is a dirty idea!" She felt deeply wounded in her purest feelings.

No indeed, these sincere people, who duly honour both their bodies and their souls, and live in accordance with the laws of Nature, have no reason for indulging in excess. For if we keep a physiological urge within proper bounds, it never overexcites us. Only morbid deviations lead to over-stimulation, and none so much as a too protracted compulsory abstinence. Only then will passionate indulgence be an inevitable consequence. For in such a case, if once one gives way, he is certainly no longer master of himself, and plunges into debauchery. That is the constant danger of excess, which the preachers of abstinence always hold before our eyes as a spectre; but it only exists in their own heated imagination, perverted by abstinence.

The sexual appetite, physiologically considered, is like all other periodic needs. One should learn to control one's reflexes, but when appropriate occasions arise, they should not be deliberately suppressed. Nature makes her laws known to us by her barometer of the blood-pressure and the pulse. On the wedding-night, a certain amount of moderation and discretion should be observed; with of course, a little more of giving way on both sides during the honey-moon, for the newly married couple must get used to each other gradually. As a regular habit for the married in the heyday of their lives, indulgence every day of the week is certainly too often, every other day may be taken as a reasonable average; as time goes on they will gradually lengthen the rest periods by themselves, and Luther is said to have given the well-known rule: "twice a week". Later on in life, once a week will perhaps be found sufficient, and then, with the advancing years desire gradually dies down. If we live thus exactly according to natural rules, the foundation of married happiness is secure, and this is the best safeguard of harmonious spiritual love.

Once, when on a visit, I heard the mistress of the house exclaim: "Every dinner is a banquet for me, when I sit down to table"; so the consummation of our marriage should never be a thoughtlessly accomplished routine, but a constantly renewed occasion of festivity and joy.

Chapter 65

MISERABLE SUBSTITUTES FOR
IDEAL SEX SATISFACTION WHICH ARE SCORNED
BY OUR NEW GENERATION

WE ARE so far removed from sexual excess, that we are often tempted to go to the other extreme, and employ miserable makeshifts. These are the melancholy ailments from which our love-life suffers, and which are so difficult to avoid because, like other sorts of ailments, they partly arise from individual and partly from social-economic causes. We have referred to them several times in former parts of this work, for just as we learn to appreciate light in contrast to darkness, so we can only truly realise the value of the good, when we see it contrasted with the evil. But in order to be able to attack the evil at its source we must now consider it thoroughly as a subject of the greatest importance.

I will begin with masturbation (so-called *onanism*), which we have already thoroughly discussed. If we wish to form an opinion about a case of masturbation, or to attempt its cure, then we must consider first of all the age of the person addicted to it; for the diagnosis, and especially the prognosis of the case, varies considerably with the age.

There are many different sorts of masturbation.

In this connection I would first name the handling of the external genitals in quite young infants, which can scarcely be termed masturbation, because nothing really sexual can be said to exist in the child so far.

Then there is, later on, the more systematic fingering of the genitals by little children, when they do not know what to do with themselves, and this may also become a blind passion with them, just as when they were babies it was impossible to break them of sucking their thumbs or their dummies, even by force, because the local stimulation, like all other forms of massage, is accompanied by pleasurable sensations.

Even mutual masturbation in young children may be regarded as only a variation of the usual mutual teasing and tickling that

287

they so readily practice in all parts of the body; preferably of course, on the most sensitive parts.

As they grow older it becomes more serious at the approach of the age of puberty. Then there arrives the usual stage in which the school children use their hands under the desks, if the teacher does not take great care; the artful device of keeping the hands in the breeches pockets; and the bad habit of using the hands under the bed-clothes, if mothers do not watch their children when putting them to bed.

Then when the age of puberty has been reached, we have masturbation with actual emission; perhaps at first simply as an experiment, out of curiosity, so as to see what the sexual organs are really for. This is far more dangerous than the infantile masturbation, because from this time onwards it becomes a need unless we combat the habit strongly.

If at this age masturbation becomes a confirmed habit, it may endanger potency later on.

The nearer we are to the prime of life, the greater the danger of an uncontrollable and shameless manifestation of masturbation. In boarding schools where there is insufficient supervision, where the pupils are thought to be in perfect safety because there is no co-education, mutual homosexual practices are not infrequent, and in big pensions and barracks there is often the most shameless collective self-masturbation. It must always be thought a lucky thing if young men do not learn to frequent houses of ill-fame: first in their youth before they are even engaged, and again at the approach of old age when marital intercourse is no longer possible. In the brothel there it not, as with masturbation, only the danger of harming oneself, but as a result of a single night's folly one may ruin not only one's own health and happiness, but that of the future wife and children as well.

Leaving all higher ethical considerations out of the question, compared with the question of prostitution, masturbation is the lesser evil.

When two young people are courting, they keep at first within the bounds of modest caresses; but gradually getting bolder, easily get into the habit of mutual heterosexual masturbation as a foretaste of marital bliss.

In married life itself, masturbation often plays an important part. It is generally only an occasional makeshift, if one or other of the pair is away or ill, or if the wife is obliged to refuse her husband on account of advanced pregnancy, or for other reasons. Occasionally also, mutual masturbation is habitually practiced be-

288

tween married people if they do not know of better preventive measures, or have none at their disposal.

Unfortunately, there is also melancholic masturbation, a cryptogamic blossom of the lonely soul, as the picture of the blighted dreams of a defective love-life.

Then, finally, we have senile masturbation, when impotence has supervened, as a barren reminiscence of the pleasures of youth. It is not uncommon to find its shameless practice in old age as a symptom of a second childhood.

It is only when we admit this biological law that it really becomes possible to stop the process of degeneration and to postpone the advent of old age. Self-control is the magic remedy, the only infallible remedy, which enables us to preserve our finer sensibility in its purest form. Not that that need mean an absolute denial of all sexual life, but only an ethical and reasonable mode of life as we have outlined in the whole of this work.

If we desire to wage effective warfare against this evil, we must judge each case upon its own merits, firstly, as we have already mentioned, according to the age of the subject, and then taking other details into consideration. If it is simply a case of yielding when the urge becomes too strong, it may be that when the person is drowsy and half asleep, the slightest movement of the warm bed-clothes suffices to precipitate the climax, and the difference between a half-involuntary ejaculation and a nocturnal emission during sleep almost entirely disappears. But the more it is a case of a voluntary and forcible induction of the symptoms of excitement, the greater both psychic and physical exhaustion become. In this connection the frequency of the act is of the greatest importance. For masturbation is far more liable to be practiced to excess than is copulation, because for the latter two people are always required, whereas in masturbation the pleasure can be heightened at will, and herein lies the real danger of the habit.

As in so many other bad habits and morbid conditions, the essential point is to begin the treatment early, before the habit has become too firmly ingrained. It is advisable not to appear angry or upset when one learns of the habit, and to treat it as though it were simply something "not quite nice"; for if we make too much fuss about it and punish it too severely at first, we only drive the children to hide their evil propensity, and then it becomes finally incurable. The most important point of all is to direct the attention of the little sufferer to other things, and by means of constant occupation, and especially fatiguing muscular exercise to leave neither time nor energy for day-dreaming. Then a careful supervision by the parents, if necessary a rational system of rewards and punishments, not as coercion, but only to maintain the child's interest in the fight against the habit.

If masturbation has already become habitual, we can adopt the same system as in weaning an *habitué* from morphia or alcohol, and choose either the direct or the gradual method.

If the first is chosen, the patient should be given a change of scene, under careful supervision, avoiding all the exciting causes that have been observed in his case, and with the categorical injunction that he should give up the evil habit once and for all. His good resolution should be helped and strengthened by associating with good playfellows, regular occupation of mind and body and good advice. So we seek to overcome evil with good, and to awaken higher ideals. When we are dealing with adults, we may hold out the prospect of a happy marriage, at least if the patient[1] is not already too far ruined physically and mentally, and if the evil can first be cured.

If we choose the second, or gradual method, which one is obliged to do in the great majority of cases, because the will power has become too greatly weakened for such a vigorous mode of treatment as the first, and perhaps also because the bodily strength has already suffered too greatly for it to be able to support this sudden change of habit, then one must imitate the mothers who want to wean their babes, who space out the intervals of giving the breast in a systematic manner. For adults, the plan regulating their conduct should be written out in detail, preferably by the doctor, tutor, or clergyman. If the patient has a relapse, it is not necessary to start again right at the beginning, but the treatment can be recommenced at the half-way stage, according to the severity of the relapse.

This second way is longer and more troublesome, and more uncertain of ultimate success; but it may prevent a complete failure which might otherwise so easily happen, if after the first effort relapses occur, although the patient was full of hope that he was already cured. And he might only too easily be tempted, simply from disappointment at his failure, to throw himself more unreservedly than ever into the evil habit, abandoning all hope of permanent cure.

The second is more of an educational method inasmuch as the task of improvement that is set the patient each time is always

1. This is meant generally speaking: it may be either a male or a female patient. Only in females masturbation is very difficult to observe. But even with young men it is not easy to distinguish between the stains in bed-linen, etc., caused by masturbation and those arising from nocturnal emissions. Both dry hard, harder than milkspots and softer than the small stains produced by gonorrheal discharge.

290

one possible of attainment, and its difficulty is increased proportionately with the patient's degree of training. Even if absolute
success is never attainable with this gradual method, yet the ideal
is worked for, and one comes a step nearer that ideal, which
makes the patient feel each time that he has accomplished something after all, and he is cheered on his way. He is, on the whole,
at last on the high road to recovery.

And then, later on perhaps comes marriage, or he moves away to another
locality, or he gains wisdom with maturer years. Like the physician who does
not merely regard his work as an effort to save his patient's life (for he often
fails in this), but rather as an effort to help the patient to improve all his mental and physical energies, to help him in the fight against his troubles both
bodily and mental, which almost always meets with success. And, therefore, this
second method is usually crowned with relative success at last.

To remain constantly in sympathetic touch with those who have contributed
to his cure, just as a total abstainer does with the Order of Good Templars; and
here and there with some moral society that preaches against masturbation, is
also very important as an aid to keeping the good resolution. The best advisers
are generally the parents, or elder brothers or sisters, or some intimate friend.

The greatest danger lies, I repeat, in loneliness and boredom. Bad companions bring other dangers with them, such as aggravation of the evil through dirty
talk and false theories; or they incite to mutual masturbation, which can easily
lead to shameless vice and prostitution.

If, however, the evil habit finally cannot be overcome[2], then
at least no effort should be spared to reduce the ill effects to a
minimum. Great care should be taken that the patient does not
become shy of company or feel desperate, he should not be subjected to excessive mental strain which would exhaust his nervous
system, and his bodily health and strength should be carefully at-
tended to so that he may not suffer in this respect either. Thus
a period of equilibrium may be reached, in which, although his
condition is not altogther satisfactory, it is at any rate quite en-
durable. In very serious cases, in which there are symptoms of
profound moral disturbance or mental derangement, it will usually
be found that it is not masturbation that is at the root of the mental disorder, but that mental deficiency is the primary lesion, and
that the excessive masturbation is only an accessory symptom, consequent upon it. Sometimes an alternation of the two conditions
occurs.

One should be most careful not to frighten the patient by men-
dacious accounts of the terrible dangers and hopeless sinfulness
of masturbation, as this would only make matters needlessly worse.
It is serious enough as it is.

2. In any case the evil habit must be kept within certain limits, even in the most
severe cases. The extreme limits of the permissible frequency must be judged by
the details given at the end of the foregoing chapter, for no matter how mod-
erately masturbation may perhaps be practiced, it is far from exerting the soothing and beneficial effect of normal copulation.

It is an easier matter to frighten people and to drive them to desperation than it is to cure them of their evil habits. Simply because it is so much less trouble to frighten the young folks than it is to exercise watchful care and control over them, many parents hold the danger of hell-fire before them as punishment for the masturbation habit.

The unfortunate subjects, who are already in a somewhat nervous condition, incident to puberty (see end of chapter 55), or suffering tortures from enforced celibacy, are in especial need of careful supervision, and at the same time of loving care and sympathy, and if they do not get it, being of weakened character, they give up and consider themselves forever lost.

And so it unfortunately happens, if the spiritual leaders and moral guides of the people are themselves blinded by ignorance, and dualistically wander far from the truth, even neglecting to acquaint themselves with the real facts, as far as they are known to every medical man.

The simplest things in hygiene are treated from the ideological point of view, and thus in regard to marriage, a certain form of idealism is created, which always leads to disappointment, while in the case of masturbation the victims are driven to despair—far worse than the vice itself.

If, however, we devote attention to the facts, which are surely serious enough to warn us of the evil, then we can, by comparing cause and effect, save many useful human lives from destruction by means of our timely advice and mutual help.

Some people think, when speaking of unsatisfactory substitutes for natural intercourse, that the use of contraceptive appliances by married people is one of the worst of them all. This opinion, however, does not agree with the facts.

It is true that certain preventive methods are very harmful; but there are some appliances that give absolutely no trouble and in fact cannot be noticed by the wearer during the night. It is, however, not within the province of this work to go into this subject in detail; for the whole subject, I beg to refer my readers to Mr. Coudray's English translation of my book, "Rassenverbesserung" (Eugenics and Birth Control), pub.: Richard A. Giesecke, Dresden-A. 24, 1923.

Many persons are hungering and thirsting for love, but owing to unpropitious circumstances are prevented from marrying. It often happens that they find a substitute in the intimate companionship of another person of the same sex, and live together. Not that there is anything of a homosexual preference, such as we dealt with in Chapter 59, but because in their inner consciousness they feel that friendship, after all is the greatest thing in the world, and because it reconciles them to their fate.

Such an intimate friendship may be as faithful and inseparable a union as the most beautiful of heterosexual marriages, and very often is quite as happy, because the identity of the sex so frequently includes an identity or great similarity in tastes and wishes.

We often meet with (or suspect) such very intimate friendships especially

292

among the most intellectual of women; and that for two reasons: firstly, because whether she marries or not, a woman is always more dependent on her own cleverness than a man; and secondly, because as a general rule, men have a far wider circle of friends and acquaintances to choose from for friendship, and when they want to satisfy their sexual desires only too often stray from the straight path.

One might even go a step farther and declare that the institution of marriage itself, as we know it today, is a very poor substitute for that ideal state of bliss of which lovers so fondly dream.

Of course the objections that may be raised against our modern marriage system as it is at present organised, are numerous and serious. In many respects it is a worn-out and defective institution, originating in abduction of the desired woman, and based on the crudest form of private property-owning, as though both wife and children were mere goods and chattels of the husband.

Milder manners and the idealism of a higher degree of civilisation have of recent centuries somewhat ameliorated the unhappy state of affairs, but it is still far from satisfactory. Wherever in this work I have spoken of marriage, I have not meant the legal institution of marriage such as we are all acquainted with, but rather ideal marriage as it should be, and as fortunately it often is, in spite of all the enormities of the law.

Why should not the special conditions of each individual marriage contract be left to the parties themselves, at least if they demand it? The State should then simply ascertain and certify whether such a private contract may not possibly contain something that might prove prejudicial to a third party, and in particular, whether the interests of potential children are sufficiently guaranteed.

It has been demanded in many quarters for a long time now, that if a State grants marriage licences, it should also require medical certificates from the contracting parties, guaranteeing them to be free from any ailments or hereditary tendencies as may prejudice the health of possible children of the marriage. The legislator can, however, never find time for such "unimportant things"! And yet this is no party question, but touches on the highest and most important interests of all individuals.

Ages ago there were many people of a low standard of morality who neglected legal marriage from carelessness; in our modern times, on the other hand, there are many more people of a high morality, who offer themselves as martyrs for an ideal, and refuse on principle to enter the official bond of matrimony, preferring to contract a "marriage of conscience" or a "free love association", quite openly, and as a protest against compulsory and indissoluble unions.

293

Others drag out their engagements as long as possible, regarding this period as the happiest time of their lives, until better laws make their appearance on the statute books.

Yet we must admit that these substitutes for regular marriage are but poor expedients, because they lead to difficult situations for the descendants, which can only be overcome with a great deal of trouble, or sometimes not at all. And then in such cases, the condemnation of public opinion is always much harder and more cruel than the law itself.

In very many cases, the environment and accompanying circumstances do not allow a man to openly declare the situation, and the secrecy that must be maintained inevitably leads to endless hypocrisy. How far this is from the ideal! Yes, it may still happen that as a compensation one must be satisfied with a purely ideal worship of the beloved ideal, a love that does not demand any love in return, and that never betrays its own existence. Clergymen and physicians are often the ideals of these dream pictures: or the hero of a novel, or a historic figure, or an ideal from the Scriptures may fill a yearning heart with its luminous halo. Unfortunately, however, that is no reality. The small amount of religious freedom that we ourselves enjoy was wrested from the powers that be by the blood and tears of our forefathers; but how many more tears must flow in silence and solitude before even the most reasonable of our desires for sexual freedom will be recognised as the indisputable right of man!

Even in the most ideal organisation of the sexual life, there will certainly always be difficulties enough, and there will be every day tiny differences between the two parties in domestic life, and not always perfect harmony between the two characters. These little differences will always be just enough to make us feel the charm of love anew through the effect of contrast. For we must not forget that we are dealing with two persons: and how often it really happens, when one must decide for oneself alone, that one cannot be at harmony even with oneself.

And then it is a lucky thing that monogamy is the rule with us. Bigamy would, however, be a better term for our marriage, because there are always two persons in every marriage. Here again we have a stupid state of things, that this rule is made and fixed by the law and any deviation from it is punishable. We are not very idealistic after all, if we believe in the boundless character of our sympathy, if three persons may not be allowed to conclude a marriage bond together, when all three earnestly desire it. One would think that should not matter to the legislator.

But, of course, even without any such stringent regulations, in normal cases monogamy will always continue to be the ruling form of marriage; for even in countries where polygamy is permitted it is only a few of the richer families that can afford such a luxury as a plural marriage. There are many reasons in favour of monogamy, both of a higher and lower order. The jurist should, however, not lose sight of the fact that there are always exceptional cases which must not be overlooked.

As long as the couple love each other, the official indissolubility of the marriage bond is superfluous; but as soon as it happens that the continuation of the union is costing one of the partners all his life's happiness, then it is an immoral bond that should most certainly not be upheld by any power or third party. And it is a very doubtful kind of happiness for the children if there are any, if the parents are forced to live together against their will.

The yoke falls most heavily on those people who, when they were engaged (see end of chapter 57), had only one common ideal or one common interest, no matter how enthusiastic they may have been, limited to one sphere: art, or science, or music, for instance, or perhaps sensual pleasure, or bodily comforts alone; and this would be all the more likely to happen, the more the one object of mutual admiration threw everything else into the background. Future marital happiness is far better assured if there is a moderate liking for things of wider scope, and a mutual sympathy for the past in each other's lives is expressed by the two lovers.

The more their love before marriage was a blind passion, a passion with exaggeratedly high ideals set before it, the greater and more painful will the disappointment prove later on. Furthermore, if blind passion makes us strong in love, it is liable to make us very weak in legal matters, for love gives itself freely and gladly without reserve. And thus it is that, as a general rule, we see engaged couples, especially those that are fearfully in love with each other, not only cast away the few precautions that are allowed, not only do they neglect to avail themselves of them, but prefer to sacrifice them entirely, as though these were a treason against love.

And if we have been very happy in our married life, and have shared our joys and sorrows with each other for many years, as soon as one of us is taken away by death, the other feels desperate grief. Engaged couples too often forget, when marrying, that some day one of them must go first, although they have the indissolubility of marriage impressed upon them. For the faithful wife who has devoted herself all her life with body and soul to the "indissoluble bond" instead of standing alone and living as an individual for herself, the loss of her husband and life's companion is a catastrophe hardly to be borne. In many cases, when the wife has nursed her husband through a long and lingering illness, a severe nervous depression sets in, which undermines her health and threatens her life. And the loneliness at night is not without its deleterious influence, just as with children and in the case of elderly persons, grave feelings of anxiety may occur.

The tragic sufferings of widowed persons are greatly misunderstood, little appreciated, and often ridiculed by the majority of people. The gentlest coercive measure applied to the widow in olden times was that she should be confined in a "philanthropic" institution. If, however, the widow is left to her own resources, her fate may be quite different, according as she is in pecuniary want, or has been left only without her usual occupations. In the first case it often happens that she makes an unwise second marriage, so that she may have a comfortable life once again, or, in the hope of finding another husband, she takes in lodgers, which is sometimes a sort of "widow-prostitution", particularly only at the "dangerous" age. To the second category, however, belong the more frequent cases of "widow's melancholy", often accompanied by a tendency to suicide, in order to follow the loved husband into the grave. We can thus the better understand the Hindoos, with their exalted Oriental temperament, allowing their widows to immolate themselves in the "suttee". This is the most terrible example of the upholding of marriage as the downfall of woman and of womanly individuality.

We now come to the subject of prostitution, the antithesis of marriage.

In order to be able to appreciate the various forms of sexual intercourse at their true value, we should never do as many thoughtless folks do: i.e., confine ourselves to only one alternative, that is, if it is not marriage, it must be prostitution.

No, we must not be so old-fashioned; we must admit the fact that marriage and prostitution are the extreme ends, the terminal links in a long chain of gradations, endless in their variety. We must not judge from one criterion alone, but from different viewpoints: for instance, the length of time certain relations have continued, the degree of affection displayed between the partners, and how far private motives rule.

According to this principle, one may say that marriage has as its object a complete loving surrender for life, and is practically always bound up with a community of property; while prostitution, on the other hand, is a passing event, an act of the moment, without affection as its *raison d'être*, and always for money or other reward.

When we go into the historic and prehistoric evolution and development of these two ancient institutions of prostitution and marriage, the categorical contradistinction between them becomes much more clearly apparent.

It was considered that it was far less evil for a few girls of the poorer class to fall victims to prostitution, as long as they could herd them together in an out-of-the-way part of the town, and that this had the advantage of allowing their respectable virgins and matrons to remain free from danger. As though it were not prostitution which, more than anything else, poisons the family life of the married and seriously undermines the institution of marriage itself.

Sterility and celibacy were the concomitants of prostitution. Even before the last war, nearly one-half of the marriageable women in western Europe were unmarried; and as to the sanitary benefits of prostitution, all the strictness of state-control has never been able to exclude the danger of infection.

Whether the controlled prostitute is found to be suffering from disease or not is of no importance to her visitor. Be she ever so healthy, perhaps only because she has an immunity to venereal diseases, she may nevertheless act as carrier of the infection from one man to another. And even if one were to attempt to subject every one of her clients to medical inspection, unfortunately diagnosis of these diseases is not simple, and a superficial examination is worse than useless. It is a fixed law that the danger of infection increases in ratio to the concentration of sexual intercourse, and so every brothel and every prostitute must therefore be looked upon as hotbeds of infection, and every frequenter as a suspect.

The halo that once glowed around prostitution has faded for other reasons also. Times are changed. After the era of crude desire for orgasm we now have the era of a desire for contraction and of mutual affection. One is no longer satisfied with a mere pouring out of the reproductive secretion in return for payment in money. The new generation wants the pleasures of love, and prefers any other kind of relations, if they only depend on a certain amount of affection, and feels a decided disgust for the mercenary practice of prostitution.

Prostitution is not only the most dangerous, but also the most miserable of makeshifts.

Because it has already been amply proven by an unspeakable amount of suffering that the two extremes (marriage with the tyranny of the husband on one hand, and prostitution on the other) are both contemptible, it is evident that although the legislator obstinately continues to refuse a proper evolution to the institution of marriage, better standards must be developed. more in accordance with our higher ideals and with the practical necessities of our modern life. It is of greater value for our spiritual evolution to seek and strive after this "Excelsior" than to remain forever steeped in a traditional dogmatism. We begin already to meet with unsanctified unions that are as honestly intentioned as official marriage and often felt to be far more ideal.

297

Chapter 66

SEXUAL RESTRAINT
versus COMPLETE SEX ABSTINENCE

ALTHOUGH sexual abstinence in the child seems angelically pure, and in the young man so honourable, we are much to be pitied if we have reached the summit of our lives without having found what we sought, or if we have found it and lost it again, or if for any other reason the greatest happiness of life is withheld from us.

A certain amount of restraint in the fulfillment of our marital duties is always necessary; this only increases our sexual potency, our will-power is thereby strengthened and our love sanctified. By an adequate control of our sexual life — see Chapter 44 — we ceased to be animals and became men; and our finer ethical virtues have only been developed through the manifestation of due chastity and reserve — see Chapter 30. But in married life, absolute abstinence is always dangerous if too long protracted, and may end by completely undermining the happiness of our lives.

Of course the degree of abstinence varies with individual temperament and circumstances; abstinence that is only a necessary rest for one, may prove a terrible privation to another; but absolute abstinence as a permanent state, especially where there is great mutual love, must always be felt as a great source of misery. Only in exceptional cases, in which there is some special and weighty reason for it, do we admire and honour it; otherwise we can only sympathise with the sufferers, because with abstinence disappears all the beauty which, as we have seen in this work, is so closely associated with the realisation of love's ideals. Voluntary abstinence in married life may even ruin our character and lead us to imagine we are better and nobler than everyone else.

Some people used to think that abstinence was physiological economy of our strength. But for healthy, vigorous men and women at the summit of their life's energy, the biological principle is just as true in this case as in that of any other function, that normal exercise stimulates growth and strength. It is that normal exercise which we term life. Whatever the disastrous consequences

298

of a permanent absence of sexual satisfaction, they cannot be properly studied in the married, as here no control is possible. For an elucidation of this problem we must turn to the unmarried; not to lead them into stupid ways, or to confuse their minds by empty sophistry, as has so often been done, but to call upon them to take up the fight in an energetic manner, so that they, too, in their turn, may learn what marital happiness is. The dangers of excessive intercourse are greater, certainly, than those of abstinence; but that is no reason for denying the misery and dangers that are attendant on the latter. On the contrary these should be duly brought to our notice, so that not only the sufferers themselves, but also all right-thinking people shall join in the effort to ensure such an improvement of our social organisation as shall guarantee to every adult man and woman, if they so desire, their reasonable share of sexual happiness.

There are indeed still doctors and professors who stoutly maintain that sexual abstinence is *never* injurious, but such generalisation cannot be scientifically supported, because in order to make this statement a law, one must first be acquainted with *all* cases and *all* their consequences.

Others make the more careful statement that they personally have never seen any harm accrue from it; but the reason for this may be that they are specialists or have never practiced outside a hospital or again have not been careful observers. One witness who has really seen something is worth more than a hundred who have seen nothing. It is, however, the height of presumption to say that no medical practitioner, or none of any importance, has ever observed ill effects from sexual abstinence. Such a statement is either due to excessive naiveté or is a direct falshood.

And yet, in regard to sexual abstinence, there are still people who preach it, as though it were something sublime and pleasing to the Almighty.

This disregard of the physiological optimum is excused on physiological grounds: namely, the neglect of the other physiological needs of the human body are punished by death, while, they say, this is not the case with the sexual life. That statement, however, by no means proves that a limitation of the sexual life does not lead to danger and suffering. These latter, however, are liable to be overlooked, because unlike privation in breathing and eating, the initial effects of a too protracted sexual abstinence are purely psychic, and with a little dogmatism the subsequent material untoward results may be readily attributed to other causes than abstinence itself. It is then easy to say that the morbid symptoms proceed from the fact that the patient has worried too much about

299

the matter and has not tried hard enough to conquer. Those who interpret symptoms in this *a priori* manner, must take the responsibility themselves, of course.

If, however, one wishes to establish the real facts of the case, it is certainly preferable to judge from one's own observations as a medical practitioner, and so I shall now mention my own experience in the course of some 25 years of practice as a general practitioner in Rotterdam. Only in such a family practice is it possible to become sufficiently acquainted with the life-history and environment of one's patients.

First of all, we must enquire whether it is really a case of sexual abstinence. We can only find this out, when we have won the confidence of our patient; the majority of cases occur in females, because on account of the external position of the male organs, men diagnose the trouble for themselves, and indeed usually find a way out on their own initiative, their remedy often proving worse than the disease. Especially if the doctor himself is a man, it is the more easily possible, with care and delicacy, to test how the patient reacts, which helps to ensure a correct diagnosis.

The most difficult of all cases to decide are those in which we are in the presence of only a relative degree of abstinence, cases in which during certain periods extra-marital intercourse or a liaison has been temporarily interrupted: as a consequence of which later on the abstinence is doubly felt, something like the suffering endured in widowhood.

In the early days of my medical practice I used to think that cases of illness leading to the diagnosis of sexual abstinence as an etiological factor were rather rare, and this led me to pay more attention to them than I should otherwise have done. But the more such cases one has already seen, the more one learns properly to appreciate the value of studying all the trifling symptoms as a symptom-complex, and then one finally observes that there is scarcely a case of genuine life-long abstinence to be found that does not show the characteristic symptoms. Very often, it is true, the symptoms may be only slight, but still they *are* symptoms, and are quite sufficient to shroud the patients' lives in sadness.

It is very depressing, when we are granted a glimpse into the lives of the many adult virgins who are compelled to remain unmarried, and who, one is quite certain, are not in the habit of having any sexual gratification whatsoever. In former days, when most young ladies of the upper classes lived more secluded lives and did not go in for any kind of sport or exercise, all these nervous symptoms were attributed simply to physical weakness.

Nowadays, however, most of them go in for some useful occupation, and yet we find that, no matter how zealously they may throw themselves into this work, they still suffer from their sexual abstinence.

At first their ailment only manifests itself in a certain amount of psychic depression; the patient feels herself out of sorts, weary, listless, takes no interest in her work and loses all her energy. There is no organic lesion to be found; the functional disorders are all little complaints that are not ordinarily so severely felt. When one gradually wins her confidence, one learns that life is cold and devoid of charm. She takes no interest in anything. Poor souls: They often betray their longing for a little affection by petting an animal, or raising plants or flowers[1] or they develop a tremendous liking for a clergyman or doctor; for the richer their spiritual life, the more do they feel the need of affection.

No medicines, no pleasure trips, no holidays at the sea-side or in the mountains can help this condition.

In more advanced cases, one finds the patient nervous, excitable, emaciated, always unsatisfied, though she herself cannot tell why. She feels terribly lonely and passes restless, sleepless nights, always tormented by her unhappy lot. It is noteworthy that the more she suffers from sleeplessness, the less appetite she has.[2]

Then she begins to get weak, pale, and thin.

She tries every means of escaping from her uncomfortable situation. She endeavours to give her time and strength for laudable objects, she would like to perform impossible deeds, but accomplishes nothing, because her mental and physical energy is already too far broken down. In everything she finds only disappointment.

I could quote a large number of such cases from my practice, severe cases of complete loss of energy. The patient's parents and friends lose patience at last. If the spinster is no longer quite young, then behind her back they say harshly and cynically: "What she wants is a husband." In such cases the medical adivser can of course do nothing.

So, slowly but inevitably, a condition of anaemia, a chlorosis and debility develop, with all their concomitant psychical and physical troubles— that vague but familiar picture which one so often sees in the unmarried, and which only too easily pave the way for other, more definite diseases. Of course, it is a matter of general knowledge how greatly all conditions of exhaustion predispose to pulmonary tuberculosis and many other constitutional diseases[3]. Then later it happens that one is hardly able to distinguish in the individual case which was the cause and which the effect.

When we gain time, we gain a great deal. If these patients did not so often meet with an early death through this class of bodily ailments, there would remain the possibility that when in the course of time their sexual activity ceases, their psychic life also reaches a period of repose, and thus at last a day of general mental and bodily peace and relative health and comfort may dawn for them.

In the early stages, when the morbid condition has not become too chronic, there seems to be every possibility of cure; especially if there is a prospect of a happy marriage. This latter, is however, always somewhat risky, for if in such a case it should turn out later that the patient was already too far gone, then there would be two unhappy people instead of one. But if the morbid condition has made too great progress, all help comes too late; after all her disappointments, everything that may remind her of sexual things has become unbeautiful, or even hateful. Bitterness and tragedy are written in her face; one hears them in every tone of her voice, sees them in her every movement. And

1. The patient herself often says that she feels the whole trouble to be due to the fact that she ought to be a mother. Really, it is a crying injustice of public opinion to deny her the right which the legislator has not denied her; but whether motherhood would cure her of her unhappy condition is doubtful, just as it is uncertain that her child would find much joy in life.

2. An association of symptoms that is constantly found in other cases.

3. We physicians have always wondered why it is that consumptives are so often passionate in their sexual inclinations. This enigma may possibly find its solution in the fact that those who suffer severely from sexual abstinence are particularly predisposed to contract scrofulous and tuberculous diseases.

the unkind world, that so readily mocks at all suffering, calls her in derision "old vinegar-face".

But in the prime of life the mental suffering often becomes acute, even when no complications that might be termed a menace to life appear. For psychical disturbances may acquire a very threatening character.

Here I must devote a few lines to the subject of hysteria. This ailment takes on so many protean forms, and every practitioner finds so many variations of it in his clinical observations, that he forms his own definition of hysteria from his personal experience. This much is, however, certain, that in innumerable cases of hysteria, the continued enforced abstinence plays the most important part in its causation. At the first the sexual abstinence occasions a loss of mental equilibrium, and in the course of time unbalances the central nervous system, which may give rise to the strangest symptoms, often accompanied by bizarre behaviour, which attracts attention to the patient. She suffers so keenly: and if no one seems to understand her, if no one sympathises with her, she feels compelled to bring the most terrible charges against people and even to simulate the most alarming symptoms. We doctors have a great deal to put up with from this class of patients! In a few cases our remedies have some little success; in others no matter what one prescribes, nothing has the slightest effect; there are even cases in which drugs only do harm and aggravate the symptom. The most extraordinary cramps and irregular reflexes may also in reality render the patient's life quite unbearable and drive her to desperation. The family doctor may then diagnose *"globus hystericus"* without hesitation, while the patient, in her despair of ever getting better, is often inclined to commit suicide to put an end to her sufferings. In another case, a typical erotically delirious patient developed epileptiform attacks, which usually originate from some deeper pathological condition.

Sexual abstinence may really lead to the most serious neuroses and to complete insanity. The causal nexus may be distinctly traced through a certain parallelism in related cases.

There were three daughters in a respectable family. One of them was subject to hysteria, but the family doctor was able by dint of constant attention to keep her in equilibrium; the second had a love affair with a bookkeeper; the third was for some time so mentally deranged that she could not be cared for in an ordinary hospital, and was kept at home, where she even annoyed her father with her erotic importunities.

We find such cases most instructive, because we can thus observe how differently sexual abstinence affects three closely related persons. The first mentioned, the youngest daughter, was easily saved, the second refused to remain celibate, while the third daughter was driven by her intolerable nymphomania to attempt incest and was also mentally deranged.

I was called to another family where I found a severe case, a young and most excitable girl, who had been complaining that she was constantly pursued with amorous offers in her father's business where she was employed. From the next-door neighbour, who was also a patient of mine, I learnt that one of the young girl's sisters had on one occasion caused a terrible scandal at night with one of the young employees. The third sister, my patient went on to say, had been married but had lost her husband soon after; she told her neighbour one evening when she had been invited to tea with her that she was longing to get married again; but the next morning she was found drowned; she had thrown herself into the water.—Meanwhile I found that the young sister I had

302

been called to see was in such a nervous condition that we had to send her to an asylum. She got no better. The specialist who examined her stated that he had no doubt her symptoms were the consequence of sexual abstinence. So here we find the trio: seduction, suicide and insanity[4].

The evidence of the causal factor is far better brought to our notice than in such parallel cases, when in pronounced cases a cure follows a cessation of the abstinence. I have seen this happen in a case that was apparently hopeless.

I had been medical adviser for many years to a wealthy family which counted several Catholic priests among its relatives. The daughter was a very pretty girl, who had always been remarkably healthy until shortly before the time when I was called in. The parents complained that for some time, about a year in fact, she had been very melancholy and given to frequent fits of weeping. She got steadily worse. At last I found out that she worried and thought herself lost because, as she thought, a young chaplain had put her in the family way at an evening party.

He had only kissed her.

Very likely the girl had had a fully pleasurable voluptuous sensation from the passionate kiss that the young man had given her, as often happens in such cases. But in reality she was in a perfectly normal condition and not pregnant at all. Although we assured her a hundred times over that if she had been *enciente,* something would have been noticeable long before, as a year had elapsed since the incident and that the medical examination proved that there was really nothing the matter with her, she only shook her head in a helpless manner, and continued to wander about in her father's house all day and half the night, a prey to melancholy and despair. A very experienced physician, a specialist in mental affections, was called in consultation, as the parents could not keep her at home any longer. We were of the opinion that her internment in a suitable institution was absolutely necessary, and certified to that effect.

What, however, was our surprise to learn shortly later, that instead of sending her to the institution recommended, the parents had found a husband for her. Our young patient has, since then, always enjoyed the best of health as a wife, and even under the most trying circumstances never lost her balance.

I only learnt all these details when, sometime afterwards, I had a similar case of dementia to treat; that of a young lady who was only kept from suicide by placing her under restraint, and who had to be watched day and night. "For God's sake, don't send our daughter to an asylum," begged her parents.

I related the details of the former case to the relatives of this second patient, and also to the gentleman for whom she had been an excellent housekeeper. Her condition continued to become steadily worse, and at last I considered it imperative to send her to an asylum. Her employer frequently went to see her on visiting days; and after a time took her back into his service, and the experienced observer could not fail to remark that the patient's gradual restoration to health coincided with an affectionate union between the two. Death alone put an end to their affectionate relations.

4. One may readily understand how many girls, seeing no hope of getting married, get so sick of their lives that they end them, and this is a frequent result of chronic abstinence. Physiologically speaking, life is, and must always be, a succession of periods of pleasure and pain; if everything were always agreeable, it would not seem to us to be so; we must have contrast. Normally, both factors almost balance each other. But if one is deprived from any cause whatsoever, of the enjoyment of one of the richest sources of human happiness, what else can we expect than a life that is no longer worth living?

The most conclusive, however, are the less frequent causes in which the medical adviser, taught by experiences such as those above mentioned, finds himself in a position to discreetly encourage an engagement or such a love affair as may be morally permitted, with a resulting cure as a direct consequence of the changed conditions. Absolute proof that the sexual abstinence was the only cause of the morbid state can never be adduced. But the experience that such an experiment leads to the patient's recovery, is certainly a contribution to our scientific knowledge.

I have been fortunate enough on several occasions to witness this, and under circumstances which leave no shadow of doubt as to the efficacy of marriage. Sexual satisfaction has a decided therapeutic effect, even if the improved condition is only apparent so long as the sexual relations continue, and in proportion to the intensity of the same. If, however, the morbid condition is found to be of too long standing, and has become chronic, the treatment may be of no avail. Only the approach of age can then peacefully terminate this state of things.

In conclusion, I must mention how great an effect protracted sexual abstinence may have on the intellectual and moral sensibilities of some sufferers, inevitably driving them to despair and profound melancholy, not infrequently also unhinging their minds. How many highly cultured people have been led, as a result of their endless struggle against their purely natural feelings, to abnormalities and perverse practices, sometimes giving way to the most frightful sadism, or even to rape and lust-murder.

My friends, the next time you read in your newspaper of a crime committed in a passionate moment by an unmarried schoolmaster or a celibate priest, you should have pity on the unfortunate man, as well as on his victim. Was the guilty man really wicked? No, he only lost control of himself for a mad moment. If he had been a man of low ideals, he would long ago have associated with common prostitutes; but he had fought down all such temptations, he had always tried to win the mastery over his passions, until one day he was off his guard... and then... the thing happened! All his remorse is then too late! The real guilt for these occurrences lies with our hypocritical upbringing, our traditional glorification of an oriental asceticism. We must all share the blame with him.

Scientifically speaking, the following points are the most important. Because the suffering entailed by sexual abstinence starts with nervous and mental disturbances, people were always inclined to think that the trouble was only something subjective, the consequences of suppressed longing or unsatisfied desire, or possibly disappointment over a presumably wasted life. But cases have often come to my notice in which the same distressing symptoms and dissatisfaction with life were observable in elderly spinsters who were innocent of all trace of sexual desire, who were indeed quite cold in this respect, and in these cases it became evident that any cure presented far greater difficulty, because not only did these ladies not seek the remedy, but even avoided it.

This experience throws quite another light on the morbid picture. Quite independent of any subjective wishes and inclinations, the normal exercise of the sexual function is an essential condition of the proper development of our full health and our full vitality to which we have so often referred in this work, and on which we laid special stress in Chapters 26 and 40.

In view of the practical importance and the highly complicated nature of this question, I will endeavour once more to outline here the various deleterious influences concerned.

The more the energy of the vegetative growth approaches its terminal point in our youth, the more do we perceive a certain indifference and loss of energy or listlessness, a condition which may easily amount to depression. As soon as, with the arrival of the period of puberty, the stimulus of sexual desire makes itself felt, this new stage of growth may easily cause in sensitive individuals a certain degree of exaltation, which then alternates with periods of fatigue. If, later on, at the climax of our life-energy, in the prime of life, the sexual urge becomes so insistent that its suppression is felt to be an imperious necessity, then a compulsory and continued abstinence becomes a deeply-rooted evil resulting in depression, and this is made far worse by the harmful effects of all sorts of unsatisfactory substitutes for normal, healthy and regular sexual intercourse.

In those cases where the sexual urge is not felt at all by the individual, the due revival of the life-energy ceases to appear. Even when asexual frigid women marry in later years, and cohabitation takes place regularly, this symptom of deficiency will make itself more or less apparent, because they never feel the least sexual desire, and have no idea what it really is.

But the morbid picture of the suffering entailed by sexual abstinence is by no means completed by the enumeration of the above symptoms; it only indicates the preliminary stage and the less severe cases. We see quite other symptoms, far less easy to diagnose in really grave cases. The effects of sexual abstinence, as we physicians observe them in unmarried women, often give the impression, with their typical chlorosis and cachexia, that one is in the presence of an auto-intoxication. It would be highly interesting to inquire

305

more fully into the causes of this impression; unfortunately we must be content for the present with mere hypotheses.

We may, however, suppose the case to be as follows: adulthood is that particular life-period in which the special organochemical substances are poured into the blood-stream and are thus enabled to exert their important stimuli on all the tissues of the body. Those individuals in whom this phenomenon occurs in an insufficient degree, frequently display the loss of interest, depression and mental inferiority typically seen in eunuchs.

If, however, this union occurs normally, then in due course, perhaps through a cumulative effect, all the organs and body-fluids become so thoroughly permeated and saturated by the organochemical substances, that at the climax of our life-energy, the sexual urge becomes manifest in an enormous degree. If in this case there is no biological neutralisation of the individual organochemical toxins of one or the other sex, by the exercise of regular cohabitation or kissing, etc., it seems to me to be very plausible that as a result of the excessive one-sided effect of one's own endocrine secretions being retained, blood-poisoning, as in all other auto-intoxications, may readily occur. This hypothesis agrees with the known fatal properties possessed by all these endocrine poisons, which can only be directed into their proper channels if they counterbalance each other, that is to say, if they neutralise each other biologically.

Further, it is well worth while enquiring whether retention of secretions in the genital tract may not occasion auto-intoxication, just as it does in the urinary system and in the intestinal canal, unless the secretory functions are sufficiently stimulated by regularly repeated sexual intercourse. For we do not meet with the more serious cases of sexual abstinence in early manhood or womanhood, at which period the sexual urge is most pronounced, but only much later on in life.

Especially in the female organism, this morbid predisposition seems to me not at all improbable; which would explain why the effect of sexual abstinence in woman shows so much more definitely a toxic character than in man.

Many readers may possibly think that if abstinence from sexual intercourse is fraught with such serious danger, a voluntary or involuntary abstinence from child-bearing must have a very prejudicial effect on the maternal organism, for it has always been looked upon as the "raison d'être" of the sexual life. Experience however, does not bear out this view. On the contrary, the somatic and physical damage and the dangers of pregnancy and motherhood unfortunately weigh far too heavily in the balance!

But no matter what the theoretical solution of all these problems may eventually be, the hygiene of the future will always strive towards the goal of an ideal mode of living; and energetic vegetative development, which will in due course be crowned by the most beautiful of sexual blossoms.

Chapter 67

SEX SUBLIMATION *versus*
BEAUTIFUL SEX RELATIONS IN MARRIED LOVE

WHAT is meant by this word that moralists are so fond of, as though it were a magic cure for all the ills that follow on sexual abstinence?

In the foregoing chapter we have seen how so many people, at the very best period of their lives, suffer from depression and dissatisfaction simply as a consequence of a too protracted sexual abstinence, and how deeply miserable and thoroughly disheartened they may be when vanquished in the conflict. But even those who issue apparently victorious from the hopeless fight against their natural passions are generally to be pitied, as something narrow and "old-maidish" persists in their character, an inevitable one-sidedness, which we shall now study a little more closely.

First of all, there comes to my mind the case of many a good spinster getting on in years, who has experienced many disappointments, and has ended by renouncing everything. Once upon a time the sexual life may have inspired her with great hopes, but in the end it has brought her only sleepless nights and bitter awakenings. Now at last she feels she has had enough of it. She cannot and will not nourish any more false hopes; everything sexual is most distasteful to her. She will be more reasonable in the future; she will seek consolation in "higher things"; she still has plenty of energy and will employ it along other lines.

She is fitted for something superior: for music, theosophy, or other forms of mysticism; she feels spiritually exalted. As time goes on, she feels great sympathy for those similarly situated, and is quite at home in their society. She pursues these new ideals with all the enthusiasm of passion; for the fire of her primitive feelings is by no means extinguished. Her passion is only sublimated; it has been directed into higher paths. If she were really dead to the world her renunciation would be of a more resigned character, something like the calm of people in advanced old age.

And so at last, renouncing everything "base", she has attained

307

Chapter 68

DEGENERACY OF THE SEXUAL LIFE
Facts that Should Be Widely Known by Parents, Teachers, Judges, Ethical Leaders

IT IS now a very unpleasant task, but my duty, to refer to some of the forms of perversity and erotomania that come to the surface here and there in the sexual life. The general practitioner in every big town or city meets with such cases in his practice, and comes to know them only too well. From the scientific point of view, pathological deviations from the normal are of less importance than a knowledge of the normal itself; the endless variety of individual abnormalities has not the fundamental importance of the normal. This must always be taken as our standard for all observations; besides, all these pathological complications are much more difficult to understand.

How often we observe in cases of senile degeneracy, old people who instead of normal sexual pleasure, find a dirty delight in playing with their own excreta, when they have reverted to a second childhood, or relapsed into complete idiocy[1]. And how cruelly these aged degenerates inflict moral and physical suffering on their unhappy partners, and even on themselves, solely in the fallacious hope that these abnormal stimuli will awaken a temporary return of their own lost sexual forces; this may even lead to lust-murder in the violation of women and children.

And then what strange association of ideas, thought and feelings, it is when they feel sexually excited by the handling or contemplation of a lock of hair, or of an article of female clothing, for instance, and when no other objects possess the least charm for them, or have the least effect on them sexually! In former times all such cases, as soon as they led to serious acts, were looked upon as misdemeanours; the Mosaic law, for instance, punishing all connection of men or women with animals with death. Krafft-Ebing and other psychiatrists, however, have studied

1. Little girls sometimes wet the bed when they take to the habit of masturbation, while in little boys, on the contrary, habitual bed-wetting often disappears as they reach the age of puberty.

this question more closely, and are more and more inclined to the opinion that these sexual abnormalities are generally the result of psychic derangement, and frequently of deep-seated mental trouble.

Thus our judgment of these people has become severe. And further investigation has also convinced us that in most cases we may blame false education and training, erroneous impressions received in childhood, or perhaps simply an individual natural peculiarity[2].

Krafft-Ebing, for instance, mentions a case of erotic cruelty in a young man, who experienced sexual satisfaction for the first time in his life as he was wringing a fowl's neck. As in my own practice I remember a case of so-called "fetichism", that of a young man who never obtained satisfaction unless he was holding a lady's slipper, which can only be explained by the fact that his first emission occurred when fondling one of his own sister's slippers. Of course, one must also be somewhat unfavourably predisposed and badly trained, if one can be so exclusively and permanently influenced by a single experience, or even if it occurs repeatedly.

And the feeling of necessity for the dirty and the obscene in word and deed may also easily arise from a false training in one's youth, if, as so often happens, all things sexual are stigmatised as the height of impropriety, And it may also be that with such erroneous over-refined training, all actual contact with, or experience of, dirt and violence are avoided as much as possible, so that when these actually occur later, they possess the attraction of novelty, as though they were something quite original; but this is a rough sort of stimulation, only to be played as a cynical trump card at the end of one's life, when all normal, agreeable and tender charms have lost their power.

These errors can now be better avoided, because new light breaks in upon the etiology, i.e., the causation of such cases, and such unfortunate degenerates are more humanely treated. If for some reason or other they are brought up before the judge, they are now more likely to be sent to a suitable home than to prison.

And the further we pursue our investigations into the chain of causes, the greater is the possibility of a complete cure.

Although an erroneous education or training is frequently the cause of sexual aberration with improper behaviour, yet in other cases the *causal nexus is* quite different, and it is such cases to which Krafft-Ebing has devoted special attention. In Chapter 65 we referred to something similar in the more serious forms of nervous affections arising from excessive masturbation. In serious cases of sexual morbidity, the primary cause often proves to have been some affection of the central nervous system, and the psychopathy can then, therefore, only be regarded as more or less causal manifestations of the functional morbidity.

The lay public, however, believes just the contrary to be the case, always expects a cure from an appeal to reason and throws all the blame on the sex-

2. We have already referred to the erogenous and erotofugal zones in the normal sexual life.

Chapter 69

UNCONSCIOUS POWERS OF INFLUENCE ON OUR SEXUAL LIFE

WE now come to the most intimate feelings of our psychic life. This is the realm of secret and magical powers, dating from the origin of humanity; powers which have more influence over us than any others. This occult force is like a fairy godmother watching over us from our childhood, until we are old enough to shift for ourselves; and although she makes us rather timid of the good things, she often helps us to avoid the bad.

Every powerful emotion drives the blood with renewed energy through our blood vessels, and we have already mentioned (in chapter 20) how the sexual life, especially, is liable to affect our emotions and to cause congestion in our circulation. It is more especially the sexual impressions that so frequently conjure up the rosy blush on our cheeks. And the shyer a child is, the more charming we find such blushing which becomes much more intense at the time of puberty, even making us lose our presence of mind.

The intense sensitiveness of the youthful soul is often betrayed by it. Generally it is caused merely by some little surprise, because one finds onself, for instance, suddenly in an unwonted situation. Sexual impressions may easily give rise to a certain timidity if the sexual has developed late in life and only become customary in old age, so that it has lost its first natural charm; though indeed many an old roué at this latter stage of life, falls into the other extreme — a coarse cynicism.

And the young people who are most subject to this sort of thing are those from whose training, co-education or friendly contact with the opposite sex, has been the most carefully excluded, and in whose case safety has been sought by keeping them from the "wicked" world. And on this account they feel a double need of sympathy and affection, but all is wrecked on the rocks of this stupidity! Many a tenderly blossoming young affection is thus nipped in the bud; and although it only leads to misery and disappointment, many of them seek consolation in loneliness.

314

Especially, also, must those young people suffer from this travesty of modesty, who from lack of natural modesty try to behave exceptionally well, and yet are so blinded by immodesty as to be unable to notice their own faults.

Very often in such cases, it is only a concomitant symptom of sexual abstinence.

So it is not at all difficult for us to understand how it is that a hardened Don Juan generally meets with success with the ladies; he has long forgotten how to blush and is never at a loss! Really, this indefinite modesty is of very doubtful value in our education. And it has a still worse effect when we find ourselves in bad compnay, and we need all our strength of character not to give way to temptation; our blushing timidity leads us to brave it out, and to do the same as the others so that we shall not be thought stupid.

So it is modesty that warns us of the approach of every temptation; something like the warning that pain gives us of some physiological danger to our bodies. Both warnings are life-saving a hundred times over, and are the first condition necessary for self-preservation. When once the sick man no longer feels his pain, or one is so far on the downward path in life that he is lost to all shame, then both have gone too far to be rescued.

Because this blushing from guilt cannot be distinguished in appearance from the so-called blushing from embarrassment, we must not be surprised that both are called by the same name, and that we are so often really misled in our judgment of innocence or guilt. For both of them are accompanied internally by similar palpitation and a feeling of anxiety in the region of the heart. In very serious cases it seems to us as if our heart would cease to beat altogether; it very nearly does so, and then the deep blush on our cheeks suddenly fades away, and we are deathly pale. But often before it proceeds as far as this, the reflex comes to our relief, and the tears flow.

This shame feeling from guilt is the most faulty grounding that can be imagined for the moral training of the young.

I shall now endeavour to cite a few examples of how in the course of time the human shame-motives have been modified, corresponding to the stage of evolution, to living conditions, to the security of the laws, and to improved education.

In the primitive state of nature, when our savage forefathers constantly had death from hunger or violence before their eyes, all the various kinds of bloody ceremonies and customs then prevalent, such as human sacrifice and the eating of human flesh were only reflections of these conditions, and these customs were perhaps indispensable for the preservation of the tribe. Any man who rebelled against them would surely have been put to death, or at any rate would be in constant fear of discovery. But, gradually, as the economic situation improved, these usages came more and more to be perpetuated only as traditional festivals; and anyone who tried to evade participation in them was only ashamed before the others on account of *differing* from them. As man reached a still higher stage of development, human consciousness of higher things led him to abandon such atrocities and to hold the view that fear of giving up such manners and customs was only false shame; until at last nothing is left of these traditional festivals but a few symbolical mysteries and sacraments whose origins nobody knows.

Another example. At first, the safety of a tribe, and, of course, that of each of its members, was only guaranteed by a complete solidarity among them; and at this primitive epoch there was no other way to keep this intact, except by forcing all the members to act similarly and simultaneously in all circumstances. Any failure to do this was necessarily regarded by the others as high treason, and was swiftly followed by exemplary punishment in the presence of the whole tribe. Anyone who had so rendered himself liable to capital punishment, perhaps died at once from consciousness of his own guilt.

And now, when we feel it our duty to act in defiance of public opinion, we know very well that the shame that prevents us from doing so is false shame.

Since, in the course of its evolution, the shame-motives have undergone such essential changes, it is quite evident that not every individual and class living in the same locality, and still less all the different races and sects that go to form a nation, can possibly have passed through the same stages of evolution with the same rapidity; their living conditions are far too varied. So, in the conception of shame, there develop sharp boundary lines between people at different stages of moral evolution which often conflict most bitterly.

Now we can far better realise the danger of taking the feeling of shame as the foundation of ethical education.

It is certain, for instance, that when a young man who has been brought up in a quiet and retiring little provincial town where rules of modesty and shame were instilled into him, comes up to town and is thrown into cosmopolitan society, he will surely not only throw over the shame-motives of his early days, but also others which he should always hold sacred.

The feeling of shame is honoured as the foundation of morality by those people who still affirm that one is only moral and correct when conforming to the traditional and universally accepted etiquette, morality or custom, a principle of morality that excludes in anticipation all evolution of the individual to a higher ethical standpoint. In such circles, false modesty is encouraged and held up as the most laudable of all virtues, so that they may wear the halo of extraordinary morality or of aristocratic ways, while in reality all this is only travesty on virtue. Thus the so-called feeling of shame becomes a barrier against which all real progress founders.

And the shame of nudity is quite typical. Formerly, when a family was so poor that the children were forced to run about bare-foot like savages, even in inclement weather, they felt terribly ashamed of their poverty; for of all social transgressions, none is so great as poverty.

Among those people who are a little better off in the world, it is considered perfectly shocking if they are not fully dressed, and when they are caught in the midst of their toilet, incompletely attired, they feel frightfully embarrassed before strangers.

Now, however, we have arrived at an era when the richer folks proudly lay aside certain articles of clothing which are useless from a hygienic point of view,

316

but which were formerly held in high honour. They can thus flout public opinion, because everyone knows that they are not at all poor. So now our children run about very often with naked legs, and our young men without hats or caps, although in former times the head was covered (except during prayer) as a sign that one was a free-born citizen. And false shame in the presence of nudity is also beginning to disappear.

Only, at least in our cold northern climate, bashfulness in regard to denuding the whole body will persist for a long time, for reasons of expediency. For as soon as we throw off our last articles of underclothing, we feel all the currents of cold air as something that is almost always uncomfortable and even disagreeable.

And to this must be added another motive actuated by our reason: the exposure to view of our sexual organs, which may lead to other complications. For in females it shows their fitness or otherwise for the married state, and in males their actual sexual feelings at the time, which in the presence of third parties may cause a suspicion of wilful provocation, or at any rate, the most undesirable associations of thought and feeling.

In this case there are not only the shame-motives of embarrassment to be taken into consideration, but also serious motives of reason, which in many cases render it a duty to observe the greatest reserve and discretion. And yet, in family circles and in the world of art[1] and science, for instance in medical consultations, all this shame of nudity has long been recognised as misplaced modesty, unless special contra-indications exist in these cases.

So now we find ourselves back again on our sexual theme, and here, above all, the feeling of shame has always reigned; but here also the force of natural evolution has worked the most striking changes, which are still progressing.

Originally the sexual life was not so much a source of friendly sentiments, as a focus of animal desire, an endless source of envy and conflict, leading to the use of force and murder, and naturally of shame and a feeling of guilt.

Later, with the advent of a more regular social and sexual organisation, the sexual shame-feeling is more especially produced if one has offended against traditional or conventional moral laws, whereby one soon acquires a bad name or may be involved in the greatest difficulties. And sometimes, if one has been informal or impolite, though often this is only false shame.

These various sets of shame-motives are as yet but little eliminated from our sexual life, because as we mentioned at the beginning of this chapter, the sexual urge occurs so late in our lives, and, therefore, always seems to us something unusual. And this is why, in the

1. See the artistic edition of "Ideal Human Forms", seven volumes of which already appeared in the "Schonheit" Verlag, proprietor Richard Giesecke, Dresden-A. 24.

public eye, everything sexual is essentially shameful. And these vitally important organs have been dignified (in the Latin and German languages at least) with the epithet of our "shame" — (Pudenda and Scham). Shame! Why, we should only feel ashamed that we have wandered so far away from Nature. Evolution has certainly still a long way to go.

Now that we have read this review of the evolution of the feeling of shame as a general manifestation of the gradually increasing moral feeling of mankind, the way is cleared for a better understanding of our individul conception of what shame is. The most delicate touchstone of our own ethical viewpoint is the manner in which we regard this feeling of shame; and we shall thus be able to improve and to adopt a higher personal standpoint.

When we were quite young and felt ourselves dependent on our environment, we were ruled by motives of fear and sensitiveness, and this cost us many a bitter tear! But we have forgotten all this years ago. And because we idealise everything that belongs to an earlier state, and cast a halo around it, although as adults we have our consciousness of being quite grown up, we have not lost the habit of surrounding our childish false modesty with its halo.

As we grew up, we always sought to be more and more free and independent; and when finally we really became adult, we studied cause and effect and tried calmly and worthily to master our feelings.

As far as we were able to accomplish this, our shame-motives took less and less importance in our lives, until with our advancing years they ceased altogether.

So long, however, as hot young blood rushed through our veins, blushes suffused our cheeks, sometimes at awkward moments, with varying intensity and from the most different motives, which depended upon our education and moral development. How different the case may be: a terrible fear of being caught at something we ought not to do, bashfulness if we accidently say something improper, and that false shame that we have of saying or doing anything not in accordance with custom, and so on.

And only now do we fully realise that that feeling of shame is not the highest ideal that we should really strive after. On the contrary, it is our duty to avoid everything that we could possibly be ashamed of; indeed we wish also to entirely conquer all false shame, and to rise superior to it. The more we bring our sexual life under the control of reason and of our full consciousness, the more will this vague feeling that we call shame retreat into the background, with all its poetry and danger.

The higher emotional motives will then take its place: an aesthetic refinement of feeling, a desire not to wound others, an enthusiasm for all that is good and that can raise us to higher things, and especially enthusiasm for pure love. In this way the blood will circulate more warmly through our veins; without the slightest anxiety or shame; only the lofty aim at a higher and greater life-energy.

Chapter 70

MAKING THE SEXUAL LIFE
A THING OF BEAUTY

IN THE last six chapters we have discussed the ways in which the love-life may be overcast. Although the delicate morning-mist of modesty may sometimes enhance the brightness of love, the fog of ignorance, and the black thunderclouds of immorality and lust may unfortunately totally eclipse the light of day, and fill our hearts with trouble and anxiety.

Yet, although the sun may be obscured by clouds, we cannot deny that it is still there, and for this reason I do not wish to close these pages with the melancholy subjects that have filled the last chapters, but rather to cast a farewell glance over the whole panorama that shows us the sexual life as the focus of psychic life and the summit of the curve of our life itself.

Within us we have always felt this, every time that the sexual urge has stirred us deeply; but we scarcely dared to admit it. Modesty was the cause of this. And then our whole academic education forced us into the path of a prejudiced intellectualism, and we felt that to be very cold, for our reason affords us light, but light without warmth. And old honourable traditions were there to punish us, as though a longing for sexual affection were something sinful, and sexual passion a temptation of Satan.

Throughout the whole of this work, however, the beauty of the sexual life has been clearly emphasised, as we have always felt it, whenever our hearts have beat joyfully from the charm of love. Now we are more content with ourselves, and we shall no longer nourish the wish to stifle our sexual life, but shall devote every effort to render it a thing of beauty. Now when the flowers bloom and the birds sing, we join in with them and feel the same intoxicating joy of living, and our life is a life of sunshine at last.

Written words are too feeble to express the enthusiasm of love. Even the poet is scarcely equal to it. The nearest approach to an expression of this wonderful feeling and joyous enthusiasm, is through the most spiritual of the arts, that of music; from the

319

...cation of the oriental Gamelan, to the most charm-
...ntal songs.

...re comes to my mind the wonderful Ninth Sym-
...hoven, with the Ode to the Ecstasy of Love at the

Joy, beauteous spark of the gods!
Love, a shaft of Light from Heaven!